Certified Wireless Design Professional (CWDP) Official Study Guide (CWDP-302)

First printing November 2015

ISBN: 978-0-9963279-3-0

Errata, when available, for this study guide can be found at: CWNP.com

Technical Editor
Tom Carpenter

Content Contributor
Keith Parsons

Project Manager
Brad Crump

Copy Editors
CWNP Staff

Production Supervisor
Josie Miller

Introduction

"Coverage is easy, capacity is hard," says Keith Parsons, a WLAN engineer and CWNE, and he is right. Capacity requires WLAN design skills, coverage requires the ability to turn on a sufficient number of APs. This study guide and the Certified Wireless Design Professional (CWDP) certification exam were created to ensure WLAN designers know how to properly plan, design, implement, and validate WLANs.

This book is first and foremost a study guide for the CWDP certification offered by CWNP. It is a reference to important topics related to WLAN design, but the primary focus is on helping you pass exam CWDP-302. It will act as an excellent addition to live instructor led courses, CWNP e-learning courses, CWNP practice exams and other self-teaching resources.

The first step to preparing for any CWNP exam is to gain an understanding of the objectives. The following sections provide an overview of the CWDP-302 objectives.

CWDP—302 Exam Objectives

The CWDP-302 exam is organized into five knowledge domains with assigned percentages. This structure simply means that 20% of the questions on the exam will be in the first knowledge domain, 20% in the second, and so on. In the objectives listed on the following pages, pay close attention to the percentage breakdown for each knowledge domain. It will help you understand the number of questions, out of 60 on the exam, that will come from that knowledge set.

The following detailed objectives list should be used as your guide during exam preparation. All exam questions are written to the objectives.

CWDP—302 Objectives

Requirements Analysis—20%

1.1 Understand the requirements analysis and documentation procedures required to design a WLAN including information gathering, business justification, business requirements, user requirements, technical requirements, regulatory requirements, and budgetary procedures.

1.2 Determine the client device types to be used and understand the impact they will have on the WLAN design related to coverage and capacity including laptops, tablets, mobile phones, 802.11 VoIP handsets, and additional mobile and non-mobile computing devices such as Internet of Things (IoT) and sensor-based networks.

1.3 Discover the planned applications and document the impact they will have on the WLAN related to coverage and capacity including web-based, mobile, real-time, and high-data volume applications.

1.4 Define the security requirements of the WLAN including security solutions, BYOD/MDM, guest access, roaming, and monitoring.

1.5 Document the physical coverage requirements of the WLAN including common, industrial, outdoor, service, and guest areas.

1.6 Determine requirements for bridge links and other link types including point-to-point, point-to-multipoint, and mesh connections.

1.7 Understand and implement the knowledge require to upgrade existing WLANs including phased, forklift, modular, software upgrades and performance, compatibility, and security testing.

1.8 Discover and document the building factors impacting the WLAN design including building materials, square footage, ceiling heights, multi-floor structures, wiring and power limitations, blueprints, and facility access requirements for on-site planning work.

1.9 Demonstrate knowledge of documentation generated as the output of the WLAN requirements analysis processes including

- scope of work
- NDA
- hold harmless
- network diagrams
- site survey deliverables
- bill of materials, and
- network design acceptance criteria

Site Survey Procedures—20%

2.1 Explain and perform the different types of site surveys commonly used including manual (active and passive), predictive, and hybrid

2.2 Understand and utilize site survey tools including protocol and spectrum analyzers, site survey software (predictive and manual), throughput testers, and various hardware used in the process including laptops, tablets, mobile phones, batteries, APs, PoE injectors, carts, and cabling.

2.3 Ensure that proper site survey procedures are followed including gaining access clearance, acquiring floor mappings with application- and user-specific needs notations, and approval to perform the site survey.

2.4 Define metrics and other information collected and reported during a site survey including signal metrics (RSSI, SNR, noise floor, interference), cell coverage, application and connectivity data (data rates, throughput, latency, jitter, loss, and retries).

2.5 Ensure scenario-specific requirements are met and appropriate plans are in place including arranging escorts, performing training (safety and operations), provisioning equipment (lifts, ladders, tools), meeting access requirements (clearance and badges), taking into account single-floor versus multiple-floor installations requirements, and abiding by industry specific requirements such as union assistance and patient privacy.

2.6 Understand the different methodologies used in site surveys for varying applications and architectures including VoIP, video, data, location services, and multiple (MCA) and single channel architecture and single channel architecture (SCA).

2.7 Explain and perform procedures required for outdoor site surveys including outdoor client access WLANs and bridge links.

WLAN Design—40%

3.1 Demonstrate knowledge of WLAN architectures and solutions including management solutions, communication protocols, data forwarding models, scalability, redundancy, encryption methods, controller- and cloud-based solutions, autonomous solutions, centralized data forwarding, distributed data forwarding, and the advantages and limitations of various architectures.

3.2 Plan for RF management including channel usage, MCA and SCA, RRM, solutions for co-channel interference, non-overlapping adjacent-channel interference, overlapping adjacent-channel interference, and non-802.11 interference all within regulatory constraints and including client station considerations (interference at client locations, high density of clients, mobile, and non-mobile clients).

3.3 Design appropriate 802.11 channel plans including channel widths, frequency bands, output power levels (including DFS and TPC requirements), channel reuse, 802.11n and 802.11ac channels, and advanced channel features (80+80, RTS/CTS enhancements, etc.).

3.4 Select access points (APs) and define their configuration and installation parameters including indoor and outdoor APs, internal antennas and external antennas, PoE-and wall outlet powered APs, mounting solutions, and staging procedures.

3.5 Understand and explain the varied configuration processes for different AP deployment models including MCA, SCA, controller-and cloud-based, distributed, autonomous, and additional models commonly used in modern WLANs.

3.6   Design infrastructure services and connectivity to existing services required to support WLANs including RADIUS and DNS services, LDAP connections, DHCP provisioning, PKI and RBAC implementation, NTP availability, firewall configuration, ACL and VLAN management, BYOD/MDM, onboarding, and NAC integration.

3.7   Ensure availability of appropriate cabling and power provisioning including backhaul speeds, PoE, redundant connections, and connectivity to required services.

3.8   Design branch and remote office WLAN deployments including authentication services, WAN connections, VPNs, split tunnel forwarding, and AP selection and configuration.

3.9   Design mesh networks including mesh access networks, mesh backhaul solutions, channel planning, band selection, and redundancy.

3.10   Design bridge links including determination of appropriate line of sight (visual and RF), band, antenna, and channel selection; output power levels and data rate; requirements; link budgets; and PtP and PtMP links.

3.11   Design for varied client devices including tablets, mobile phones, laptops, stationary devices, supported PHYs, data rates, channels allowed, channel widths, DFS support, and receive sensitivity levels.

3.12   Design for varied application types including roaming and latency requirements, data throughput demands, specialty devices (barcode scanners, healthcare devices, ID badges, location tracking systems, wireless cameras), and voice/video.

3.13   Design end-to-end QoS solutions including 802.11 QoS, wired QoS, WMM, airtime fairness, band steering, load balancing, QoS markings, and queues.

3.14   Design standard security solutions including RADIUS server and EAP type selection, encryption solutions, passphrase-based implementations, and WPS.

3.15 Design advanced security solutions including Per-User PSK (PPSK), VPN implementation, endpoint security, Wireless Intrusion Prevention Systems (WIPS), BYOD/MDM/guest access and onboarding, captive portals, network segmentation, and content filtering.

3.16 Given a scenario, plan for secure roaming including 802.11-2012 roaming methods, Opportunistic Key and PMK Caching, SCA roaming, pre-authentication, and pre-shared key implementations.

3.17 Design WLANs for specific use cases and vertical markets including high-density design, large public venues (LPV), healthcare, education, retail, hospitality, outdoors, public hotspots, and government deployments.

3.19 Understand the use of network planning tools including site survey software design features, network diagramming tools, throughput testing tools, and link calculation software/spreadsheets.

WLAN Deployment—5%

4.1 Perform device staging according to organizational policies and design recommendations and install devices according to vendor specifications and the WLAN design.

4.2 Implement channel plans according to the design recommendations including manual channel assignments through controllers, cloud solutions, and autonomous configurations. Configure automated channel management features according to common operational method provided by major vendors.

4.3 Configure infrastructure devices where necessary to support the WLAN including routers, DHCP servers, DNS services, and switches.

4.4 Understand the basic installation procedures used for different WLAN architectures including controller-based, cloud-managed, distributed, autonomous, and virtual controller.

Design Validation—15%

5.1 Identify the purpose and methods of post-installation site surveys including application validation, coverage assurance, capacity requirements, and load handling.

5.2 Describe remediation processes used when validation fails including making channel and output power adjustments, installing additional hardware, removing hardware, and changing additional configuration options.

5.3 Understand and use the appropriate tools in the validation process including spectrum and protocol analyzers, throughput testers, and documentation.

5.4 Understand and implement methods for troubleshooting coverage and capacity problems, roaming delays, low-data rate clients, QoS failure, security configuration, and client connectivity issues.

Target Audience

As stated previously, this book is written for those preparing for the CWDP certification and not as a general guide to WLANS that also happens to include wireless design topics. You will find, in the very first pages that this book is written to an individual who understand wireless networking from a functional perspective already. No review of basic 802.11 fundamentals is included. If you are CWNA certified, which is required as a prerequisite to becoming CWDP certified, you are ready to begin exploring this book with full understanding. However, if you are not CWNA certified, you should have extensive knowledge of wireless networks before venturing further.

Book Errata

Errata, when available, for this study guide can be found at: CWNP.com

Acknowledgements for Content

Finally, we at CWNP would like to thank the following individuals for assisting us in the production of this resource. They provided valuable content that greatly improved the book to help CWDP students and security professional everywhere.

Keith Parsons and Andrew von Nagy provided significant content for the appendices. Their addition to this guide is much appreciated.

Keith Parsons is the managing director at Wireless LAN Professionals, Inc. He is a respected industry expert and has performed WLAN design, consulting, troubleshooting and training in countries all over the world. He is CWNE #3 (CWNP) and also holds certifications with Cisco, CompTIA, Microsoft, and even NetWare. His blog can be found at WLANPros.com, and videos of his exceptional WLAN Professionals Conference can be found on Vimeo and YouTube. Keith is also a frequent delegate at Wireless Field Day events and a popular speaker at both vendor and industry conferences.

Andrew von Nagy is an accomplished multi-discipline computer networking professional with over 15 years of experience in the education, retail, and WLAN industries, and a recognized WLAN networking expert having achieved two of the industry's highest certifications, CCIE #28298 (Cisco Systems) and CWNE #84 (CWNP). In his spare time, Andrew writes about relevant Wi-Fi industry topics on the Revolution Wi-Fi blog, which provides expert analysis on the wireless LAN industry. He has also served as a technical editor for wireless LAN publications, including the CWNA Study Guide: 3rd Edition (ISBN #978-1118127797), 802.11n: A Survival Guide (ISBN #978-1449312046), and the CWNA Study Guide: 4th Edition (ISBN #978-1118893708).

Table of Contents

Chapter 1:

Introducing WLAN Design

In this chapter:

- Importance of Design
- Design Process

Wireless LAN (WLAN) design is an art and a science. It is a science because essential skills can be learned. It is an art because experience will enhance those skills resulting in greater success as a WLAN designer. The Certified Wireless Design Professional (CWDP) Official Study Guide will help you to build the essential skills you will need.

This chapter introduces important concepts that will surface many times throughout the book. First, you will explore the importance of design by discovering some of the problems that may occur without a proper design. Then you will investigate the design process and the different phases through which the WLAN designer navigates. This chapter quickly introduces WLAN design and provides a foundation for the remainder of the book.

Importance of Design

The importance of design for WLANs cannot be overstated. The best way to grasp the importance of good design is to consider the problems that occur because of bad design, cookie cutter designs, or no design at all. This section provides an overview of these issues.

Problems with Bad Design

When WLANs are poorly designed, several problems exist:

- **Insufficient coverage:** Without sufficient coverage dead spots and low-data rate areas occur. Dead spots are simply areas where the wireless signal is not sufficiently strong to provide a connection. Low-data rate areas are those locations where connections may be accomplished but are too slow to perform needed operations. You can eliminate low-data rate areas by simply disabling lower data rates on the APs; however, this also results in more areas that could be categorized as dead spots. Therefore, the only solution to insufficient coverage is sufficient coverage. For purposes of this book and the CWDP exam, **sufficient coverage** is defined as the availability of a wireless connection that provides the required data rate and stability demanded by the clients. *Figure 1.1* depicts insufficient coverage, assuming that coverage is desired in the areas without signal.

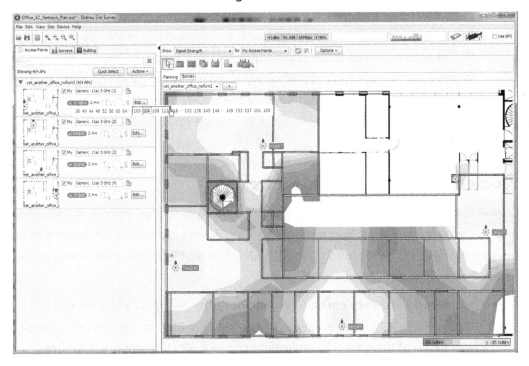

Figure 1.1: Floorplan Showing Areas without Coverage

- **Insufficient capacity:** Another problem with poorly designed WLANs is the lack of needed capacity. Capacity is simply the ability to accommodate the demands of all supported clients. More specifically, it is the ability to provide supported clients with access at needed data rates resulting in the achievement of required TCP/UDP throughput for the user applications. With sufficient coverage and insufficient capacity, the WLAN still fails.

- **No scalability:** Scalability defines the ability of the network to grow with increasing demands. A WLAN designed to meet today's needs with no thought for tomorrow's needs will perform well for a short period of time (typically 6–12 months), but as new users and devices are added, the performance will suffer. Scalability must be considered in the design process.

- **Lack of required functionality:** The final major problem with poor design is still common even among well-trained WLAN engineers because they often focus on the RF and miss the need for capabilities on the network. Functionality such as onboarding, guest access, and more are not necessarily RF issues, but they must be planned for and designed into the solution. Without them, even the best RF network, in relation to coverage and capacity, fails to meet the needs of users. While the WLAN design professional is required to know RF, more than just RF knowledge is needed to be successful.

Problems with Cookie Cutter Designs

Cookie cutter designs are those designs that are often described as one size fits all or one guideline for everyone. Suggestions like "one AP per classroom" or "ensure RF is seen everywhere" do not result in good WLANs. The problems incurred when cookie cutter designs are used include:

- **Increased hardware costs:** Many cookie cutter designs call for more APs than are typically required because it is the only way for the designs to work well much of the time. This utilization of more APs than required is often called over-engineering. The costs of the installations are increased because of the extra APs. A good WLAN design will result in the right number of APs for today and some point in the future, but will not overemphasize scalability to the point of breaking the budget.

- **Poor performance:** If the cookie cutter design is not over-engineered, it is very likely to be under-engineered. The result of such a deployment is poor performance for the users. This is often the case when the design calls for the WLAN signal to simply exist everywhere—also known as coverage only. Such a design rarely performs well today.

Note: It is often argued that cookie cutter designs may result in over engineering, but they also save money on the front-end in relation to consulting fees for surveys and designs. In some scenarios, this trade off may be true and beneficial, but it is certainly not the most common. This is the position of CWNP.

Problems with No Design

No design scenarios are common. Such scenarios include evolutionary implementations of WLANs and the installation of APs based solely on availability of Ethernet ports.

Evolutionary Implementations

When a WLAN is implemented little-by-little, over time, it is an evolutionary implementation. Such an implementation typically fails in the final result because each cell may be designed well for its individual use, but the cells are not designed with the other cells in mind. The result is often excess co-channel contention (also called co-channel interference), and improper coverage in needed areas. Additionally, throughput challenges typically exist as the WLAN was not engineered as a whole with consideration of the back-end infrastructure needed for it to work optimally.

Ethernet Availability Implementations

These implementations choose AP locations based on the current availability of Ethernet ports or, even worse, PoE ports (as there are typically fewer PoE-capable ports in any given network than standard Ethernet ports). The result is poor coverage in needed areas as APs are often placed in less than ideal locations, and then output power is adjusted to cover a large physical space. The result is often coverage in areas where it is not needed and non-existing coverage where it is needed.

To prevent these and other problems you should always implement wireless networks with a full design in mind. The next section introduces the basic WLAN design process.

Design Process

In this final section of Chapter 1, you will review the basic design process used in WLAN design. This includes defining, designing, and implementing the network based on the design, and then validating that the network design performs as you intended.

Define

The Define phase of a WLAN design and installation project includes important tasks like

- requirements analysis
- information gathering, and
- pre-site survey checklists.

Requirements analysis requires several skills, including:

- **Communication Skills:** The WLAN designer must be able to communicate the capabilities of vendor solutions to the customer and understand the customer's needs. Without effective communication skills, the designer will face great challenges throughout the project. For example, if the designer fails to gather the proper information, he may have to approach the customer multiple times during the design process to gather the missing information. This behavior frustrates customers and can result in unsatisfied users at best and the loss of a contract at worst.

- **Wireless LAN Knowledge:** The WLAN designer, of course, must have in-depth knowledge of WLAN technologies. This knowledge will serve the designer well as she surveys users and explains how business needs will be met by proposed solutions. It will help the designer communicate what can and cannot be accomplished with current technologies in relation to the customer needs.

- **Wired LAN Knowledge:** It is not enough to know WLANs, the WLAN designer must also have a mastery of wired LAN technologies. This book does not cover wired networking in-depth, but it is assumed that you have basic knowledge of switches, routers, and IP networking. In later chapters, you will learn about the services running on the wired network that impact the WLAN. Knowledge of wired LANs will be of great benefit as you plan for network connections, roaming solutions, security configuration, and other required capabilities of the WLAN.

The Define phase is covered in detail in Chapter 2 of this book. To learn even more about requirements analysis, consider the book **Software Requirements (3rd Edition)**, *Karl Wiegers and Joy Beatty, 2013, Microsoft Press*. While the book primarily targets software developers, a significant portion of the book will also be useful to WLAN designers.

Design

The Design phase of the project includes site surveying and the design of the WLAN. The site survey may be predictive, AP-on-a-stick, or a mixture of these (hybrid). Predictive site surveys are performed using software that simulates RF propagation based on blueprints and proper data entry about materials. AP-on-a-stick involves placing APs at locations that are likely to provide the needed coverage and then testing to ensure that they do. This description is a bit simplified and the details will be presented later in this book, but it is accurate to the basic concept.

The purpose of the site survey, whether predictive or manual (AP-on-a-stick), is to determine the proper locations of APs and the settings required on those APs in order to meet the requirements determined in the define phase. At this point, it is important to note that if the Define phase is not completed properly, all other phases will fail as well. The WLAN designer cannot design a network that meets requirements of which he is not aware.

The Design phase also involves the actual design of the WLAN, which includes multiple designed components such as the wired-infrastructure services, power provisioning, AP settings, controller settings, Quality-of-Service settings, and more.

The resulting design documents may include blueprints with AP locations marked, AP configuration settings, infrastructure settings, a Bill of Materials (BoM), and others.

The Design phase is covered in extensive detail in Chapters 3–5.

Implement

Deployment or implementation of the WLAN is the next logical step. Once the design plans are approved, the network can be configured and installed. This action typically follows a sequence similar to the following:

- **Configure Infrastructure:** Before installing the APs, it is important to get the proper foundation. This means configuring the infrastructure to support the new or upgraded WLAN installation. Items such as DNS, DHCP, and routing must be configured to support the newly-scaled network and the extra demands that the WLAN will place on the infrastructure.

- **Provision Power and Network Access:** With the infrastructure in place, providing power to the APs and network connectivity is the next logical step. Both may be provided through a single cable, or power may be provided through wall outlets with network connectivity provided through the Ethernet cable. Either way, this is an essential step that must take place before the APs themselves can be deployed.

- **Configure and Install APs:** Finally, each AP must be configured and installed or installed and configured, depending on the WLAN architecture chosen. In some installations, you will configure the AP and then install it at the assigned location. This process is particularly true in autonomous, small WLANs. In other installations, the process varies, and you may install the AP and the configuration may happen from the infrastructure, but, in truth, you have still first configured it and then installed it. It's just that you configured the AP in the controller, cloud, or manager before connecting the AP.

WLAN implementation or deployment is covered in greater detail in Chapter 6.

Validate

The final phase of the WLAN implementation project is the Validation phase. In this phase, the network is evaluated to ensure that it meets the requirements determined in the Define phase. Therefore, the Validation phase is a cyclical procedure. You must validate and tune (or adjust) the network components as many times as required to accomplish the demands of the original requirements. This phase may take a single afternoon for smaller networks and several days or weeks for large-scale deployments.

Many vendors have implemented some form of automatic-channel management to help with this issue, often called radio resource management (RRM), but it is no replacement for a skilled WLAN designer and troubleshooter in critical WLAN installations.

The validation process is basically an active site survey performed after the installation. At minimum, three items should be verified:

- coverage,
- capacity, and
- capabilities.

Coverage ensures that a sufficient signal is available in all required areas. Capacity ensures that the WLAN can provide the needed throughput defined in the requirements. Capabilities include features like fast secure roaming, guest registration, onboarding, security, and more.

The Validation phase is covered in greater detail in Chapter 7.

Chapter Review

In this brief introductory chapter, WLAN design was explained from a bird's eye view. The chapter provided an overview of what will be covered in the rest of the book and gave insights into the importance of proper WLAN design while also introducing the basic WLAN design process of define, design, implement, and validate.

Facts to Remember

Be sure to remember the following facts as you prepare for the CWDP certification, and be sure that you can explain the details related to them:

- Bad design results in insufficient coverage, no scalability, insufficient capacity, and lack of required functionality.

- Cookie cutter designs often result in increased hardware costs and poor performance.

- Failing to perform any design functions often results in excessive co-channel contention, poor performance, and limited capabilities.

- The WLAN design process can be divided into four basic phases: Define, Design, Implement, and Validate.

- The Define phase includes requirements analysis.

Chapter 2:

Requirements Analysis

In this chapter:

- Understanding Requirements Analysis
- Determining Client Device Types
- Planning for Applications
- Defining Security Requirements
- Defining Physical Coverage Requirements
- Documenting Building Factors
- Preparing for Bridge Links and Other Link Types
- Planning for WLAN Upgrades
- Creating Documentation

Objectives

1.1 Understand the requirements analysis and documentation procedures required to design a WLAN including information gathering, business justification, business requirements, user requirements, technical requirements, regulatory requirements, and budgetary procedures.

1.2 Determine the client device types to be used and understand the impact they will have on the WLAN design related to coverage and capacity including laptops, tablets, mobile phones, 802.11 VoIP handsets, and additional mobile and non-mobile computing devices such as Internet of Things (IoT).

1.3 Discover the planned applications and document the impact they will have on the WLAN related to coverage and capacity including web-based applications, mobile apps, real-time applications, and high-data volume applications.

1.4 Define the security requirements of the WLAN including security solutions, BYOD/MDM, guest access, roaming, and monitoring.

1.5 Document the physical coverage requirements of the WLAN including common, industrial, outdoor, service, and guest areas.

1.6 Determine the requirements for bridge links and other link types including point-to-point, point-to-multipoint, and mesh connections.

1.7 Understand and implement the knowledge required to upgrade existing WLANs including phased, forklift, modular, and, software upgrades, and performance, compatibility, and security testing.

1.8 Discover and document the building factors impacting the WLAN design including building materials, square footage, ceiling heights, multi-floor structures, wiring and power limitations, blueprints, and facility access requirements for onsite planning work.

1.9 Demonstrate knowledge of documentation generated as the output of the WLAN requirements analysis processes including scope of work, NDA, hold harmless, network diagrams, site survey deliverables, bill of materials, and network design acceptance criteria.

I t is not uncommon to hear complaints about WLANs such as the following:

- "The network is way too slow."
- "I can't even access Wi-Fi from my office."
- "When I walk down the hallway while on a call, I lose the call every time."
- "The initial connection to the wireless network takes way too long."

If you've heard these or similar complaints, you've probably dealt with unhappy users in cases where requirements analysis was not executed properly, if at all. Providing a WLAN that grants users the needed capabilities is the primary goal of the Define phase and requirements analysis.

This chapter introduces Requirements Analysis in general and then addresses specific issues of the process for WLANs. Then, planning for WLAN upgrades and creating documentation are addressed.

Understanding Requirements Analysis

Requirements Analysis can be defined as the process of discovering a project's requirements. A requirement is anything, physical or logical, that must be provided by the product of the project in order for the project to be considered successful. Simply stated, the requirements are the things that you must achieve at the completion of the implementation of your WLAN. The product of a project is defined as the result or outcome of the project. It is what the project gives you. The requirements, then, are those things that the product must provide in order for the project to be deemed successful.

The following definition structure of a requirement is from the *IEEE Standard Glossary of Software Engineering Terminology*:

1. A condition or capability needed by a user to solve a problem or achieve an objective.

2. A condition or capability that must be met or possessed by a system or system component to satisfy a contract, standard, specification, or other formally imposed document.

3. A documented representation of a condition or capability as in number one or number two above.

This definition structure raises some important questions. Who sets the objectives? What contracts, standards, specifications, or other documents define conditions or capabilities related to WLANs? When you answer these two questions, you are on your way to performing requirements analysis.

The objectives, in most organizations, are defined by the organization and user actions are performed in order to accomplish tasks that ultimately result in the achievement of those objectives. When considering a WLAN, these objectives must play a role. The WLAN should help the user achieve the tasks that result in the achievement of the objectives. The objectives define the business requirements. Tasks performed by the users define the user requirements. The capabilities required to achieve those tasks define the technical requirements. The fact that the WLAN provides the ability to get it all done provides the business justification. In addition to this, WLANs must comply with regulatory requirements and, of course, organizations do not have an unlimited supply of cash so budgetary procedure must be considered. Each of these is explored in more detail throughout the remainder of this section.

Business Requirements

Business requirements are known as the objectives of the organization, sometimes also called high-level objectives because they are the objectives of the entire organization and not just a specific department or team. The customer, project sponsor, or project launch team will often provide business requirements. The WLAN designer should acquire a copy of these objectives, if they already exist. If they do not exist, they should be generated in relation to the WLAN so that the design can accommodate the current focus of the organization.

Business objectives provide an explanation for the desire to implement a WLAN. They describe the purpose behind the implementation. A vision and scope document, also called a project charter, is a good place to define the business objectives related to the WLAN.

Business requirements are frequently a superset of user requirements. The user requirements should be things that help the users act in such a way so as to achieve business or organizational requirements. Business requirements come from two primary sources—internal business requirements and external business requirements. **Internal requirements** are based on organizational objectives and policies such as security policies, employment policies, and so on. **External requirements** are based on regulations from local regulatory bodies such as federal and local governments and their agencies.

An example of a business requirement would be to say that the WLAN must allow the users to perform at the same level they have been able to perform on the wired LAN. Ultimately, this business requirement is born out of the objective to improve performance, or at least maintain it, while also providing mobility. In this case, the organization wants to move forward in the area of mobility, but not backward in the area of performance (data throughput). Modern applications are far more throughput-intensive, and it is usually unacceptable to reduce data throughput in comparison with the existing network with any modern network implementation.

User Requirements

User requirements include the goals or tasks that users must perform when using the WLAN. For example, users may need to roam throughout the organization's facilities while using a Voice over WLAN (VoWLAN) phone. They may need to transfer files that are rather large without taking an unacceptable amount of time. This last one is a perfect example of the kinds of "requirements" you often get during user interviews that require you to dig deeper into the intentions of the user. In this situation, you might ask, "How much time would be an unacceptable amount of time?" and "What size are the large files you will be transferring?" You will be more likely to meet the requirements of the users if you gather specific rather than vague user requirements.

The point is this—when a user or group of users informs you of a requirement that is stated in non-specific language, always ask for clarification. The example in the preceding paragraph is very illustrative. Users or managers will often use the term unacceptable without defining what they mean. For example, if the users must be able to transfer large files without requiring an unacceptable amount of time, you must get the answers to three questions:

1. What is a typical size for these large files?

2. What period of time would be unacceptable?

3. To or from where are the files being transferred?

The first question clarifies the size of the referenced files. The second question could also be stated in the positive as, "What period of time would be acceptable?" Either way, you will gain a more specific number for your analysis. The third question is of utmost importance in this scenario. If the users are transferring files to or from an FTP server on the Internet that is out of your control, you will have a limited amount of impact on the performance the users perceive. You can only control the performance from the users' client stations to the Internet connection. The speed of the Internet, the remote network, and the remote FTP server may be completely out of your control. In cases such as this, you must be sure to communicate what you can and cannot promise.

Imagine the users tell you that they are transferring files that are typically 5 MB (megabytes) in size and that they are transferring them to and from an internal FTP server. Furthermore, they tell you that the files should be transferred in less than one minute to be seen as acceptable. You also determine that as many as three users could be transferring these files at a given time. This results in the following equation:

$$5 \times 3 = 15 \text{ MB per minute}$$

$$\text{(file size)} \times \text{(number of users)} = \text{transfer rate}$$

You now know that you must provide a WLAN that will allow the users to transfer 15 MB per minute. Assuming you also determine that 1 MB of normal or other network traffic will be transferred per minute, you actually need to be able to transfer 16 MB per minute. Since you are implementing an enterprise-class access point with approximately 18–24 Mbps of actual data throughput (resulting in 2.25–3 MBps), you are confident that the WLAN will be able to maintain the demands of the users.

In addition to the current needs, you must be sure to plan for future growth. You should ask "Will you be running Voice over IP (VoIP) communications on the WLAN in the future?" If so, you must consider not only data rates but latency issues. Also, consider speaking with the different IT divisions to discover new projects that are planned for the future. These projects may eventually demand more throughput of the WLAN than is required at the time of network implementation.

Technical Requirements

Finally, functional requirements, also called technical requirements, are those technical capabilities that, when implemented, allow your WLAN to meet the requirements of users and the business. For example, fast secure roaming may be required to support the user requirement of roaming from a BSS in one building to a BSS in another without losing voice connections. Fast secure roaming implements robust security network features such as CCMP and fast authentication methods like pre-authentication, which allows for fast and secure roaming by requiring only the 4-way handshake at the time of actual roaming. Additionally, specific QoS devices may be required. The point is that multiple functional requirements may be needed in order to meet one user or business requirement.

Table 2-1 provides a reference of these different requirement types, their definitions, and examples of their application.

Requirement Type	Definition	Example
User	User goals or tasks that users must perform using the WLAN.	Walk around while maintaining connectivity to a Web server.
Business	Business goals or objectives that must be met by the WLAN.	Compliance with corporate security policy.
Functional	The technical capabilities of the WLAN that allow for or support user and business requirements.	Wireless LAN fast secure roaming support or IEEE 802.11i support.

Table 2.1—Requirement Types

Regulatory Requirements

The final type of requirements is the regulatory requirement, sometimes also called a regulatory constraint. These can be requirements imposed by regulations such as Sarbanes-Oxley or HIPAA, among others. They can also be requirements imposed by parent companies in many situations. Whatever the source, they force specific implementation features to be utilized. As an example, any U.S. government or non-government agency currently connected to the DOD-GIG (Department of Defense-Global Information Grid) must comply with policy DODD 8100.2 and amendment DODD 8100.2p in relation to the wireless devices that are attached to the networks as defined in the policy and amendment. This type of regulatory requirement will often answer the question of whether you can implement a WLAN or not. If you cannot implement a WLAN that meets the regulatory requirements (due to budget constraints), you cannot implement a WLAN at all.

Budgetary Procedures

Many projects begin with the words, "Can you get this done for X amount of dollars?" The project begins with the budget already set before the plan has even been created. To make it less painful, this kind of budget is often beautifully named a top-down budget. Of course, the opposite is a bottom-up budget, where you are asked to determine what it would cost to implement a WLAN that meets all requirements. Either way, you will likely run into budget limitations as there is simply a practical limit to how much money is available. This budget constraint may impact decisions such as the wireless equipment you purchase or the saturation of wireless devices you can afford. In turn, this can impact available throughput in a coverage area. The point is simple: what you can implement is directly linked to the demands of the users and the available resources.

As a WLAN designer, budgeting may be required from at least two perspectives. First, you may be an internal project manager responsible for the entire project from initiation to handover. In this case, you will manage the entire budget including man hours and materials. Second, you may be an internal employee called upon to select the hardware for use in the WLAN or a contractor performing this role and you may be asked for a **Bill of Materials** (BoM) only. In this case, you simply need to create a design that includes the number of APs, controllers or managers, new infrastructure equipment or software, and any other needed items (CAT6 cables, PoE switches, etc.). The BoM will act as the materials budget and the project manager can use this to perform complete budget management.

All projects have constraints that can be recalled with the acronym CSSQ, which stands for cost, scope, schedule, and quality. The budget is concerned with the cost. The requirements help define the scope and the quality. The schedule is established based on the scope of the project and the resources available to perform the design, implementation, and validation.

The budget may be a rough order of magnitude (ROM) estimate, which typically allows for variance of 15–20% over the actual costs or it may be based on specific quotes from vendors when addressing only hardware and software licenses. When managed in a project, the work/materials for a given task can be tracked with standard methods such as budgeted cost of work performed (BCWP), actual cost of work performed (ACWP), and budgeted cost of work scheduled (BCWS). The terms are self-explanatory. BCWS exists at the beginning of the project before any tasks are complete. BCWP and ACWP are used after a task is complete to see if the task involves a cost variance (CV). A CV exists when ACWP is subtracted from BCWP and the result does not equal 0. Technically, when the result is a positive value, it is still a CV; however, in most cases only negative value CVs are a concern because they indicate that the project may be over budget.

Business Justification

Showing that the WLAN helps to achieve business objectives is a major part of business justification. From the business perspective, the objectives should be written in the language of business outcomes. For example, all organizations, whether for profit, not for profit, or governmental, have the following objectives at practically all times:

- Quality improvement
- Efficiency improvement
- Cost reduction
- Increased production
- Organizational continuity

The first four are commonly known as better, faster, cheaper, and more. The last one simply indicates that the organization wishes to remain and not cease to exist. Many regulatory constraints cause us to implement projects for the sole purpose of organizational continuity. Sarbanes-Oxley, for many organizations, is a perfect example of something we implement for organizational continuity; however, with a little analysis, you can often discover ways to improve quality, efficiency, cost management, or productivity while implementing an imposed solution.

Most organizations desire to improve quality at all times. Improving quality means doing what you do better. Sales representatives may be able to respond to customer inquiries more quickly if they have a wireless mobile phone connected to a WLAN. Inventory management employees may be able to keep the inventory data more current if they have a tablet with WLAN connectivity that they carry with them while checking stock. These are both examples of improving the quality of your process outputs: the customer response and the inventory data.

WLANs have been very helpful in the area of performance improvement. Performance improvement is about doing what you do faster. Wireless LANs help by providing connectivity anywhere and mobility. Users can respond to e-mails more quickly, enter data from any covered location, and receive alerts shortly after they are issued. The ability to be notified quickly of an alert (a price change, a network intrusion, a factory accident, and so on) is very important. In the past, pagers and cell phones were often used to accommodate the speedy delivery of alerts. Today, you can accomplish this with WLANs and mobile connected devices, as well.

Of course, reducing costs and increasing production are always top of mind for managers and executives. WLANs help you reduce costs by removing costly delays and saving business deals that would be lost if not for the timely response provided by instant communications across a WLAN. They can increase productivity as well. As an example, a warehouse management system (WMS) utilized the benefits of a wireless LAN. The warehouse workers used handheld devices based on tablets to enter information about inventory and to process barcodes. In the past, the workers were required to peel stickers off boxes as they were received and then take those stickers to a central (and shared) PC that had a barcode scanner attached. The process of adding new inventory was very time consuming. Now, the WLAN connected scanners immediately transfer the information back to a central database. This also provided notification to the sales staff. The sales staff was immediately aware of new inventory and could begin selling this inventory to waiting clients.

From this information you can see how a business objective might look like any of the following:

- Increase user mobility and therefore easy access to information.

- Reduce delays in digital information delivery.

- Implement a secure wireless network that also meets the performance demands of the organization.

Such business objectives can help in proving business justification.

In addition to the linkage to business objectives, it is important to understand that the cost of the WLAN must factor into business justification. For example, if employees will be 5% more efficient because of the WLAN, but this provides a reduction in cost of only $250,000, then a $2.5 million WLAN may be difficult to justify on the objectives of increased efficiency alone. However, when you add in increased employee retention and morale, reduced errors and other factors, you may well be able to justify the WLAN.

Information Gathering

The process of requirements analysis is ultimately all about information gathering. The WLAN designer must discover the needs of the organization and design a WLAN that meets those needs. According to Wiegers and Beatty, in *Software Requirements*, the requirements development or information gathering process can be described in four steps:

1. **Elicitation:** Eliciting needs from individuals and the organization so that requirements can be clearly defined.

2. **Analysis:** Analyzing the elicited information to determine user and organizational goals, which link to requirements.

3. **Specification:** Creating a requirements document that lists the expectations of the WLAN.

4. **Validation:** Gaining approval of the requirements from those with authority to greenlight the project.

Determining Client Device Types

The WLAN clients often drive design decisions. Whether you require fast secure roaming or not, depends on the clients and applications used. The security solution selected will often be derived from the security requirements and the client devices in the user population. For these and other reasons, the WLAN designer must ensure that she has a proper understanding of the clients likely to participate in the network.

This section provides an overview of common client types and the issues they present to the WLAN designer. These client types include laptops, tablets, mobile phones, 802.11 VoIP handsets, wireless desktops, Internet of Things, and sensor-based networks.

Laptops

Laptop computers are among the most common Wi-Fi clients. They present few issues to most WLAN designs because they typically have strong wireless adapters with better antennas than tablets or mobile phones. However, they also present some challenges.

Laptops come with many different wireless adapters in them. Some are single stream. Others are multi-stream. Some are 802.11n (or even 802.11g) and others are 802.11ac. Even if all laptops in an organization use 802.11ac, they will still use varying features of the standard. For example, they may or may not support transmit beamforming. They may or may not support multi-user MIMO.

One advantage of most laptops is the powerful batteries they use. This allows for better Wi-Fi connectivity in many instances due to higher output power for the Wi-Fi radio.

As a WLAN designer, selecting a good laptop and adapter combination is key. For example, choosing a MacBook Pro with 802.11ac 3x3 chipsets allows for packet capture without the need for odd adapters and external antenna kits. Figure 2.1 shows a MacBook Pro laptop with 802.11ac support.

Figure 2.1—MacBook Pro Laptop

All client devices—laptops, tablets, mobile phones, and the rest—include a wireless radio. Without this radio, the devices could not participate in the WLAN. More specifically, it must be an 802.11-compliant radio. Each wireless LAN client device is composed of a similar set of hardware components and software elements. The hardware components include chipsets for radio control and management, antennas for RF transmission and reception, and interfaces for connectivity to the device intended to communicate on the wireless network. The interface used to connect to the device (laptop or tablet) is something like a PCI or ExpressCard interface. The form factor, whether it be PCI, ExpressCard, or Mini-PCI, determines the interface to the communicating device.

The chipset and antenna are points of differentiation. Chipsets provide the actual implementation of the 802.11 PHYs that are supported by the client device and, therefore, the radio. For example, a chipset may support only the transmission of 2.4 GHz signals and support the DSSS, HR/DSSS, ERP and HT PHYs, or it may support the 2.4 GHz signals and the 5 GHz signals as well, which allows for support for the OFDM and VHT PHYs in addition to the PHYs operating in the 2.4 GHz band.

A device that supports both the 2.4 GHz and 5 GHz PHYs is often referenced as an 802.11a/b/g/n/ac adapter. Most of these devices cannot operate both PHYs at the same time but must switch between them or operate on only one of them. The same is true for most HT (802.11n) and VHT client adapters. The HT and VHT clients can usually operate only in one frequency band at a time, and many support only one frequency band.

Sadly, it is still not uncommon for 802.11 client adapters to support only the 2.4 GHz band, which means that they are not as useful in enterprise deployments. In most enterprise deployments, the 5 GHz bands will be used since more channels are available in these bands.

Client devices usually have built-in antennas, but many devices also support the use of external antennas. By supporting external antennas, the vendor allows for the device to be used in unique ways for testing and site surveying purposes. For example, the device can be set up with an external semi-directional antenna to compare communications quality as opposed to a dipole antenna.

While the information about chipsets and antennas is universal to 802.11 client devices, laptops tend to have more battery power than other mobile devices and can even use USB adapters that have higher output power and antenna gain. Therefore, the laptop is rarely the lowest-quality client on most modern WLANs. However, laptops are still frequently used to perform site surveys due to their combination of processing power and mobility. As tablet form factors become more and more powerful leading up to 2018, they will become ever more useful in site surveying. The Surface 3 tablet is already an example of this reality (see Figure 2.2). With an external adapter, the Surface Pro 3 can be used to perform site surveys easily.

Two additional examples of current (2015) laptop category devices that work well for site surveys would be the Lenovo Yoga series and the Toshiba Radius series. Both laptops convert to tablet mode and support external adapters that could be used for site surveys. Due to the lack of 3x3 802.11ac devices, in 2015, calculations may have to be made to determine coverage at various data rates given the current pool of available devices. While many site survey applications support 802.11ac, the hardware limitations prevent 3x3 surveying unless a MacBook Pro is used or special hardware is introduced to the kit. This reality is likely to change in 2016 and beyond. Figure 2.3 shows the Toshiba Radius 15.6 model.

Figure 2.2—Microsoft Surface Pro 3

Figure 2.3—Toshiba Radius 15.6

When defining requirements, it is important to know the following about laptop computers:

- How many are expected to be used within the WLAN?

- What PHYs will be supported by the laptops?

- How often are laptops refreshed in the organization?

- Are laptops used in a stationary manner within work areas, while moving, or both?

- Will laptop users use only internal adaptors, or will some use external adapters?

- Will any laptops use high-gain antennas?

- What EAP types are supported by the supplicant?

 Note: **While the Linux operating system is not popularly used in the user community, it is an excellent choice for the WLAN designer from a chipset analysis perspective. Linux reveals much more information about the wireless adapters in a laptop than Windows.**

Tablets

Tablets matured greatly from 2009 to 2015. At the time of writing, tablets had increased in power to the point where they can perform practically any function that can be performed by a laptop computer. This is particularly true with some of the crossover tablets like the Surface Pro 3.

Many tablets run the Windows operating system and can therefore be considered a full computer. However, they typically have less powerful hardware in the areas of processing and memory and may also use slower wireless chipsets to conserve battery power. For example, they may use a single-stream chipset instead of a two-stream chipset, which is more common in laptops.

Tablets can play a role in site surveys just as laptops can. Some vendors have released tablet (or mobile phone) apps that can be used to capture signal information within an environment and then allow for loading of that data into desktop/laptop versions of the software for full design analysis.

When defining requirements, it is important to know the following about tablets:

- How many are expected to be used within the WLAN?

- What PHYs will be supported by the tablets?

- What EAP types are supported by the supplicant?

- Will the tablets be in complete control of the organization's internet technology group, or will personal tablets be allowed on the network?

Figure 2.4—iPad Tablet

Mobile Phones

Today, mobile phones are really nothing more than small-form-factor tablets from the perspective of acting as a Wi-Fi client. For this reason, the same considerations should be made for mobile phones as are for tablets.

An additional consideration should be made for mobile phones. Because they are actually devices that work on a provider network, transition from the provider network to the WLAN should be planned. If the mobile phones are owned by the organization, it can provide a significant cost savings to the organization to have them automatically connect to the enterprise WLAN when it is available. This will allow for reduced-sized data plans for all employees with employer-owned phones.

When defining requirements, it is important to know the following about mobile phones:

- How many are expected to be used within the WLAN?

- What PHYs will be supported by the phones?

- What EAP types are supported by the mobile phone supplicant, if any?

- Will the phones be configured to transfer to and from Wi-Fi automatically?

Figure 2.5—Samsung Galaxy S6

When defining requirements, it is important to know the following about mobile phones:

- How many are expected to be used within the WLAN?

- What PHYs will be supported by the phones?

- What EAP types are supported by the mobile phone supplicant, if any?

- Will the phones be configured to transfer to and from Wi-Fi automatically?

802.11 VoIP Handsets

There was a day when we might have said that Voice over IP (VoIP) brings benefits to this or that industry, and you are likely to see it used there. The landscape has certainly changed. Today, it is a rare enterprise that does not utilize VoIP. The only question is how are they using it, and will they be using mobile 802.11 VoIP handsets?

VoIP includes several components, such as the call manager, voice gateway, and the infrastructure routers. However, for the purposes of the CWDP, it is most important to know about the handsets, including their capabilities and requirements. VoIP handsets are also simply called wireless IP phones or wireless VoIP phones.

Most VoIP handsets or phones have the following basic features:

- IP address assignment

- Firmware updatable

- VLAN support

- Security features like WPA/WPA2 pre-shared key (PSK)

- 802.11a/g/n wireless PHY support

- Transmit power of 25 mW or more

- Variable range depending on output power and other factors

As a WLAN designer, you must plan for several factors to support the VoIP handsets. When defining requirements, it is important to know the following about VoIP handsets:

- How many are expected to be used within the WLAN?

- What PHYs will be supported by the phones?

- What security features are supported?

- What services do they require and how will access to those services be provided?

- How will roaming be supported?

- What is the transmit power of the intended phones?

- What VLAN will be used by the phones?

- What Quality of Service (QoS) configurations must be in place?

- What VoIP protocols are used (SIP, H.323, etc.)?

 Note: **It is important to know that some wireless VoIP phones are not intended to be mobile handsets. Figure 2.6 shows such a phone. This desk phone supports 802.11n in 2.4 GHz and 802.11ac in 5 GHz for WLAN connectivity for the complete wireless workspace with wireless computers and phones.**

Figure 2.6—Cisco 8861 VoIP Desk Phone

Wireless Desktops

As the preceding device illustrated, even non-mobile devices are often using wireless connections these days. This trend is likely to continue now that 802.11ac is in wave two and future standards will be faster still. The wireless workspace provides several advantages to the IT group:

- No need for cable runs to each workspace.

- Easy speed upgrades through replacement of Wi-Fi adapters.

- Easier moves from one workspace to another.

However, adding Wi-Fi-enabled desktops to the WLAN introduces a new challenge and that is that, in addition to mobile devices, non-mobile devices must be connected to the network. The result is a demand for greater density and faster pipes through the Wi-Fi connections.

Wireless desktops may be equipped with onboard Wi-Fi, internal Wi-Fi adapters, or USB adapters. In many cases, the supposed onboard Wi-Fi is really just mini-PCIe included with the motherboard. However, this configuration is actually advantageous as it means that the adapter can be replaced to gain faster or different Wi-Fi capabilities according to your needs. The internal Wi-Fi adapters are typically PCI or PCIe with antennas that protrude out the rear of the computer case. Of course, USB adapters connect to USB ports.

When defining requirements, it is important to know the following about wireless desktops:

- How many are expected to be used within the WLAN?
- What PHYs will be supported by the desktops?
- What EAP types will be supported by the supplicant?
- What adapter type will be used, and where will the antennas be placed?

Internet of Things

Internet of Things (IoT) is a reference to devices that communicate with one another over the internetwork provided without necessarily requiring human interaction. These include medical devices, automation systems, tracking devices, and personal devices. The key concept is that they communicate regularly, some constantly, across the network. They may transmit small amounts of information, but they transmit frequently. The end result is many devices communicating with each other all the time—often 24x7.

These technologies, which are set to grow rapidly through the year 2020, demand network access and stable network communications. Many, if not most, of them use wireless communications. Some are Bluetooth, others are Wi-Fi, and some use proprietary wireless communications. But the focus here is on the Wi-Fi-enabled devices or devices that operate in the 2.4 GHz and 5 GHz frequency bands used by Wi-Fi.

The first Internet was the Internet of people. People communicated with other people using computing devices that were globally interconnected. The second Internet is the Internet of things. Things (devices) communicate with other things using the internetwork, which is typically connected to the Internet.

As of early 2015, there were estimated to be 10 billion devices on the Internet. This number is expected to explode to more than 50 billion by 2020. Cisco has predicted that the year 2017 will be the pivot point when Wi-Fi devices drive more of the Internet than wired devices. The important point is simple, with 50 billion devices by 2020 and most of them (the vast majority) using Wi-Fi, it is essential that these devices be considered in our Wi-Fi designs.

When defining requirements, it is important to know the following about IoT:

- How many devices are expected to be used within the WLAN?
- What PHYs will be supported by the devices?
- What will the expected load generation be from the devices?
- What is the growth rate expectation of such devices in your organization?

Planning for Applications

Applications add an extra layer of complexity on top of the client devices. When considering the client devices, the WLAN designer is focused primarily on the hardware capabilities of those devices, with the common additional focus of supported security options. The applications used on the devices further impact their operations. Some applications require massive amounts of throughput, while others require little. Some applications require great speed in delivery, while others can tolerate delays. Understanding these application issues is key.

This section provides an understanding of the common application types used on enterprise networks today and the issues they may present on that network. Application types include Web-based applications, mobile apps, real-time applications, and high-data volume applications.

Web-Based

Web-based applications use Internet data protocols for communications between client applications (browsers, possibly with special plug-ins), and the Web server. A very popular example of this type of application is Microsoft SharePoint Server, which is a collaboration server providing list management, document sharing, and social communications.

The primary communications protocol used with Web-based applications is the Hypertext Transfer Protocol (HTTP). It uses a request/response architecture wherein the client sends requests and the server responds with requested files. Files include text files (HTML, HTM, and other formats), graphics files (JPG, PNG, GIF), audio files (MP3, WAV), and more. Modern web-based applications are also dynamic in that they can update content in regions of the displayed page without updating the entire page. This modern method is sometimes called AJAX as this is one common open implementation of the dynamic development model.

When planning for Web-based applications, consider the following questions:

- What is the average communication size in kilobytes?

- How many communications will each client make per minute?

- How many clients will use Wi-Fi to connect to the application server?

Mobile Apps

Mobile apps are used on mobile phones and tablet devices. Such apps are acquired from the Apple Store, Google Play, and the Windows Store. Mobile apps often have the following characteristics that should be considered:

- Frequently update data though the sizes of the updates are usually in the range of less than 1 kilobyte to less than 20 kilobytes.

- The apps themselves are updated more frequently than traditional desktop applications and such updates range from 2–3 megabytes to more than 100 megabytes.

- Some apps can be configured to work only on Wi-Fi.

- Many apps are ad-driven and may require access to sites blocked by the firewall to function.

In the requirements analysis phase, it is best to determine whether the organization will allow users to connect personal mobile devices to the network (support for BYOD), and if they will allow the use of any and all personal apps. It is not uncommon for the average mobile phone to consume 1–2 megabytes of throughput per hour which can impact the Internet connection within the organization in a significant way when thousands of personal mobile devices are connected on the campus.

Real-time

Real-time applications include both voice and video applications. These types of application include Voice over IP (VoIP), video conferencing, and media and audio streaming. Unless buffering is used, real-time data transfer must occur in order to prevent audio or video loss.

Because VoIP is widely used and sensitive to network latency and irregularities, this section will focus primarily on IP telephony.

You know about data networks and telephone networks, but how do we get telephone conversations to travel over data networks? The answer is a simple one—covert the audible telephone conversation into digital data packets. This conversion is accomplished with encoding standards, and the voice data packets are then transferred using standard or proprietary voice communication protocols. It's really no different than any other data communications process as to its technical nature; however, voice data packets do come with demands that are not seen in traditional data packets.

For example, if you are sending a file to a server using FTP, it doesn't matter if a few packets arrive out of order or if there happens to be a delay between the arrival of one packet and the arrival of the next packet that is greater than a particular threshold. Of course, if there is an extended delay it will slow down the communications, but the data will eventually arrive at the destination. Voice traffic will not tolerate such occurrences. If an extended delay occurs, the call will be dropped or quality will suffer.

If you think about it for a moment, you'll understand why this low tolerance is needed. Humans are at both ends of a VoIP communications link. They will both talk and listen and they have expectations that have been set by the analog telephone network. If they do not hear any sound for some variable length of time, they will assume that the call has been dropped or the person on the other end has disconnected. If the sound quality is inferior, particularly to the point where they cannot understand one another, they may give up on the conversation. Expectations of quality exist that must be met with VoIP data that have not traditionally been required of other data types. In fact, we often refer to "carrier grade" or "carrier quality" VoIP communications. This term means that we have accomplished a quality of sound and communication speed that is, at least, equivalent to the traditional PSTN.

Since we are transmitting the VoIP packets over the same physical network as traditional data packets (think e-mail, database access, file transfer, printing, etc.), we can say that we are layering voice over the data network. We are using the same network devices, cables, and software that are used for traditional data to transfer voice data. This layering places a new demand on the network. The demand is that the data network must be able to differentiate between different packet types and give priority to voice data so that the quality expectations of the VoIP users are met. The needed technology is known as Quality of Service (QoS).

Since voice traffic must move at a rapid speed across the network, and since it would not provide a benefit to resend the traffic if it is corrupted or lost in transmission, we use UDP to send most VoIP data packets. UDP is a connectionless protocol, unlike TCP. TCP has far too much overhead to transmit voice packets as rapidly as they must be transmitted.

You may wonder why there is no benefit from resending corrupted or lost voice packets. The reason is simple. Think about how long it takes you to say the word "don't". If you're like me, it will take you far less than a second. Now, imagine you're having a conversation on a VoIP phone and you say the following sentences: "Don't push the button. Pull the lever." Further imagine that the word "don't" was lost in transmission, and the system decided to resend it. Because of the sequencing problem, the user on the other end hears the following: "Push the button. Don't pull the lever." This reordering could theoretically happen because the phrase "push the button" made it through while the word "don't" didn't make it through. When the word "don't" was retransmitted, it was placed before the phrase "pull the lever." The result is a complete opposite of the intended message. Do you see why retransmitting lost audio packets would be useless and possibly damaging?

Instead, the listener would just not hear the word "don't;" however, the reality is that it all gets a bit more complex. More than likely the listener would hear something like, "D---t pu—the ---ton. Pu-- --- --ver." All the dashes represent either sounds that are unintelligible or complete silence. The point is that the network doesn't usually drop exact words, but rather portions of audio much less than a complete word, resulting in what we usually call a "bad connection."

Digital voice communications require encoding and decoding. This encoding and decoding takes time, and there is additional time accrued due to the actual transfer of the data from one endpoint to another endpoint. While encoding and decoding allow for the transmission of voice as data, compression allows for faster transfer of this data through the utilization of less bandwidth. The following paragraphs outline all three factors—encoding, decoding, and compression.

To convert analog sound waves (specifically voice waves in this case) into digitized bit streams, a coder/decoder (codec) is used. In order to convert the smooth variations in analog information to the abrupt changes in digital information, sampling rates are applied. The sampling rate is the number of times per second that the analog information is analyzed to convert it to digital information. A typical sampling rate is 8000 times per second. This notation would be written as 8 KHz (kilohertz) because it is a sampling rate or sampling frequency of 8000. The Nyquist Theorem suggests that a sampling rate of at least two times the highest frequency component of the analog information set results in an acceptable and accurate representation in a digital form. Analog to digital conversion is often called A-to-D or ADC.

When a higher sampling rate is used, the audio quality is improved on playback. However, a higher sampling rate means that more data is generated. When more data is generated, more bandwidth is consumed to transfer the data. Therefore, an acceptable loss in audio quality must be tolerated in order to use the bandwidth most effectively. This loss is why an individual's voice sounds different on a telephone than it does in person. We only sample enough and in the right frequency range to transfer intelligible communications with acceptable quality.

There are many standards for encoding audio in telephony networks. These include H.261, H.264, and the G7xx encoding algorithms.

The International Telecommunications Union (ITU) developed the H.261 codec in 1990 for the transmission of video over ISDN lines. H.264, also known as MPEG-4, is a video encoding standard also developed by the ITU. H.264 is used for video conferencing, HDTV, and VoIP. The big difference between H.261 and H.264 is that H.261 does not work well over Frame Relay or TCP/IP networks, and H.264 does work well in these environments.

When it comes to audio codecs, the G7xx series of standards are the most commonly utilized. Audio capability is the minimum standard required of an H.323 endpoint (they may support video as well), and so any H.323 endpoint must support the G.711 codec at a minimum. The G.7xx series of codecs are outlined as follows:

- G.711   Supports uncompressed audio encoding at 64 Kbps. This codec is required by H.323 in that any device claiming H.323 compliance must support it. You are not required to use it, but it must be supported.
- G.722   Encodes at 64, 56, and 48 Kbps.
- G.723/723.1   Encodes at 5.4 and 6.3 Kbps.
- G.729/729A   Encodes at 8 Kbps.

A form of bandwidth reduction used by many codecs is known as silence suppression. In most voice conversations, about half of either end's audio is silent. The G.729 codec will remove this silence before encoding the audio. G.711 doesn't remove this silence and makes for much larger bandwidth consumption rates. In addition, codecs may use advanced compression algorithms that look for redundant bits and other factors that allow for even greater compression of the voice data. Ultimately, the compression algorithms must balance the need for reduced bandwidth consumption and quick transfers of the audio data. All the compression must happen in a matter of microseconds for each voice packet.

Voice companding refers to the process of compressing the audio on the transmitting end and expanding the audio on the receiving end. Compressing and expanding equals companding. G.711 defines two different companding algorithms. Each is based on mathematical formulas or laws, and each is named for this law. The first is μ-Law (pronounced mu-law), and the second is a-law.

Here, μ-Law is a mathematical algorithm used for pulse code modulation (PCM). The algorithm represents analog amplitude values as compact digital codes. Three binary bits represent one of eight different ranges of amplitude values. Four more bits are used to represent an amplitude value within the range specified by the first three bits. The μ-Law algorithm is used in T1 lines in the Unites States and J1 lines in Japan.

A-Law is also a mathematical algorithm. The specifications are the same as for μ-Law in that the first three bits represent the range and the last four bits represent an amplitude in that range. A-Law companding is used primarily on E1 lines in Europe.

Several VoIP protocols should be understood in greater depth by the convergence technology professional. These protocols include:

- RTP/RTCP
- H.323
- SIP
- MGCP

The Real-time Transport Protocol (RTP) is, as its name implies, a transport protocol. Unlike FTP and many other protocols, RTP is usually implemented with the UDP protocol instead of TCP. TCP is connection oriented and has more overhead than UDP. UDP is normally a send-it-and-forget-it protocol, which is perfect for the transmission of voice information. Resending voice packets is not only useless, but it can also cause unnecessary network consumption. So RTP is used to transfer the stream of information that is the voice data in a phone conversation.

RTP was first published in 1996 as RFC 1889; however, RFC 3550 supersedes RFC 1889 and defines the current standard for RTP. RFC 3550, published in July of 2003, defines a standardized packet format used for the delivery of audio and video over internetworks. The focus of RTP is on real-time applications. According to the RFC:

RTP provides end-to-end network transport functions suitable for applications transmitting real-time data, such as audio, video or simulation data, over multicast or unicast network services. RTP does not address resource reservation and does not guarantee quality-of-service for real-time services.

Contained in this quote are two key facts you should know. First, RTP is used between two or more endpoints. The term end-to-end indicates that it is used for the real-time transfer of data between these endpoints. Second, RTP has no internal QoS mechanisms and does not ensure the required resources for its operation. However, RTP layers over the IP protocol, which does offer QoS capabilities. RTP can take advantage of the QoS capabilities in the IP protocol implementation.

RFC 3550 provides four basic services for the delivery of real-time information:

- Payload Type Identification: Because RTP can carry any real-time information, the RTP header provides a field for payload identification. The field can identify the codec used and the sample rate. It is a 7-bit field.

- Sequence Numbering: The sequence number for each RTP packet is stored in a two octet (two byte) field within the packet header. The sequence number allows for detection of dropped packets or out-of-order packets.

- Timestamping: The timestamp is a 32-bit field, which is used to determine the timing of the current packet's data within a stream. This allows for proper sequencing of packets that are encoded out of sequence (for example, the sequence numbers do not reflect the actual required order of playback).

- Delivery Monitoring: Delivery monitoring and all other monitoring is provided through the RTCP component defined in RFC 3550. RTCP is covered later in this section.

You should be familiar with the following terminology, as defined in RFC 3550, in order to fully understand the functionality of RTP and RTCP (the definitions have been extracted directly from the RFC and any references to sections are in reference to the RFC itself and not this book):

- RTP payload: The data transported by RTP in a packet, for example audio samples or compressed video data. The payload format and interpretation are beyond the scope of this document.

- RTP packet: A data packet consisting of the fixed RTP header, a possibly empty list of contributing sources (see below), and the payload data. Some underlying protocols may require an encapsulation of the RTP packet to be defined. Typically one packet of the underlying protocol contains a single RTP packet, but several RTP packets MAY be contained, if permitted, by the encapsulation method (see Section 11 [of RFC 3550]).

- RTCP packet: A control packet consisting of a fixed header part similar to that of RTP data packets, followed by structured elements that vary depending upon the RTCP packet type. The formats are defined in Section 6. Typically, multiple RTCP packets are sent together as a compound RTCP packet in a single packet of the underlying protocol; this is enabled by the length field in the fixed header of each RTCP packet.

- Port: The "abstraction that transport protocols use to distinguish among multiple destinations within a given host computer. TCP/IP protocols identify ports using small positive integers." [12] The transport selectors (TSEL) used by the OSI transport layer are equivalent to ports. RTP depends upon the lower-layer protocol to provide some mechanism such as ports to multiplex the RTP and RTCP packets of a session.

- Transport address: The combination of a network address and port that identifies a transport-level endpoint, for example an IP address and a UDP port. Packets are transmitted from a source transport address to a destination transport address.

- RTP media type: An RTP media type is the collection of payload types that can be carried within a single RTP session. The RTP Profile assigns RTP media types to RTP payload types.

- Multimedia session: A set of concurrent RTP sessions among a common group of participants. For example, a videoconference (which is a multimedia session) may contain an audio RTP session and a video RTP session.

- RTP session: An association among a set of participants communicating with RTP. A participant may be involved in multiple RTP sessions at the same time. In a multimedia session, each medium is typically carried in a separate RTP session with its own RTCP packets unless the encoding itself multiplexes multiple media into a single data stream. A participant distinguishes multiple RTP sessions by reception of different sessions using different pairs of destination transport addresses, where a pair of transport addresses comprises one network address plus a pair of ports for RTP and RTCP. All participants in an RTP session may share a common destination transport address pair, as in the case of IP multicast, or the pairs may be different for each participant, as in the case of individual unicast network addresses and port pairs. In the unicast case, a participant may receive from all other participants in the session using the same pair of ports, or may use a distinct pair of ports for each.

The distinguishing feature of an RTP session is that each maintains a full, separate space of SSRC identifiers (defined next). The set of participants included in one RTP session consists of those that can receive an SSRC identifier transmitted by any one of the participants either in RTP as the SSRC or a CSRC (also defined below) or in RTCP. For example, consider a three-party conference implemented using unicast UDP with each participant receiving from the other two on separate port pairs. If each participant sends RTCP feedback about data received from one other participant only back to that participant, then the conference is composed of three separate point-to-point RTP sessions. If each participant provides RTCP feedback about its reception of one other participant to both of the other participants, then the conference is composed of one multi-party RTP session. The latter case simulates the behavior that would occur with IP multicast communication among the three participants. The RTP framework allows the variations defined here, but a particular control protocol or application design will usually impose constraints on these variations.

- Synchronization source (SSRC): The source of stream of RTP packets identified by a 32-bit numeric SSRC identifier carried in the RTP header so as not to be dependent upon the network address. All packets from a synchronization source form part of the same timing and sequence number space, so a receiver is able to group the packets by its synchronization source for playback. Examples of synchronization sources include the sender of a stream of packets derived from a signal source such as a microphone or a camera, or an RTP mixer (see below). A synchronization source may change its data format, (e.g., audio encoding) over time. The SSRC identifier is a randomly chosen value meant to be globally unique within a particular RTP session (see Section 8 [of RFC 3550]). A participant need not use the same SSRC identifier for all the RTP sessions in a multimedia session; the binding of the SSRC identifiers is provided through RTCP (see Section 6.5.1 [of RFC 3550]). If a participant generates multiple streams in one RTP session, for example from separate video cameras, each MUST be identified as a different SSRC.

- Contributing source (CSRC): A source of a stream of RTP packets that has contributed to the combined stream produced by an RTP mixer (see below). The mixer inserts a list of the SSRC identifiers of the sources that contributed to the generation of a particular packet into the RTP header of that packet. This list is called the CSRC list. An example application is audio conferencing where a mixer indicates all the talkers whose speech was combined to produce the outgoing packet, allowing the receiver to indicate the current talker, even though all the audio packets contain the same SSRC identifier (as that of the mixer).

- End system: An application that generates the content to be sent in RTP packets and/or consumes the content of received RTP packets. An end system can act as one or more synchronization sources in a particular RTP session, but typically only one.

44

- Mixer: An intermediate system that receives RTP packets from one or more sources, possibly changes the data format, combines the packets in some manner, and then forwards a new RTP packet. Since the timing among multiple input sources will not generally be synchronized, the mixer will make timing adjustments among the streams and generate its own timing for the combined stream. Thus, all data packets originating from a mixer will be identified as having the mixer as their synchronization source.

- Translator: An intermediate system that forwards RTP packets with their synchronization source identifier intact. Examples of translators include devices that convert encodings without mixing, replicators from multicast to unicast, and application-level filters in firewalls.

- Monitor: An application that receives RTCP packets sent by participants in an RTP session, in particular the reception reports, and estimates the current quality of service for distribution monitoring, fault diagnosis, and long-term statistics. The monitor function is likely to be built into the application(s) participating in the session, but may also be a separate application that does not otherwise participate and does not send or receive the RTP data packets (since they are on a separate port). These are called third-party monitors. It is also acceptable for a third-party monitor to receive the RTP data packets but not send RTCP packets or otherwise be counted in the session.

Non-RTP means: Protocols and mechanisms that may be needed in addition to RTP to provide a usable service. In particular, for multimedia conferences, a control protocol may distribute multicast addresses and keys for encryption, negotiate the encryption algorithm to be used, and define dynamic mappings between RTP payload type values and the payload formats they represent for formats that do not have a predefined payload type value. Examples of such protocols include the Session Initiation Protocol (SIP) (RFC 3261 [13]), ITU Recommendation H.323 [14] and applications using SDP (RFC 2327 [15]), such as RTSP (RFC 2326 [16]). For simple applications, electronic mail, or a conference database may also be used. The specification of such protocols and mechanisms is outside the scope of this document.

The preceding definitions are Copyright © The Internet Society (2003). All Rights Reserved.

To help you better understand how the RTP protocol works, consider the RTP header and the functions of each part. Figure 2.7 shows the structure of the RTP header in ASCII representation as it is displayed in the RFC.

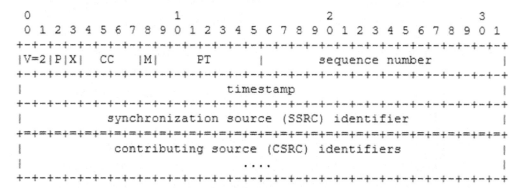

Figure 2.7—RTP Header Details from RFC 3550

If you've never read an RFC, RFC 3550 might be a good first read. It is an easy read in comparison to many other RFCs. However, whether you read it or not, most RFCs use formats like the one in Figure 2.7 when they need to represent the frame formats or packet structures for networking protocols.

The first thing to note about the RTP frame structure is true of all networking frames. This truth is that all frames are a series of bits. The frames are a collection of organized ones and zeros. The payload is just a collection of ones and zeros itself, but the carrying protocol (in this case RTP) doesn't really need to interpret the payload data in any way. The carrying protocol provides the information needed to properly transport and process the payload information. The RTP header, as defined in the RFC and depicted in Figure 2.7, provides this needed information.

The following descriptions address each field in the RTP header:

- Version (V): This first 2-bit field is used to indicate the version of RTP in use. Currently, version 2 is the newest version. Version 1 was the draft standard and version 0 was a more proprietary solution. Because the field is 2 bits, it can contain any number from 0 to 3 in decimal.

- Padding (P): This 1-bit field is set when the packet contains padding bytes at the end. The padding bytes are not part of the payload and are used with encryption algorithms requiting fixed block sizes. Padding bytes may also be needed when carrying multiple RTP packets in a lower-layer protocol. Because the field is 1 bit, it can contain the value of 0 (no padding octets) or 1 (padding octets included).

- Extension (X): The extension bit is a 1-bit field. When the extension bit is set (the value is 1 and not 0), the header must be followed by a header extension. An RTP header extension is used to allow customizations to the RTP header for specific use profiles.

- CSRC Count (CC): The CC field specifies the number of CSRC identifiers that come after the fixed header. This is a 4-bit field.

- Marker (M): The marker field is interpreted differently depending on the profile. RTP works based on profiles and the profiles identify different use scenarios (such as VoIP or video streaming). The marker field is 1 bit and is used to identify significant events like frame boundaries in the packet stream.

- Payload Type (PT): The PT field is 7 bits and is used to indicate the format of the RTP payload and how that payload should be processed by the receiving application. RFC 3551 identifies default mappings for audio and video payloads. For example, RFC 3551 suggests that G.729 should be PT 18 and G.723 should be PT 4. Table 2-2 provides a listing of the default PT values for different protocols based on RFC 3551. If a receiver is unaware of a defined PT, the standard dictates that the packet must be ignored, which provides better security.

- Sequence Number: The sequence number is a field in the RTP header and it is a 16-bit value. The sequence number increments by one for each RTP packet sent. The receiver can use this number to detect lost packets or to restore the packet sequencing if they arrive out of order. The standard recommends that the initial sequence number value be determined by a random algorithm.

- Timestamp: The timestamp field is 32 bits. The timestamp reflects the sampling instant of the first octet (byte) in the RTP packet. It is used to allow synchronization between the communicating machines and to perform jitter calculations.

- Synchronization Source (SSRC): This 32-bit field defines the synchronization source. The source is identified randomly so that no two sources within the same RTP session will have the same SSRC identifier. Because random algorithms can generate the same value (though it is less likely with 32-bit numbers), the RTP protocol must implement algorithms to detect and resolve collisions. Section 8 of RFC 3550 provides a mechanism for collision detection and resolution and indicates that the probability of two sources having the same identifier is roughly 10-4. The code listing following this RTP header field list is the algorithm suggested by RFC 3550.

- Contributing Sources (CSRC): The CSRC field may contain from 0 to 15 items of 32-bits each. The list defines the contributing sources for the payload in the packet and is applicable in conferencing scenarios where multiple audio streams are combined. When more than 15 CSRCs are included, only 15 may be identified. The CSRCs are added by mixers (conferencing servers) and the individual SSRCs are used.

Table 2-2 shows the Payload Type (PT) values of common codecs.

Codec	PT Value
GSM	3
G.723	4
G.728	15
G.729	18
G.726(16)	dynamic
G.726(24)	dynamic
G.726(32)	dynamic
G.726(40)	dynamic
H.263	34

Table 2-2—PT Values for Different Codecs

Because RTP is used to transfer the data packets and provides no session setup or management, another protocol is needed for the monitoring of a data stream. This is where the RTCP protocol comes in.

The RTP Control Protocol (RTCP) is used to provide four basic functions.

- The first and primary function is providing feedback on the quality of data distribution. The information provided may be used for control of dynamic or adaptive encoding solutions and it is critical for fault detection within the distribution system (such as frame loss, jitter, and delay).

- The second function is the transfer of a persistent transport-level ID for each RTP source known as the canonical name or CNAME. The CNAME is similar to DNS names on the Internet. The SSRS may change due to conflicts; however, the CNAME will remain the same. This construct is similar to the way an IP address may change while the DNS host name remains the same. These first two functions of RTCP are critical to the operations of a media-transport network and are most important in a multicast environment such as conferencing or multicast audio and video streaming.

- The third function of RTCP is the management of rate so that all participants can send RTCP packets. The rate at which packets are sent directly depends on the number of participants in the communication.

- The fourth function, which is optional, is used to convey session control information. This information may include participant identification. The methods by which session control information is generated is beyond the scope of this book or RFC 3550.

Five major RTCP packet types are defined in RFC 3550. These five types are:

- **Sender report (SR):** The sender report includes transmission and reception statistics from active participants in the communication. The RTCP header identifies a SR packet with the PT field set to 200.

- **Receiver report (RR):** The receiver report includes reception statistics from non-active participants in the communication (such as listeners of an audio stream who cannot talk). The RTCP header identifies an RR packet with the PT field set to 201.

- **Source Description (SDES):** Source description items such as the CNAME. While the CNAME is mandatory, other optional items may be included. These items include the NAME (a personal name), the EMAIL (the email address of the participant), the PHONE (the participant's phone number), the LOC (user's geographic location), the NOTE (notice or status information), the TOOL (the application or tool name generating the stream), and private extensions for application-specific SDES values (PRIV). The RTCP header identifies an SDES packet with the PT field set to 202.

- **BYE:** Used to end participation in an RTP session. The RTCP header identifies a BYE packet with the PT field set to 203.

- **APP:** Provides for application-specific functions. The RTCP header identifies an APP packet with the PT field set to 204.

RTCP packets, like RTP packets, begin with a fixed header and then end with flexible lengths depending on the RTCP packet type. All RTCP packets must be divisible by 32-bits. This constraint is imposed so that multiple RTCP packets can be stacked and placed into a compound RTCP packet.

The most important of these RTCP packets are the sender and receiver reports. These reports are used to make adjustments to the RTP streams to accommodate actual operations on the network. They can also be used to locate the source of a problem (on your local network, on the WAN, etc.). The sender reports include the following useful information:

- **NTP timestamp:** The actual time (wall clock time) when the report was sent. Used with RTP timestamps to calculate round-trip times and other values.

- **RTP timestamp:** Relates to the NTP timestamp, but is defined in the same unites and random offset as the RTP timestamps in the monitored data packets.

- **Sender's packet count:** The total number of RTP data packets sent since starting the transmission.

- **Sender's octet count:** The total number of octets (bytes) sent in the payload of RTP packets since starting the transmission.

- **Fraction lost:** The number of RTP data packets lost since the previous sender report or receiver report.

- **Cumulative number of packets lost:** The total number of lost packets since the transmission began.

- **Interarrival jitter:** An estimation of the variance in RTP data packet arrival times.

The receiver report contains the same information minus the NTP and RTP timestamps and the sender's packet and octet counters. According to RFC 3550 several calculations may be valuable and processed against the sender and receiver reports:

It is expected that reception quality feedback will be useful not only for the sender but also for other receivers and third-party monitors. The sender may modify its transmissions based on the feedback; receivers can determine whether problems are local, regional or global; network managers may use profile-independent monitors that receive only the RTCP packets and not the corresponding RTP data packets to evaluate the performance of their networks for multicast distribution.

Cumulative counts are used in both the sender information and receiver report blocks so that differences may be calculated between any two reports to make measurements over both short and long time periods, and to provide resilience against the loss of a report. The difference between the last two reports received can be used to estimate the recent quality of the distribution. The NTP timestamp is included so that rates may be calculated from these differences over the interval between two reports. Since that timestamp is independent of the clock rate for the data encoding, it is possible to implement encoding- and profile-independent quality monitors.

An example calculation is the packet loss rate over the interval between two reception reports. The difference in the cumulative number of packets lost gives the number lost during that interval. The difference in the extended last sequence numbers received gives the number of packets expected during the interval. The ratio of these two is the packet loss fraction over the interval. This ratio should equal the fraction lost field if the two reports are consecutive, but otherwise it may not. The loss rate per second can be obtained by dividing the loss fraction by the difference in NTP timestamps, expressed in seconds. The number of packets received is the number of packets expected minus the number lost. The number of packets expected may also be used to judge the statistical validity of any loss estimates. For example, 1 out of 5 packets lost has a lower significance than 200 out of 1000.

From the sender information, a third-party monitor can calculate the average payload data rate and the average packet rate over an interval without receiving the data. Taking the ratio of the two gives the average payload size. If it can be assumed that packet loss is independent of packet size, then the number of packets received by a particular receiver times the average payload size (or the corresponding packet size) gives the apparent throughput available to that receiver.

In addition to the cumulative counts which allow long-term packet loss measurements using differences between reports, the fraction lost field provides a short-term measurement from a single report. This becomes more important as the size of a session scales up enough that reception state information might not be kept for all receivers or the interval between reports becomes long enough that only one report might have been received from a particular receiver.

The interarrival jitter field provides a second short-term measure of network congestion. Packet loss tracks persistent congestion while the jitter measure tracks transient congestion. The jitter measure may indicate congestion before it leads to packet loss. The interarrival jitter field is only a snapshot of the jitter at the time of a report and is not intended to be taken quantitatively. Rather, it is intended for comparison across a number of reports from one receiver over time or from multiple receivers, e.g., within a single network, at the same time. To allow comparison across receivers, it is important the jitter be calculated according to the same formula by all receivers.

Because the jitter calculation is based on the RTP timestamp which represents the instant when the first data in the packet was sampled, any variation in the delay between that sampling instant and the time the packet is transmitted will affect the resulting jitter that is calculated. Such a variation in delay would occur for audio packets of varying duration. It will also occur for video encodings because the timestamp is the same for all the packets of one frame but those packets are not all transmitted at the same time. The variation in delay until transmission does reduce the accuracy of the jitter calculation as a measure of the behavior of the network by itself, but it is appropriate to include considering that the receiver buffer must accommodate it. When the jitter calculation is used as a comparative measure, the (constant) component due to variation in delay until transmission subtracts out so that a change in the network jitter component can then be *observed unless it is relatively small. If the change is small, then it is likely to be inconsequential.*

Unlike RTP, which is defined in a single RFC and updated as a single protocol, H.323 is a standard that encompasses many protocols. Much like TCP/IP, we often refer to H.323 as a protocol suite because multiple protocols are defined under the H.323 umbrella. H.323 is a standard that defines the components (roles and devices) and protocols for multimedia communications over IP or packet networks. The multimedia communications include VoIP as well as real-time video or data (such as video conferencing services).

The H.323 protocol suite includes protocols for three primary purposes. The first is endpoint or terminal control and management. These protocols allow you to set up a call and manage the features available for that call. The second is the audio and video protocols. These protocols include the codecs used to encode and possibly compress the call data. The third set of protocols is used for data communications, and they are not covered in detail here. These protocols allow for the transfer of data files and information, and they use their own proprietary Layer 4 solution (T.123). Figure 2.8 depicts the H.323 protocol suite in detail.

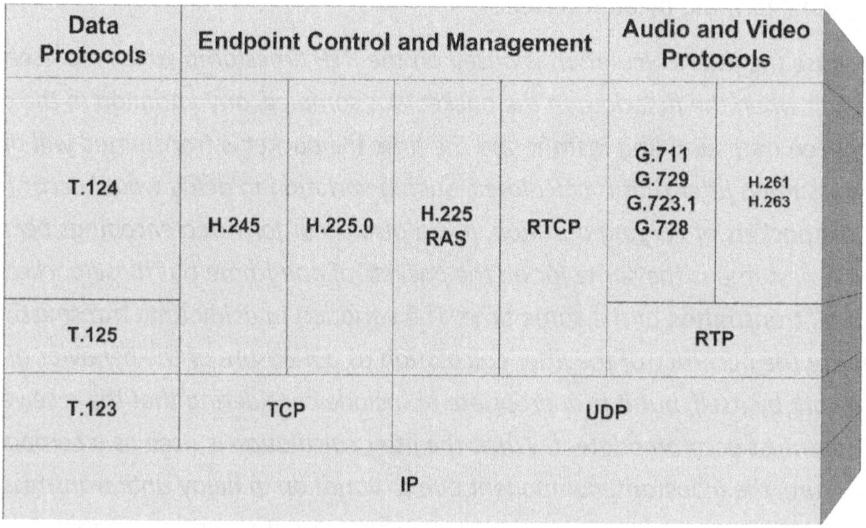

Data Protocols	Endpoint Control and Management				Audio and Video Protocols	
T.124	H.245	H.225.0	H.225 RAS	RTCP	G.711 G.729 G.723.1 G.728	H.261 H.263
T.125					RTP	
T.123	TCP		UDP			
IP						

Figure 2.8—H.323 Protocol Suite

It is important that you understand the basic purpose of each protocol. The following list should help you remember the reason each protocol is used and its role in a VoIP network.

- **IP**: The Internet Protocol (IP) is the Layer 3 protocol used on all VoIP networks; hence, the IP in VoIP. IP is used to transport the TCP and UDP packets across the routed network or across the LAN segment. IP is used in both routed and non-routed networks.

- **TCP:** When the upper layer protocol requires delivery verification, the Transport Control Protocol (TCP) is used. For H.323, TCP is used for the initial call setup with H.225.0 and H.245.

- **UDP:** When the upper layer protocol does not require delivery verification, the User Datagram Protocol (UDP) is used. For H.323, UDP is used for H.224 RAS messages, RTCP packets, and the actual data streams (audio or video encoded packets).

- **H.245:** The control signaling between H.323 endpoints (terminals) is performed with H.245. Control signaling includes capabilities or features exchange, flow-control messaging, initiating and terminating of logical channels for media streams, and other general commands or notifications. In Cisco VoIP networks, for example, the key utilization of H.245 is in feature communications.

- **H.225:** The initial connection between two H.323 endpoints is achieved using H.225. H.225 protocol messages are exchanged on the call-signaling channel, which is opened between the endpoints or between the endpoint and a gatekeeper when H.323 gatekeepers are in use.

- **H.225 RAS:** The H.225 Registration, Admission and Status (RAS) is used to transfer messages between endpoints and gatekeepers. Registration, admission control, status messages, bandwidth changes, and call termination procedures are all handled by H.225 RAS. H.225 RAS is typically used only when an H.323 gatekeeper is present on the VoIP network.

- **RTP:** The Real-Time Transport Protocol (RTP) is used to transport the actual voice data on an H.323 VoIP network. RTP uses UTP for communications. Payload identification, timestamps, delivering monitoring and sequence numbering are all provided by RTP.

- **RTCP:** The Real-Time Transport control Protocol (RTCP) is used for control services in relation to RTP. The provision of feedback is the primary function of RTCP. Quality measurements provided by RTCP can be used to adjust networking communications for QoS improvements.

- **G.7xx:** The G.7xx series of codecs are specified as ITU-T standards. H.323 terminals must support at least the G.711 codec and may support additional codecs such as G.722, G.723, G.728, and G.729.

- **H.26x:** When H.323 terminals provide video services, they will use the H.26x series of ITU-T standards. The H.261 recommendation is required as a minimum for H.323 terminals supporting video communications. H.263 and H.264 are additional recommendations that may be supported by H.323 terminals.

Session Initiation Protocol (SIP)

The Session Initiation Protocol (SIP) is a modern alternative to H.323. While H.323 was first developed in 1996, SIP began development in that same year and was finalized in 1999. The current RFC for SIP (RFC 3261) was finalized in 2002. Because of SIP's later development, it was able to learn from H.323 and incorporate the good components already there. In this section, you will learn about the basics of the SIP protocol.

SIP was created but the Internet Engineering Task Force (IETF). It is built from several other protocols that previously existed and adds new features as well. For example, SIP builds on HTTP, SMTP, DNS, and RTP. It is today more popular than H.323 in new implementations.

SIP uses text-based communications. Stated differently, the ASCII character set is used to communicate SIP messages. Because of this format, SIP is easier to analyze and understand than most other networking protocols. Instead of worrying about the number of bits in a header that represent specific data, we are looking at plain text that clearly indicates the meaning. The messages are still said to have headers, but the headers are in ASCII text format instead of binary bit format.

SIP is a simplified protocol when compared the H.323. This simplification comes from that fact that SIP includes everything needed to establish the VoIP call instead of using one protocol for call setup (H.225.0 in H.323 networks) and another for feature negotiation (H.245 in H.323 networks). Many assume this always makes SIP the better choice; however, it could be argued that H.323's componentized nature makes it more flexible for implementation. Regardless of the side of the argument you take, you must understand the basics of both protocols for the CTP+ exam.

When it comes to SIP addressing (locating SIP endpoints), the addresses may look very familiar to you. For example, an address for Joe User may look like this:

SIP://Joe.User@CWNP.com

This address format is technically known as a URI or a Uniform Resource Identifier. URIs provide a standard way to reference a resource on an internetwork. Here are some other examples of URIs:

HTTP://www.CWNP.com

FTP://ftp.download.com

Do you recognize these? You probably do because they are used all over the Internet. URIs work for HTTP, FTP, SIP, and even Gopher (although Gopher is not as popular today as it once was). You can also access a SIP device securely using the secure SIP protocol (which takes advantage of TLS) with a URI like the following:

SIPS://Joe.User@CWNP.com

As you can see, even the addressing used in the SIP world is based on Internet standards. The most important feature of the SIP protocol that has allowed it to catapult beyond its predecessors to success seems to be this use of existing Internet standards whenever possible.

When considering the components used in a SIP network, you must first realize that the network infrastructure must exist to support the SIP-specific components. In other words, SIP doesn't define DNS, but it will rely on DNS for name resolution. DNS must already exist in your network infrastructure or at least be accessible by the infrastructure.

In addition to the network infrastructure, the following basic SIP components should be understood:

- **User Agent (UA):** When SIP is used to implement VoIP, the UA is the VoIP phone on the network. The UA may be hardware when a mobile IP phone is used, for example, or it may be software when the softphone is used. Additionally, a gateway may be considered a SIP UA as it communicates using the SIP protocol.

- **User Agent Client (UAC):** The UAC is the UA that sends a request message using the SIP protocol. For example, the UA sending an INVITE message to begin a call is the UAC. The practical example is the VoIP phone that dials the call or starts the call.

- **User Agent Server (UAS):** The UAS is the UA that responds to a request message using the SIP protocol. The practical example is the VoIP phone that receives the call.

- **Server:** A server, in the SIP protocol terminology, can be one of several components. It can be the UA when it is acting as the UAS. It can be a registrar, a proxy, or a redirect server.

- **SIP Proxy:** The SIP proxy is the component that acts as a server to one UA (or another proxy) and a client to another UA (or another proxy).

- **Registrar:** The registrar server manages the registration database. The registration database contains the UA to address mappings for the local network.

- **Redirect Server:** The redirect server is the SIP server capable of directing a UA to the appropriate server with the information about the target when the

58

target is not managed in the location database (managed by the location service).

- **Location Service:** The location service uses the Lightweight Directory Access Protocol (LDAP) as the directory source for UA location. Microsoft's Active Directory also uses LDAP.

The SIP methods are the actions taken by the UAs or the requests they make. For example, when a SIP phone initiates a call, it uses the INVITE method to invite another SIP phone into the association. The SIP protocol supports several methods. These methods are listed in Table 2-3 with descriptions.

SIP Method	Description
INVITE	Used to begin a SIP session between two UAs.
BYE	Used to end a call or decline a call.
CANCEL	Used to terminate any request.
ACK	Used to acknowledge receipt of an INVITE.
REGISTER	Used to register with the SIP registrar server.
OPTIONS	Used to get information about a server's capabilities.
INFO	Used for signaling within a SIP session or call.

Table 2-3—SIP methods and Descriptions

The Media Gateway Control Protocol (MGCP) is a client-server call management protocol with a centralized control design. MGCP servers (referenced as call agents in the standard) control the gateways used to connect your VoIP networks to other networks. Several gateway types are defined in the MGCP standard including:

- **Trunking gateways:** interface between the telephone network and a Voice over IP network.

- **Voice over ATM gateways:** operate much the same way as voice over IP trunking gateways, except that they interface to an ATM network.

- **Residential gateways:** provide a traditional analog (RJ11) interface to a Voice over IP network. Examples of residential gateways include cable modem/cable set-top boxes, xDSL devices, and broad-band wireless devices.

- **Access gateways:** provide a traditional analog (RJ11) or digital PBX interface to a VoIP network.

- **Business gateways:** provide a traditional digital PBX interface or an integrated "soft PBX" interface to a VoIP network.

- **Network Access Servers:** can attach a "modem" to a telephone circuit and provide data access to the Internet.

- **Circuit switches or packet switches:** can offer a control interface to an external call control element.

The newest standard for MGCP is defined in RFCs 3435 and 3661. The original RFCs were 2705 and 3660, but they were superseded by the newest standards documents. In these RFCs, it is clearly stated that the gateway types may not be exclusive, but vendors may choose to implement a PBX gateway and a VoIP gateway all in one unit. Cisco integrated services routers are such an example of gateways that may be implemented in this way.

Cisco environments commonly implement MGCP. With MGCP, dial plans are completely controlled from within the Cisco Unified Communications Manager (UCM) because the UCM is aware of all voice ports in MGCP gateways. The dial plan includes the definitions for call routing and connectivity. This centralization of intelligence makes the configuration of the MGCP gateways much simpler; however, the configurations must still be managed in the UCM.

The UDP protocol is used to send ASCII text messages between the UCM and an MGCP gateway on UDP port 2427. Because of the ASCII message format, the monitoring and debugging of MGCP messages is simple in the same way as SIP.

Several Cisco devices support MGCP including the Cisco 2600XM series ISRs, the Cisco 2800 series ISRs, the 3700/3800 series ISRs and the Cisco VG224 Analog Phone Gateway. It's also important to know that the Cisco Unified Communications Manager Express (CME) and the Cisco Small Business Communications System (SBCS) do not support MGCP.

This extended coverage of VoIP protocols was not without purpose. It is essential, as a WLAN designer, that you understand the parts and pieces that make VoIP work so that you can plan for their operation on the WLAN. For example, you must be sure that the messaging protocols and control protocols have connectivity as required. You must ensure that the voice data protocols can transmit the data quickly and without troublesome jitter.

The same kind of considerations must be made for video conferencing and media streaming solutions. First, video (with audio) still includes voice data; therefore, the same challenges of latency exist as for VoIP. However, video overheard is also added. Most video conferencing systems will sacrifice video quality first to ensure that you can hear the audio, but these settings can typically be tuned. The point for a WLAN designer is to ensure that you understand the throughput requirements of the different video conferencing systems to be used and then ensure that the WLAN is capable of performing as required.

High-Data Volume Applications

High-data volume applications are those that transfer more than a few megabytes every hour. Some applications, for example, are designed specifically to update many other portions of a device. For example, the App Store on iOS devices may download more than a gigabyte of data to perform updates on a few dozen applications. Another example is Windows Update, which has become even more difficult to manage on personal laptops with the release of Windows 10. Windows Update may download several gigabytes of data in a single launch. Figure 2.9 shows the new Windows 10 update interface.

If you allow BYOD with personal laptops, it will not be uncommon for those users to download Windows Updates from the work network. These updates can flood the network with extra data downloads that provide no business value. As part of the Wi-Fi design recommendation, it may be useful to recommend blocking the Microsoft Update web sites to prevent this behavior. When only 10–15 laptops are allowed to connect, it may not be a significant problem; however, if hundreds of personal laptops are allowed to connect, it can overload the Internet connection quickly.

 Note: **As an alternative to blocking the Microsoft Update sites, you can consider providing an internal update server and configuring all allowed personal laptops to use that server first for updates. This will prevent overloading of the Internet connection, but it will not prevent excessive use of the Wi-Fi data throughput availability.**

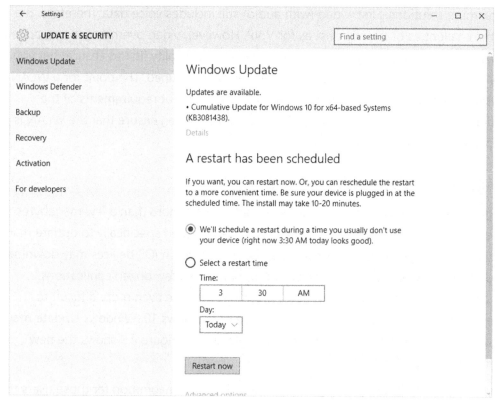

Figure 2.9—Windows 10 Windows Update Interface

Defining Security Requirements

Security is an essential part of any WLAN design. When designing security solutions, the designer must consider items such as fast secure roaming, network monitoring, Bring Your Own Device (BYOD)/Mobile Device Management (MDM), and guest access.

This section provides an overview of the information that should be gathered to properly plan for WLAN security.

Planning Authentication and Encryption

Selecting the right authentication and encryption solution can be achieved from one of two perspectives—hard requirements or client support. When selecting based on hard requirements, the organization dictates that certain authentication and encryption minimums must be supported or the client device will not be allowed. That is, if a client device does not support the security requirements, it will not be allowed on the network. This mode is often enforced using Network Access Control (NAC) solutions. An example of this is the many government implementations that have minimum security requirements like the DoD Instruction 8420, which requires:

- EAP-TLS support
- WPA2-Enterprise certification
- Implemented encryption must comply with FIPS-140

This is just one example, but it is an important example to consider. Additional examples include healthcare and payment processing systems. In environments like these, it is important to have hard requirements and only allow clients onto the network that meet these requirements.

In less secure environments, selecting security based on client support is common. For example, many WLANs are still implemented today supporting WPA-Personal because they use VoIP handsets that do not support WPA2-Personal or Enterprise. In these scenarios, the clients drive the security solutions. However, even in such cases, the security should at least meat some minimally accepted standard. For example, the

WPA-Personal passphrase should be complex and longer (15–20 characters) to avoid simple attack methods.

Fast Secure Roaming

When VoIP is used, as well as other highly mobile applications, roaming becomes very important. In early WLANs, because roaming took significant time and could even result in change of IP configuration, many environments were implemented with all wireless APs and their clients on the same VLANs, and no security or only passphrase-based security was used. As more wireless clients came onto the networks, it was obvious that a single large IP domain wouldn't work well. Additionally, early passphrase-based security solutions proved to be very weak (such as WEP). Today, Fast Secure Roaming can be implemented in several ways, but two primary methods are used—proprietary and standards-based.

Opportunistic Key Caching (OKC) is a method used by many vendors but implemented with a bit of mystery behind the scenes. The 802.11 standard now has secure roaming defined within it and the standards methods is becoming more and more common in modern WLAN hardware. The 802.11r and 802.11k amendments made it possible to begin implementing secure roaming in a standards-based method. The details of the roaming are not essential for the WLAN designer to understand, but she should be aware that three basic options are available for implementing secure roaming depending on client requirements:

1. OKC using proprietary solutions that may not work well with all devices.

2. 802.11-2012 Fast Secure Roaming that may not yet be supported with all devices.

3. WPA-Personal or WPA2-Personal, which has the widest support but increases management overhead.

It is important to note that an additional option is available with some vendors that provide a per-used pre-shared key (PPSK). This solution allows each device to have its own PSK rather than sharing a PSK with every device on the WLAN. The result is an increase in security.

Devices that require fast secure roaming include VoIP handsets, some one-to-one communication devices, and some industry-specific devices. Laptops and tablets may require it depending on the technologies used; however, when only non-real-time applications are used, slow roaming is often effective—particularly if the IP address is not lost. This is due to the recoverability in many protocols.

EXAM MOMENT: Layer 2 roaming is acceptable for most applications as it does not break the network connections of higher layers. Layer 3 roaming may cause many applications to fail or require a reset because it changes the IP address and results in lost connections for higher layers.

Network Monitoring

WLANs have traditionally been considered vulnerable to:

- Hijacking
- RF Jamming (DoS)
- Protocol Attacks
- Eavesdropping
- Spoofing
- Man-in-the Middle Attacks
- Management Interface Exploits
- Encryption Cracking
- Authentication Attacks
- Peer-to-Peer Attacks

These attacks are common and a solution exists to discover and mitigate many of them. Wireless Intrusion Prevention System (WIPS) solutions consist of a centralized server appliance with distributed sensors that are used for monitoring and sometimes interacting with the WLAN environment. Two different kinds of WIPS systems exist—integrated and overlay. Integrated WIPS are found as part of a WLAN infrastructure system where the functionality of a WIPS is built into the controller. An overlay WIP is a standalone system with its own sensors. Each type presents advantages and disadvantages.

When designing a WLAN, network monitoring or WIPS solutions should be considered. When recommending a solution, the choices are between the integrated and overlay models. The customer should understand both options and be able to make an educated decision as to which model is best for them.

In many cases, an existing WIPS solution may be in place with an older WLAN, but it is important to remember that such a system may require an upgrade itself to support full detection operations of the modern PHYs.

BYOD/MDM

Bring Your Own Device (BYOD) is a phrase or acronym used to reference the use of personal devices on the organization's network and possibly for organizational work processes. BYOD can be considered a problem, but rather than thinking of BYOD as a problem, many organizations consider it a benefit. Potential benefits include:

- **Enhanced productivity:** Users can do more work on the same devices that hold their personal information, which often enhances productivity. For example, rather than using one mobile device for corporate email and another for personal email, the user may simply use two email apps on a single device. In some cases, multiple accounts may even be aggregated into a single email app. This use case provides for enhanced productivity through reduced device or app switching.

- **Decreased costs:** Organizations can save money by allowing employees to do business work on personal devices. In this case, the benefit is very direct and measurable. Rather than purchasing a device that the user will use for personal and business uses, the organization simply allows the user the option of using their personal device for business uses. Many organizations will provide a partial reimbursement for employee participation in such a program. Consider a company with 1000 employees who agree to use their own personal mobile phone for all business processes and accept a $50 per month allowance for this participation. For many organizations, this can be a savings of $20–100 per month per employee totaling a savings of between $20k and $100k.

- **Increased satisfaction:** Employees are thankful to have the option to select the devices they desire for work activities. Some people like Apple products, others like Android, other like Microsoft, and others may prefer another provider. Rather than forcing users to learn and use a different solution, many organizations allow the use of selected products that work with their mobile device management (MDM) solution so that users can operate with devices they know well.

BYOD is not exactly the same as MDM. MDM is used to manage BYOD and, therefore, BYOD is sometimes said to be a subset of MDM. Strictly speaking, BYOD is defined as users utilizing their own devices for organizational work (and possibly personal uses) in the workplace for work processes. These personal devices include laptops, tablets, and mobile phones, but in rare cases today also include desktop computers. In most cases, desktop computers are used by telecommuters, and they do not qualify for the BYOD category, though one could place them in a BYOD category since they are using their device (Use Your Own Device). Such devices are not considered in detail here, though they may also be able to be managed by a typical overlay MDM solution.

MDM is used to manage mobile devices—both organization-owned devices and BYOD systems. MDM solutions may be integrated with a WLAN solution, or they may be selected as an overlay solution.

When considering how to address BYOD in an organization, two basic options are available—MDM or containerization. Some vendors define containerization differently than others. To some it is constrained access to others and is about secure implementation of workspaces on devices. Containerization may be defined then as the response that allows users to bring devices, but restricts them to personal or constrained uses such that they are not treated as enterprise devices or limited in relation to the enterprise apps and access in some way. With containerization, many organizations are simply allowing access to the WLAN and therefore the Internet, but they are not allowing enterprise apps on these personal devices that may allow for data leakage and other security concerns even with the use of MDM solutions. Containerization may also be defined as the process used to ensure that enterprise data on personal devices are encrypted and secured—hence, in a container or workspace.

The basic process of MDM for BYOD devices is outlined as follows:

1. Device detection determines that the device is not an enterprise device and needs to be processed by the MDM solution.

2. Device approval may involve several actions including registration or enrollment, certificate installation, profile installation, and more.

3. Device management is the ongoing management of the device once access is granted and may include updates to apps, configurations, and the profile settings.

Another movement developing momentum is BYOA (bring your own application). Driven by many commonalities with BYOD, BYOA capitalizes on the fact that many users already have Office licenses and other applications they can use to perform enterprise work. Use of these licenses can save on costs when implementing systems for users.

When planning BYOD requirements, consider the capabilities of your MDM for these specifics:

- Does it allow you to restrict settings when connected to the enterprise network that are released when connected to other networks?
- Does it provide restrictions for apps or only for hardware/OS?
- Does it work with the devices you must support?
  - Android
  - iOS
  - Windows
  - BlackBerry
  - Other
- Do you have the existing infrastructure dependencies?
  - PKI
  - Authentication service

- o Traditional network features (DNS, DHCP, etc.)

In some networks, Network Access Control (NAC), called Network Access Protection (NAP) by some vendors, is used to analyze a connecting device, determine if it meets minimum network access requirements, and then either grant or deny access accordingly.

The basic NAC process is as follows:

1. The device connects to the network.

2. The NAC infrastructure analyzes the device and processes the results.

   - If the device is in compliance, network access is granted.
   - If the device is not in compliance, network access is denied or the device is placed onto a quarantine network.
   - If placed into quarantine, the device may be updated with antivirus software or definitions and other required components.

Guest Access

When building guest networks, VLANs are often used to segregate them from the rest of the network. However, a guest network can be open or secured. In an open guest network, the users are not required to authenticate as users, but are simply instructed to connect to the guest network (based on an SSID). The guest network is not encrypted and it functions much like a traditional hotspot.

In a secured guest network, users are required to know WPA-Personal or WPA2-Personal keys or a web-based authentication code, or they are required to go through a guest registration process. Regardless of the steps, the end result is that they are connected with strong, modern Wi-Fi security.

At the WLAN level, authentication methods include both personal and enterprise options depending on the onboarding method. At the user level, authentication methods are typically Web-based.

When implementing a guest WLAN, it is best to separate it from the enterprise network using VLANs and possibly physical device separation. Boundaries can be implemented using firewalls (physical) or VLANs (virtual).

Defining Physical Coverage Requirements

Coverage requirements define the physical or geographical spaces that must have WLAN access. This is often best accomplished using a floorplan or map of the facility or area. This section provides guidance on planning for coverage in common, industrial, outdoor, service, and guest areas. The process is not complex in the requirements analysis phases as the WLAN designer need only identify the locations requiring coverage. In the Design phase, the designer must ensure that proper coverage (with needed throughput/density) is provided.

Common Areas

Common areas include the following locations:

- Workspace areas
- Hallways
- Lunch/break rooms
- Conference rooms
- Restrooms
- Stairwells
- Elevators
- Hotel rooms
- Lobbies
- Storage areas

Industrial Areas

Industrial areas are areas where manufacturing takes place. Such areas often have large equipment, shelving, and other items that cause unusual RF propagation results. Understanding the objects in the area will be important and is part of the site survey. It is important to determine which areas of the manufacturing environment require coverage as well.

Outdoor Areas

Outdoor areas can be covered easily from a coverage perspective due to the lack of walls and other barriers causing attenuation. However, this also creates greater challenges when implementing outdoor networks that support large numbers of users. It is important to not only identify the areas requiring coverage but also determine the expected number of users who will be in that area.

Service Areas

Service areas can be defined in several ways. For purposes of the CWDP exam, consider the areas where services are provided to the organization and its facility. These are areas like loading docks and other building entrance locations. Coverage in service areas should be sufficient to allow for significant changes in the environment. At times the receiving docks may be filled with shipping crates containing dense materials and at other times the materials may be easily passed through by RF signals. At other times the docks may be completely empty. Additionally, the presence of large trucks in the space can impact RF propagation in the outside areas of the shipping and receiving service area.

Guest Areas

Finally, when guest access is provided, it should not be assumed that it will be provided in all locations. Instead, the WLAN designer should gather the information to determine the areas where the guest WLAN should be available. Providing it only in required areas, prevents its use by unauthorized people in unauthorized areas and, therefore, consuming excess network bandwidth.

Depending on the chosen guest network implementation, the designer may recommend separate APs for the few areas where guest networking is required. If guest networking is required everywhere or in most places, implementing alternate

SSIDs on shared radios typically makes more sense. However, even with only a few areas requiring guest access, it can still be implemented with alternate SSIDs.

Documenting Building Factors

The building in which a WLAN is implemented will have a significant impact on the design. Several factors must be considered including:

- Building Materials
- Square Footage
- Ceiling Heights
- Multi-Floor Structures
- Wiring and Power Limitations
- Blueprints (Floorplans)
- Facility Access

This section provides guidance on these factors and considerations that must be made when designing a WLAN.

Building Materials

When gathering requirements, it is useful to learn about the building, if possible. Defining building materials is essential during the site survey process, but many times information can be acquired during the requirements gathering phase in that documentation may exist that includes information about building materials.

Older buildings with thick block and concrete walls on the perimeter and surrounding the facility can greatly reduce the range of wireless signals. Many times such building demand APs in each room even without the need for higher density deployment types. It is simply a factor of signal propagation.

Metal structures can cause significant impact as well as they may increase reflectivity. In the end, knowing the building materials can help in the requirements analysis stage in that, even without a full site survey, the experienced WLAN designer will know the relative impact of the materials and be able to better answer questions the customer may have about the number of required APs and other configuration parameters.

Square Footage

Because RF signals spread as they travel through space, the available signal and any specific pixel point location is continually reduced as they travel, as well. For this reason, even in free space, there is a limit to the distance at which an RF signal may be effectively processed. Therefore, the total square footage to be covered, coupled with the building materials, will provide enough information for the skilled WLAN designer to estimate the number of required APs based on coverage and capacity demands.

Ceiling Heights

Ceiling heights must be considered when selecting APs. Higher ceilings may impact RF coverage, particularly directly under the APs. While this information will be gathered in more detail during the site survey, building plans may already contain sufficient information. In addition to the ceiling heights, you should consider drop ceilings, plenum areas, and their impact on the AP placement decisions.

Multi-Floor Structures

When implementing WLANs in multi-floor structures, the WLAN must be planned in 3D. This is because RF signals will pass between floors. Therefore, AP mounting decisions must be made for each floor while considering the floors above and below. Simply determining the floors that require WLAN access and the locations on those floors should be sufficient in the requirements analysis stage.

Wiring and Power Limitations

In order to provide network access and power to APs, Ethernet drops must already exist or they will have to be installed where they do not exist to connect the APs. Power can be provided through PoE or though wall outlets, but the information gathering process is likely to provide information on the organization's plans for either PoE power provisioning or wall outlet provisioning.

Blueprints (Floorplans)

In order to plan the WLAN well, the WLAN designer will require floorplans or blueprints of the facility. Detailed blueprints may provide needed information related to power availability and even Ethernet drops. Simple floor plans will be sufficient for use in predictive modeling software. In multi-floor deployments, it is important to have floorplans or floor maps for each floor as walls may exist on some floors where they do not on others and these walls will impact RF signal propagation.

Facility Access

Finally, it is important to ensure that you have access to all areas of the facility that will be required during the site survey. Ask for at least two things in relation to facility access:

- Direct access to areas where you can be alone.

- Guided access to areas where you must be with authorized personnel.

Preparing for Bridge Links and Other Link Types

Bridge links are used to connect buildings over distance so that wired links are not required. They may also be used as redundant connections along with wired connections. This section introduces the issues faced by the WLAN designer when planning for bridge links and mesh connections.

Bridge Links

At the requirements stage, the WLAN designer must determine if bridge links will exist. Additionally, she must discover the networks that will be interconnected by the bridge links and whether they will be point-to-point or point-to-multipoint.

A common specialty deployment of 802.11 technology is the wireless LAN bridge. The purpose of bridging is to provide wireless connectivity between two or more wired networks. A bridge generally supports all the same features that an autonomous access point possesses, but the purpose is to connect wired networks and not to provide wireless connectivity to client stations. Although bridge links are sometimes used indoors, generally they are used outdoors to connect the wired networks inside two buildings. An outdoor bridge link is often used as a redundant backup to T1 or fiber connections between buildings. Outdoor wireless bridge links are even more commonly used as replacements to T1 or fiber connections between buildings because of their substantial cost savings.

Wireless bridges support two major configuration settings—root and nonroot. Bridges work in a parent/child-type relationship, so think of the root bridge as the parent and the nonroot bridge as the child.

A bridge link that connects only two wired networks is known as a point-to-point (PtP) bridge. Note that one of the bridges must be configured as the parent root bridge and the other bridge is configured as the child nonroot bridge.

A point-to-multipoint (PtMP) bridge link connects multiple wired networks. The root bridge is the central bridge, and multiple nonroot bridges connect back to the root bridge. Please note that the root bridge is using a high-gain omnidirectional antenna, whereas the nonroot bridges are all using unidirectional antennas pointing back to the antenna of the root bridge. Also notice that there is only one root bridge in a PtMP connection. There can never be more than one root bridge.

Besides the root and nonroot modes, bridges have other vendor configuration modes, as described in Table 2-4.

Configuration Mode	Description
AP Mode	Converts a bridge into an access point
WGB Mode	Converts a bridge into a workgroup bridge
Repeater Mode	Repeats the cell of a root bridge to a nonroot bridge
Root with Clients	Root bridge that also allows clients to associate
Nonroot with Clients	Nonroot bridge that also allows clients to associate

Table 2-4—AP Bridge Configuration Modes

Considerations when deploying outdoor bridge links are numerous, including the Fresnel zone, earth bulge, free space path loss, link budget, and fade margin. There may be other considerations as well, including the IR and EIRP power regulations as defined by the regulatory body of your country.

Mesh Connections

Mesh connections may be used to build the only infrastructure (all wireless) or they may be used to simply provide backlinks to the infrastructure. When providing the only infrastructure, the APs form a mesh network that interconnects all APs with each other and then provides one or more links to wired networks or the Internet.

When used to provide backlinks to the infrastructure, many mesh APs will use one radio for local access to client STAs and another radio to provide the backlink. The backlink may be 5 GHz while the local access is 2.4 GHz or both radios may operate in the same band. When using multiple radios for the configuration, it allows for greater throughput for clients. Some APs can provide mesh links and share a radio for the link and local access, but like a WLAN repeater, this reduces the throughput by half.

A self-forming WLAN mesh network automatically connects access points upon installation and dynamically updates routes as more clients are added. Because interference may occur, a self-healing WLAN mesh network will automatically reroute data traffic in a Wi-Fi mesh cell. Proprietary layer 2 intelligent routing protocols determine the dynamic routes based on measurement of traffic, signal strength, data rates, hops, and other parameters. Although a WLAN mesh network can be a mesh of repeater-like access points that all operate on one frequency, dual-band mesh APs are now much more common. With dual-band WLAN mesh APs, typically the 5 GHz radios are used for the mesh infrastructure and to provide backhaul whereas the 2.4 GHz radios are used to provide access to the client stations.

Planning for WLAN Upgrades

Upgrading an existing WLAN can be more complicated at times than installing a new WLAN. This is, in part, because the upgrade plan must include considerations that a fresh installation need not consider, such as employee access during the upgrade and selecting the best upgrade type. This section introduces the information a WLAN designer must know to properly plan a WLAN upgrade.

Upgrade Types

WLAN upgrades, like many other IT systems, can be performed in several ways, including phased, forklift, modular, and software upgrades.

Phased upgrades are performed over time with either single APs or groups of APs being replaced in each phase. Several problems can occur during phased upgrades. If a single AP is replaced in an area and that AP uses a new SSID or even the same SSID with a different VLAN, it can cause disruption of service for some users and may result in the removal of a roaming target in the area.

Additionally, when upgrading from older technologies to newer technologies (for example, 802.11b/g in 2.4 GHz to 802.11n in 5 GHz) clients may have difficulty or even the inability to switch between APs on 2.4 GHz and APs on 5 GHz with any kind of fast roaming.

When performing phased upgrades it is often best to do it in sections so that few users would roam from an upgraded AP to an older AP and vice versa. This can be done by upgrading one building at a time. In some cases, it can be done one floor at a time, but remember that AP signals often travel between floors and users may indeed connect to an AP on a different floor.

Forklift upgrades can be the most seamless to the user but may require more manpower to perform in a single weekend or other short period of time. With this upgrade type, all APs are replaced while users are disconnected and the next time they connect, the entire WLAN has been upgraded. Forklift upgrades also introduce a risk, though low. That risk is that the entire WLAN is upgraded and some flaw in the design prevents it from working properly. With a phased upgrade, this kind of problem is discovered earlier when fewer users are impacted. When planning forklift upgrades, careful planning is even more important.

Modular and software upgrades are performed against or with existing APs. For example, Cisco offered a modular upgrade to allow an 802.11n AP to be used as an 802.11ac AP. The module is added to the back of the AP and adds an 802.11ac radio but uses the internal Ethernet connection of the AP. Older modular upgrades used to include PC Card module upgrades.

Software upgrades add features through software. For example, new security features may be added or new management features may be added. However, new PHYs are not implemented through software. New PHYs require new radios as the PHY is implemented in the chipset. Features of a PHY may be enabled through software updates, but the PHY itself must be made available through the purchase of a new AP or a new radio for an existing AP (usually throuigh a module).

Figure 2.10—Cisco 3600 AP with Modular 802.11ac Upgrade

Performance Testing

After upgrades, performance testing should be performed to ensure the expectations of the upgrade are met. Performance tests may include:

- Throughput tests
- Coverage tests
- Roaming tests
- Latency tests
- Jitter tests

Compatibility Testing

Compatibility testing is performed to ensure that the clients can access the WLAN. Interestingly, this is not always as seamless as you may assume. An example of this occurred when Microsoft released Windows 8, which implemented Management Frame Protection, a part of the 802.11 standard. With Management Frame Protection, the Windows 8 clients would be more compatible with the 802.11 standard than most previous clients. In fact, it was more compatible than many Cisco systems in production at the time. A bug in the existing Cisco systems prevented any client implementing 802.11w from associating to the APs. In this case Windows 8 was coded and implemented properly. However, the Cisco systems had to be patched to fix the bug (CSCua29504) in the software that caused the problem. This is why compatibility testing must be performed. When upgrading the infrastructure or the clients, it is possible to introduce connectivity problems.

Security Testing

Security testing should be performed to ensure that authentication and encryption are properly implemented. A WLAN-specific protocol analyzer will provide reports for this. For example, AirMagnet Wi-Fi Analyzer and Savvius Omnipeek can provide reports on APs that are not implementing secure connections according to your policy specifications. CommView for Wi-Fi from TamoSoft can be used to trigger alarms when packets are seen that do not include proper security, as well.

Creating Documentation

The final topic of this chapter is an essential part of the requirements analysis. It is essential that all information gathered be harvested and entered into a documentation set. Documentation includes:

- **Scope of Work:** A document that defines what is to be included in the WLAN design project and what is not.

- **Non-Disclosure Agreements (NDAs):** A document signed by an individual binding them to secrecy related to organizational practices, plans, products, and processes.

- **Hold Harmless:** A document or contract between two parties that releases one or both parties from possible legal action based on accidents, damages, and other possible negative outcomes.

- **Network Diagrams:** Documents that reveal the current network infrastructure, including wired and wireless details.

- **Site Survey Deliverables:** Expectations of the site survey such as diagrams, lists, and other outputs.

- **Bill of Materials (BoM):** A document that lists hardware and needed software licenses to be acquired for the WLAN implementation.

- **Network Design Acceptance Criteria:** Requirements that must be met to say that the WLAN was properly implemented. These can be used in the validation phase to verify the WLAN.

Chapter Review

In this chapter, you learned about the importance of requirements analysis. With proper requirements analysis you have the right foundation on which to build an effective WLAN design. Without requirements analysis, it is effectively impossible to implement solutions that meet the needs of an organization.

Facts to Remember

Be sure to remember the following facts as you prepare for the CWDP certification and be sure that you can explain the details related to them:

- Requirements Analysis is the process of discovering a project's requirements.

- A requirement is anything that must be provided by the product or outcome of the project.

- Business requirements are known as the objectives of the organization.

- User requirements include the goals or tasks that users must perform when using the WLAN.

- Technical requirements, or functional requirements, are those technical capabilities that allow the WLAN to meet user and business requirements.

- Regulatory requirements or constraints are those imposed by policies or government agencies.

- Information gathering is a four phase process including elicitation, analysis, specification, and validation.

- Client devices must be considered when planning a WLAN, including PHYs they support and range of connectivity.

- Applications must be considered related to their characteristics, such as throughput requirements, data load, and more.

- Security requirements should be defined including authentication, encryption, and monitoring.

- Physical coverage requirements are essential as the WLAN must serve the users where they require service.

- Building factors should be discovered including building materials, square footage and the gathering of blueprints and acquiring facility access for the site survey when required.

- Planning bridge links includes selecting PtP and PtMP deployments.

- Mesh connections can be implemented using dedicated mesh radios to gain enhanced performance.

- WLAN upgrades can be performed as phased or forklift upgrades.

- At each phase of the WLAN design and implementation process, the right documents should be created or maintained.

Chapter 3:

Site Survey Procedures

In this chapter:

- Understanding Site Survey Types
- Using Site Survey Tools
- Site Survey Procedures
- Defining Metrics
- Meeting Scenario-Specific Requirements
- Surveying for Applications and Architectures
- Outdoor Surveys

Objectives

2.1   Explain and perform the different types of site surveys commonly used including manual (active and passive), predictive, and hybrid.

2.2   Understand and utilize site survey tools including protocol analyzers, spectrum analyzers, site survey software (predictive and manual), throughput testers, and various hardware used in the process including laptops, tablets, mobile phones, batteries, APs, PoE injectors, carts, and cabling.

2.3   Ensure that proper site survey procedures are followed including gaining access clearance, acquiring floor mappings with application and user-specific needs notations, and approval to perform the site survey.

2.4   Define metrics and other information collected and reported during a site survey including signal metrics (RSSI, SNR, noise floor, interference), cell coverage, application and connectivity data (data rates, throughput, latency, jitter, loss, retries).

2.5   Ensure scenario-specific requirements are met and appropriate plans are in place including arranging escorts, performing training (safety and operations), provisioning equipment (lifts, ladders, tools), meeting access requirements (clearance and badges), single floor versus multiple-floor installations, and abiding by industry specific requirements such as union assistance and patient privacy.

2.6   Understand the different methodologies used in site surveys for varying applications and architectures including VoIP, video, data, location services, multiple-channel architecture (MCA), and single-channel architecture (SCA).

2.7   Explain and perform procedures required for outdoor site surveys including outdoor client access WLANs and bridge links.

When implementing a new WLAN, the site survey is one of the most important tasks. Interestingly, some have suggested that site surveys are no longer needed with the use of modern WLAN equipment that is self-configuring and auto-negotiating. However, you must perform a site survey to determine that these automatic systems will work effectively or you must at least perform post-implementation analysis to ensure that the recommendations of these automatic systems have been effective. Even if you are implementing a small WLAN with one AP, you still perform a site survey. In these scenarios the survey is less complex and less detailed, but it is still required.

For example, you may determine that four client stations should be installed in a doctor's office that will access the Internet through a SOHO wireless gateway like an 802.11ac wireless router. You will then turn on your laptop and use the built-in Windows wireless client to see the networks in the immediate area and the channels they are using. Next, you turn on the 802.11ac router and configure it to use an available channel or at least an unsaturated channel. While this is a very simple example, a site survey was performed, and it consisted of two steps:

1. Determine the organization's needs. (Chapter 2)

2. Discover how the environment can support a WLAN to meet these needs. (This chapter)

This chapter is about exploring the second step and looking at the component parts so that you can understand how to perform a site survey from start to finish. You may not perform every task mentioned in this chapter on every site survey; however, you should know about all of the tasks and technologies covered in this chapter. This knowledge will help you prepare for the CWDP exam and increase your effectiveness as a WLAN designer.

Understanding Site Survey Types

Site surveys can be placed into two major categories. The first is the physical site survey and the second is the RF site survey and both will be addressed in detail in this chapter. Some resources differentiate between the physical site survey and the RF site survey; however, many overlaps exist between these two types. Is it the physical site survey or the RF site survey that would discover physical objects that interfere with RF transmissions? It seems that this is part of the RF site survey, but it can certainly be debated. Because of this potential overlap, this chapter will quickly define the intention of a physical site survey and an RF site survey. After this, the remaining sections will merge the two together and use the phrases RF site survey or simply site survey to indicate all aspects of the site survey – both physical and RF.

Physical Site Surveys

The physical site survey is an examination of the physical environment in which the WLAN or wireless links will operate. The environment is inclusive of the physical premises owned by the organization operating the WLAN and possibly physical locations leased for antenna placement or cable runs. It may also include an analysis of the physical space at the install locations of two or more wireless bridges in a point-to-point or point-to-multipoint link implementation. The primary objectives of a physical site survey are to ensure that the location can accommodate a WLAN. Questions answered by a physical site survey include:

- Can you place wireless equipment where it is needed in order to provide RF coverage in the intended service area?

- What is the best location for placement of antennas, access points, bridges, and other WLAN devices?

- For external links that are PtP or PtMP, does the proper RF line of sight (LOS) exist?

- Is power available at the intended installation locations for WLAN devices or is Power over Ethernet (PoE) required?

- Can Ethernet cables be run to the desired AP locations?

- Can you protect outdoor antennas and devices from the weather through strategic placement on or under existing structures or will you need to plan for device enclosures that are weather resistant?

While you may need to address additional specific questions for your physical site survey, the physical site survey really is about analyzing the physical space within which the WLAN will operate. One of the greatest areas of overlap between physical and RF site surveys is in the dependencies they have on one another. For example, the RF site survey will tell you how RF waves behave in the environment and this will dictate where you should place antennas; however, the physical site survey may restrict the placement of antennas so that you cannot place them in ideal locations. The result is a combination of the two types of site surveys that causes you to dynamically change your plans so that you can implement a WLAN that meets the demands of the physical space while providing the needed RF coverage. This codependence is why most treat the two site surveys as one – because it is so difficult to perform them independently and achieve success.

RF Site Surveys

The RF site survey is the process of examining the current RF activity in the physical space where the WLAN must operate and determining RF behaviors in the space. It involves evaluating how your WLAN will function within that physical space as existing RF may or may not be generated by 802.11 radios. The RF site survey should answer the following key questions:

- Is the current RF utilization low enough to allow for the implementation of my new WLAN in the desired channels/frequencies?

- How must I implement the WLAN in order to provide the needed RF coverage within the designated service areas?

- Will I need to negotiate with neighboring WLAN administrators for such demands as reduction in output power on their WLANs or even channel adjustments on the WLANs?

- Should I implement 5 GHz or 2.4 GHz or both for my WLAN?

- Will I have sufficient unlicensed channel space for 802.11n/ac (HT) channel bonding?

While it may seem simple to think of having to answer only four or five questions, many other questions must be answered in order to fully answer these five high-level questions. For example, the current RF frequency utilization is both a factor of frequency or channel usage and the signal strength of the frequency usage within the area. You might be able to detect a WLAN on the 2.4 GHz channel 6, for example, but is it strong enough to prevent you from implementing a WLAN on that same channel. Additionally, you might discover that channels 1 and 11 are utilized by networks near you that are showing strong signals; however, you could implement a BSS on channel 6 and not be seriously impacted by the neighboring WLANs. You may still have to negotiate a reduction in output power on the neighboring WLANs. These issues and more will be discussed throughout the remaining portions of this section and the remaining sections of this chapter.

Site Survey Preparation

As stated previously, you can divide the site survey process into two major steps: determine the organization's needs and determine how to implement a WLAN that meets those needs. However, these two steps can be broken down further into multiple sub-phases or sub-tasks. The details of the first step were covered in Chapter 2. The details of the second step are presented in this chapter. Consider the following more detailed breakdown of the steps:

1. Determine the Organization's Needs and Objectives

2. Determine Requirements

3. User Requirements

4. Business Requirements

5. Technical Requirements

6. Discover Constraints

7. Budgetary Constraints

8. Technical Constraints

9. Regulatory Constraints

10. Define Objectives

11. Business Objectives

12. Technical Objectives

13. Determine How to Implement a WLAN that Meets the Objectives

14. Perform a Site Survey

15. Document the Site Survey

16. Create an Implementation Plan

Performing a site survey and documenting the site survey are covered in this chapter. The final task, Create an Implementation Plan, is covered in Chapters 4 and 5.

Before you can explore site survey tools, procedures, metrics and the other topics throughout this chapter, you must know about the three basic survey types:

- manual
- predictive
- hybrid

Manual Site Surveys

The traditional site survey is the manual site survey. In this type of survey, the wireless engineer enters the physical area that is to be provided with WLAN coverage with an RF site survey kit. The engineer will place one or more APs at strategic locations and walk throughout the intended service area to test signal strengths and coverage. The APs may then be moved to another location or multiple sets of APs may be used. The use of more than one AP will allow the engineer to discover more exact roaming points and determine the best cooperative placement for the APs that result in the most effective coverage of the service area.

Manual site surveys are the most accurate for determining RF behavior and signal attenuations in an environment, assuming the engineer understands the process and results. Because the engineer is making decisions based on actual RF information in the intended coverage area, guesswork and theorized analysis is mostly removed. However, the manual site survey takes much more time when the service area being covered requires the use of hundreds or even dozens of APs. If you expect to deploy more than a few dozen APs, you may want to consider one of the alternate site survey methods. At the very least, you can perform a theoretical site survey, install the APs as suggested in the theoretical survey and then tweak and tune the configuration. Of course, this is bordering on a hybrid site survey at this point.

Predictive Site Surveys

The predictive site survey (also called theoretical or virtual site survey) is a completely hands-off site survey method. This method usually requires the import of a blueprint, aerial photo, or some other form of area map. Some tools will also provide a drawing component of their own. Next the materials of the building or the area are described and the type of WLAN desired is specified. With this input, the predictive survey tool will determine placement of APs and the configuration settings for those APs. Most applications will even generate a RF map showing the coverage patterns the suggested network will provide.

The downside of such tools is that they are usually very expensive and they require a tremendous investment of time in order to learn the application and input all the data related to materials, coverage area, and WLAN specifications. For this reason, a small or medium WLAN will often be serviced better by a manual site survey. This is because it will often take less time to perform a manual site survey than it will take to enter all the information needed by the predictive survey software. However, some companies that offer an offsite survey service. You will send them the blueprints of your facility and information about the materials and contents of the facility and they will input the data into the application and generate a report for you. Since you are not required to learn the application, this offers a good tradeoff. This service is sometimes offered for less than $1000 per 50,000 square feet (at the time of this writing).

At the same time, many facilities are built using common architectures and materials. These buildings may be able to be blueprinted, material specified, and predictive surveyed in a few hours. In these scenarios, only the cost of the application is a hindrance and that may not be a barrier for WLAN consultants who will be performing many WLAN site surveys.

In the end, when one is employed as a consultant who assists in the planning and implementation of multiple WLANs per year, site survey software with predictive capabilities is essential. The good news is that, today, all of the major site survey software vendors (Ekahau, AirMagnet, TamoSoft, etc.) offer site survey software that is both predictive and manual in capabilities.

Hybrid Site Surveys

Hybrid site surveys include elements of manual and predictive surveys. For example, you may survey the facility to validate wall attenuation levels and discover RF activity already existing in the area. Then, you can manually place and configure APs as needed in areas of existing RF activity, while allowing the software to automatically place APs in the remaining areas. Adding the actual wall attenuation data into the predictive modeling software increases the accuracy of the resulting AP placement plan.

Additional Survey Types

Automated and assisted site surveys are also available.

Automated site surveys rely on intelligent communications between the APs and a centralized controller that adjusts the APs output power and channel selection in order to automatically configure the WLAN environment. In order for the controller to properly configure the WLAN without large amounts of engineer intervention, automated site surveys often require what some vendors call overengineering. Overengineering is a term commonly used to describe placing more APs in a coverage area than are actually needed to cover that area with required signal and capacity. This overengineering allows the controller to dynamically adjust the APs to achieve the desired coverage and throughput in the serviced area.

Other vendors suggest that overengineering is not needed if the right APs are utilized. Either way, the automated site survey ends up requiring more knowledge and action on the part of the WLAN engineer than is promised. The knowledge would be required to select the right APs that do not need overengineering and the action would be required to place those APs in the right locations so that the controller can configure them appropriately. Certainly, a novice wireless administrator can make serious mistakes when implementing any kind of WLAN solution, but with automated site survey and configuration systems, the mistake may often be more expensive.

 Note: The automated site survey is really not a site survey at all from the perspective of many. Rather it is simply an automatic configuration service for the installed APs.

It certainly seems that, whether you perform a manual site survey or an automated site survey, you will need the knowledge of a WLAN engineer. Organizations that have implemented controllers that have the ability to automatically reconfigure APs (with features like Radio Resource management (RRM)) have found that much of the benefit actually comes after the installation and not during the initial planning. This reality is because the controller is able to adjust the AP settings over time to accommodate changes in the environment.

The assisted site survey is a combination of the manual and automated site surveys. Some manual work is still required, but the software performs many calculations and makes recommendations for the WLAN installation. In an assisted site survey, the engineer may perform some measurements and then input this data into the management software or the management software may make general recommendations for the facility type (including building materials, ceiling heights, etc.) that the engineer will then test in the actual service area. After this, the management software or hardware will analyze the WLAN, once installed, and make appropriate adjustments to provide the coverage and throughput needed.

Site Survey Type	Pros	Cons	Applications
Manual	Very accurate; real readings in a real environment.	Time consuming; high level of RF knowledge required.	Small and medium WLANs; large WLANs requiring exacting measurements
Automated	Dynamic reconfiguration when the environment changes; automatic power and channel management for frequency bandwidth usage	Less accurate in relation to hardware required; may require some over-engineering	Predictable environments (national chain shops and stores); open outdoor environments (city parks, open outdoor areas like corporate gardens and picnic areas)
Assisted	Requires less over-engineering than the fully automated site survey.	Requires more physical activity than the automated site survey.	Any scenario that demands a balance between the pros and cons offered by the manual and assisted site surveys.
Predictive	No or little physical activity required; RF map generated automatically	Costly software; may require large amounts of time for data entry, but typically less time than a manual survey.	Fabricated buildings; large scale installs that warrant the data entry time as it is less than the manual survey time; consulting firms that repeat similar site surveys.

Table 3-1 Site Survey Types: Pros, Cons, and Applications

Documenting the Survey

Once you've completed the work of the site survey, regardless of type, you must document your findings. Site survey software will usually generate a set of site survey diagrams and documents. Regardless of the type of site survey, there will always be some level of manual documentation required. For example, even site survey software may require that you document the details of the business objectives or security requirements outside the context of the site survey application.

At a minimum, you will need to document the business objectives, requirements (user, business and technical), and constraints. In addition, you may have to manually document the facility (blueprints or floorplans) or coverage area (location maps, etc.) if your site survey software does not do this for you.

When documenting business, user, and technical requirements, some brainstorming may be required. The most common method for defining requirements seems to be brainstorming. This method can be very useful as long as those involved in the brainstorming process understand the intended uses of the wireless network, the available WLAN technologies and their capabilities, and the constraints imposed on the particular wireless implementation. Many brainstorming techniques have been developed over the years including the following:

- Brain Dumps
- Free Association
- Clustering

Probably the most common, brain dumps seem to come natural to most people. This process involves the simple task of listing everything you can think of that you will need from the WLAN. It is the process of answering the question, "What do I need the WLAN to provide and do?," again and again. This is a useful technique as an individual, but it may result in more confusion and debate than a more organized method when performed in a group.

The free association method involves bouncing ideas off of one or more people. You may bring focus to the discussion by asking a question like, "What uses of the WLAN will impact the throughput needed?" Of course, those involved must understand what you mean by throughput and what a use is. The point of this method is to provide focus to the human process of idea or concept association. It is called free association because each individual is free to think of the uses that are most relevant to them in relation to the question presented.

The final method, clustering, involves a specific tool sometimes called a mind map. This tool looks similar to that seen in Figure 3.1. The cluster shown represents the answer to the question, "What uses of the WLAN will impact the throughput needed?" This tool can be drawn on paper or flip charts, using sticky notes or whiteboards. Regardless of the method used, many creativity experts suggest that this is the most effective brainstorming tool available. The cluster represented in Figure 3.1 was created with Microsoft Office Visio, but other tools such as Mind Manager and Mind Mapper were developed specifically for this purpose.

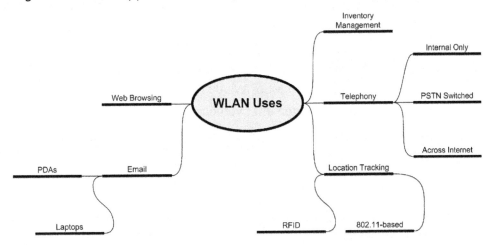

Figure 3.1—A WLAN Cluster or Mind Map of Utilization Cases

Creating an Implementation Plan

The final step, after performing the actual site survey, is to create an implementation plan. Will you implement a small pilot network first or will you simply implement the infrastructure services and then layer the WLAN over them (for example, implement a RADIUS server and then install the wireless access points)? The details of this process are provided in Chapters 4 and 5.

Systems Analysis

When it comes to determining WLAN design needs, systems analysis is a more technical method available to the WLAN designer. The process involves evaluating the existing systems (network applications and their use) in order to determine how and if they will function in a WLAN environment. The WLAN designer must look at the network as it exists today, but he must also consider future growth. He will likely perform systems analysis after user and management interviews and brainstorming. Systems analysis is really only beneficial if you already know what you desire to do with and on the wireless network.

For example, assume that you've defined seven application, which currently run on the wired LAN that must be able to run on the WLAN. You can now analyze the bandwidth consumed by these applications in your live environment (part of systems analysis) and then determine the required data rates on your WLAN. While performing such an analysis, remember that WLANs have more management overhead than wired LANs. For example, a 100 Mbps wired LAN connection may serve the application well, but a 100 Mbps WLAN connection may be too congested due to the wireless medium management overhead.

When considering the current network usage, look at the applications that are running on the network and be sure to answer the following questions about them:

- How many users use the application on the network at the same time?

- What is the average size of a data transmission resulting from the usage of this application?

- On average, how many of these transmissions are made in a given minute?

- What is the maximum transmission size?

- What is the maximum transmitted data seen in a given minute?

- Is the application WLAN aware in that it can modify its network usage patterns to work more effectively on a WLAN?

- Does the application involve bursts of large data transfers, moderate data transfers sustained over time, or both?

There are certainly application-specific questions you should ask as well, but this list may be used to begin your analysis of any application. With the answers to these questions you can determine the maximum throughput needed at peak times, the average throughput needed over time, and any specific Quality of Service (QoS) requirements that the WLAN may need to accommodate.

The change rate appears to be higher today than it has ever been and computer networks are no exception. It is a rare environment that does not have a planned change in the network at any given time. For this reason, you should be sure to consult the network administrator or IT manager to see if there are any future projects that are expected to increase the throughput needed on your WLAN.

Additionally, many WLANs are implemented so that the organization can begin using a new technology such as wireless inventory management systems, health care management systems, or even Voice over WLAN (VoWLAN). Many of the users will expect to gain the advantages of the new technology and will also expect to continue performing the work they used to do on the wired LAN using the WLAN. This expectation will demand more throughput than that which was previously required and should be a part of the site survey and WLAN implementation plan documentation.

Finally, there seems to be a tendency, in the discussions of WLAN site surveys, to assume that site surveys are only performed where there is no existing WLAN. The reality is that many site surveys are performed after a WLAN is implemented because the implemented WLAN is not performing well or because it needs to be upgraded to support modern uses of wireless such as VoWLAN, streaming video, and high-speed Internet access. The point is that you must discover both existing networks that are managed by the requesting organization and WLANs that are not managed by the requesting organization. If you can detect a WLAN from the requesting organization's facilities, it must be considered when creating your WLAN implementation plan.

Among the things you should document are the current wired LAN connections. Where are they? What speed do they provide (10 Mbps, 100 Mbps, Gigabit)? Are they all in use? Is there power at the port locations if you need to connect more switches or routers? What applications are running on the LANs and WLANs and will they continue to be used in the new WLAN?

If you can acquire network diagrams showing the switching and routing infrastructure as well as the location of authentication, authorization, and accounting servers as well as service servers (email, web, file, print, etc.), this will be very helpful. From these diagrams, you can determine where traffic flows on the network and strategically place WLAN access points so that they can have unobstructed (or less obstructed) access to mission critical servers like Call Manager servers in Cisco VoWLAN implementations.

Using Site Survey Tools

Just as the carpenter must have the proper tools to get the job done, the WLAN designer should have the proper tools to perform effective site surveys. These tools include protocol analyzers, spectrum analyzers, site survey software, throughput testers, and the proper hardware.

Protocol and Spectrum Analyzers

The primary tools used for wireless network analysis are the protocol and spectrum analyzers. Protocol analyzers are used to capture the actual WLAN frames that traverse the medium (the chosen channel). If you are purchasing a WLAN protocol analyzer today, ensure that it supports 802.11n. Most vendors have updated their solutions to do so, but you should verify this in the software specifications.

Wireless protocol analyzers can be difficult to configure properly. They tend to work with a very limited number of wireless network adapters. Sadly, with the release of the 802.11n standard in September 2009 and the 802.11ac standard more recently and the fact that many environments will be implementing 802.11n/ac hardware now, the protocol analyzer solutions purchased by many wireless administrators can become outdated. You can't simply upgrade the hardware to an 802.11n/ac client adapter, because the software doesn't understand the new frame formats. You can't simply upgrade the software to understand the 802.11n/ac frame formats, because the hardware doesn't know how to process the 802.11n/ac PHY. The end result is a complete rip-and-replace process. The software must be upgraded or replaced and new 802.11n/ac adapters, which are compatible with the software, must be purchased. The good news is that you can still analyze the older 802.11 hardware with the newer 802.11n/ac protocol analysis solutions.

A WLAN protocol analyzer is used to capture data packets as well as 802.11 MAC layer frames and decode their contents. They will also display information from the radio tap header, such as signal strength and noise floor information (though this data is often less reliable than that of a spectrum analyzer). The information is usually presented in a very readable format that is easier to understand than simply looking at a series of ones and zeros. For example, many protocol analyzers break the frame headers down in such a way that each bit is explained in real world terms and concepts. This process is often called frame or packet decoding.

Handheld and computer-based (usually used on laptops) protocol analyzers have existed for many years. Most of these applications are designed for wired protocol analysis. Because WLAN devices are so different (based on the chipsets used for the wireless communications), even protocol analyzers that are designed for WLANs or support WLAN analysis as well as wired are often incompatible with many of the WLAN network cards. For example, many early WLAN protocol analyzers supported one chipset alone. You were required to purchase that specific chipset (a network card that was based on it) if you wanted to use the protocol analyzer. Today, the situation has improved, but there are still no protocol analyzers that work with every WLAN network card. In fairness to the software vendors who create the protocol analyzers, this is—at least in part—due to the way that different operating systems interact with WLAN devices.

Protocol analyzers tend to provide features that make your life easier. For example, they can be configured to filter for specific frame types or upper later protocols. They can display performance statistics for overall throughput and frame rates on the network. They can even be configured to work with remote sensors so that you can analyze and configure alerts for the entire wireless network in your organization and not just the small portion of the network near your analysis laptop.

For site surveys, use a protocol analyzer to perform the following tasks:

- Identify WLANs in the area.

- Discover areas with high frame retries in the post-validation survey.

- Determine the packet types traversing the current network for an upgrade site survey.

- Find APs that are improperly configured in the post-validation survey.

- Track the number of clients connecting to a given AP.

- Locate the most active clients on the WLAN.

Figure 3.2 shows the OmniPeek Personal web page where you can learn about the different chipsets supported by this particular WLAN protocol analyzer.

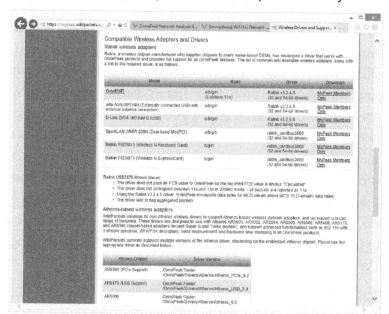

Figure 3.2— Supported Adapters for OmniPeek WLAN Protocl Analyzer

As you can see, at the time of this writing, a large pool of Atheros chipsets and drivers are supported, along with a small number of USB drivers. The OmniWiFi adapter is an 802.11n 3x3:3 adapter used for protocol analysis. To perform 802.11ac analysis, the Omnipliance is recommended. Omnipliance captures frames from APs that support remote capture. The Cisco WAP371 AP is an excellent choice for building a WLAN analysis lab or for use with site surveys where you desire to perform 802.11ac analysis and have a roaming power source to power the AP with PoE. The Cisco WAP371 AP is depicted in Figure 3.3.

Figure 3.3—Cisco WAP371 AP supporting 3x3:3 802.11ac Capture

When evaluating protocol analyzers, it is very important that you determine whether the software supports your chosen hardware. Many WLAN administrators find it is easier to build a custom laptop for WLAN protocol analysis rather than trying to find an analyzer that supports their laptop. By purchasing a laptop with CardBus (or more likely ExpressCard) support and then purchasing the recommended card (or cards) for the protocol analyzer you've chosen, you remove the guesswork from the scenario. Keep in mind that you may have to install different drivers for different protocol analyzers even though they support the same card. This can be very time consuming and some administrators have chosen to actually install multiple copies of the operating system (OS) on their computer—in a multi-boot configuration—so that they can boot into the OS installation that is preconfigured for the device and analyzer they desire to use at that time.

Newer laptop computers are now coming with ExpressCard slots. Where you used to get two PCMCIA card slots (commonly called PC Card slots), you now may have one PC Card slot and one ExpressCard slot or just an ExpressCard slot. The reality is that the vast majority of laptops do not even have ExpressCard slots as USB has won the battle for expansion ports in laptops. You may not even know that you have ExpressCard instead of Cardbus until you try to slide a PC Card into the ExpressCard slot – it won't fit! Why is this significant? With two PC Card slots, you could have one in use with your Cognio or AirMagnet Spectrum Analyzer card with external antenna and use the other one for your favorite wireless protocol analysis card with or without an external antenna. Now, you'll have to either use the embedded Wi-Fi radio on the laptop or find an ExpressCard that has a supported chipset for either protocol analysis or spectrum analysis. Vendors have been slow to accept the ExpressCard format but by the time you read this, there should be several supported ExpressCard devices on the market.

 Note: **Today, most WLAN designers are using USB-based adapters. However, exceptions do exist such as the AirMagnet ExpressCard 802.11ac capture adapter shown in Figure 3.4.**

WLAN capture is one area where the Linux operating system is actually arguably easier to use. Windows often requires much more effort to perform WLAN analysis (from a device driver perspective only) than Linux. However, Windows is more likely to provide a graphical interface for its tools than Linux (though the newer versions of the Mac OS are certainly changing this). Ultimately, you must choose the operating system that supports the tools you want and need to use.

Some administrators who use Linux very heavily and they do this even though they manage a Windows environment. The good news is that WLAN analysis and troubleshooting has evolved so that it can be performed using the Mac, Windows, Linux, and other platforms. Since the CWDP certification is vendor neutral, you will not be tested on your knowledge of Mac OS WLAN analysis versus Windows WLAN analysis and so on. Use what works for you, but be sure you understand how the technology is actually working and not just how to click the right buttons. This will make you a more effective WLAN designer, administrator, and troubleshooter.

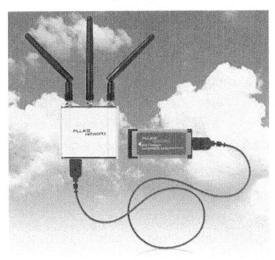

Figure 3.4— Fluke Networks AirMagnet 3x3:3 ExpressCard 802.11ac Adapters

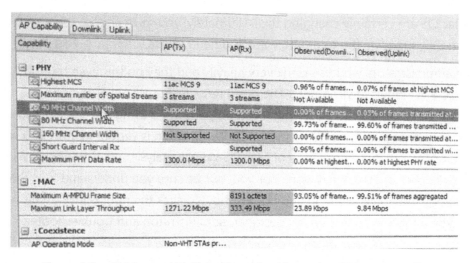

AP Capability	Downlink	Uplink			
Capability		AP(Tx)	AP(Rx)	Observed(Downli...	Observed(Uplink)
⊟ : PHY					
Highest MCS		11ac MCS 9	11ac MCS 9	0.96% of frames...	0.07% of frames at highest MCS
Maximum number of Spatial Streams		3 streams	3 streams	Not Available	Not Available
40 MHz Channel Width		Supported	Supported	0.00% of frames...	0.03% of frames transmitted at...
80 MHz Channel Width		Supported	Supported	99.73% of frame...	99.60% of frames transmitted ...
160 MHz Channel Width		Not Supported	Not Supported	0.00% of frames...	0.00% of frames transmitted at...
Short Guard Interval Rx			Supported	0.96% of frames...	0.06% of frames transmitted wi...
Maximum PHY Data Rate		1300.0 Mbps	1300.0 Mbps	0.00% at highest...	0.00% at highest PHY rate
⊟ : MAC					
Maximum A-MPDU Frame Size			8191 octets	93.05% of frame...	99.51% of frames aggregated
Maximum Link Layer Throughput		1271.22 Mbps	333.49 Mbps	23.89 Kbps	9.84 Mbps
⊟ : Coexistence					
AP Operating Mode		Non-VHT STAs pr...			

Figure 3.5—AirMagnet Wi-Fi Analyzer Pro Capturing 802.11ac Traffic

Spectrum analyzers are a completely different beast from protocol analyzers. Spectrum analyzers have no idea what the actual data is, they only see the spectrum or the energy emitted within a given frequency range. For this reason, spectrum analyzers can detect devices that protocol analyzers cannot, such as:

- Wireless phones
- Bluetooth devices
- Microwave ovens
- Incidental energy from motors and other devices
- Baby monitors
- RF generators

Spectrum analyzers are used to locate interference during site surveys and to discover rogue APs. A spectrum analyzer may be a hardware device or a software and hardware combination used on a laptop computer. While lacking the advanced features of some spectrum analyzers that cost into the thousands of dollars, the Wi-Spy series of devices by MetaGeek (see MetaGeek.com) come in at under $1000 each and provide everything the average wireless network designer will need. Figure 3.6 shows the MetaGeek Chanalyzer software, which uses the Wi-Spy adapter.

Note: The duty cycle or channel load view of a spectrum analyzer is useful in determining if a given channel is too active for use in an area as the active channel for a new cell.

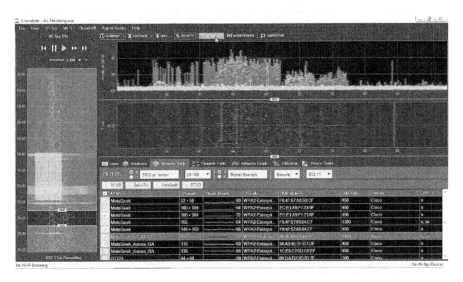

Figure 3.6—Chanalyzer Pro Spectrum Analysis Software

Site Survey Software

Site survey software is specially designed software for performing WLAN site surveys. The software typically provides the following features:

- Importing of floor plans for the generation of heat maps representing several possible metrics

  - Signal strength

  - Data rates

  - Throughput rates

  - AP coverage

- Performing walkabout surveys

- Performing predictive surveys

- Surveying multiple floors

- Calibration for accuracy

- Simulation of different APs (within reasonable non-calibrated boundaries)

- Simulation of different clients (within reasonable non-calibrated boundaries)

- Configuration of supported PHYs

EXAM MOMENT: It is important to remember to calibrate the software after importing a floor plan. This process involved selecting a long-distance range on the floor plan that has a known distance in reality and entering that distance into the software. This step allows the software to ensure proper calibration for RF signal coverage.

Site survey software is available from Ekahau (Ekahau Site Survey (ESS)), Fluke Networks (AirMagnet Survey Pro), and TamoSoft (TamoGraph Site Survey). Figure 3.7 shows TamoGraph Site Survey.

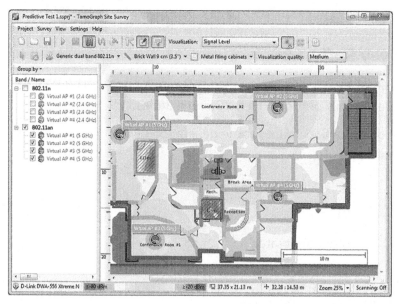

Figure 3.7—TamoGraph Site Survey from TamoSoft

The following screens illustrate the common uses of site survey software using Ekahau Site Survey (ESS) as an example.

Figure 3.8 shows the use of site survey software for the planning of AP placement and coverage within an area. Capacity is essential, but capacity is impossible without coverage. Coverage analysis is an essential part of site survey software.

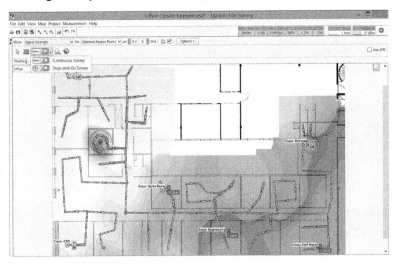

Figure 3.8—ESS Showing Coverage with a Heat Map

Figure 3.9 shows the capacity planning feature of ESS. If only coverage is provided in a site survey, the users may not be able to perform the required functions to do their job. Capacity (the ability to handle the combined required throughput and communications of all connected clients to an AP) is required.

The capacity planning feature of ESS allows you to specify requirements, such as voice requirements specified by a given vendor. These requirements result in two important metrics:

1. Signal strength

2. Number of visible APs

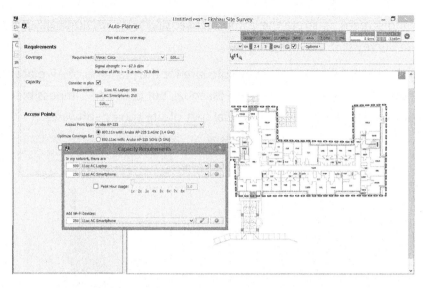

Figure 3.9—Defining Capacity Requirements in ESS

For example, signal strength is often required at -67 dB or better (remember, -50 dB is better than -67 dB because you are dealing with negative values measuring the weakness below 1 mW). The number of APs required is important for roaming and redundancy and is often said to be greater than or equal to two APs. This requirements is typically understood to mean that, ideally, more than two APs should be seen in most places, but only two APs visible in some locations is acceptable. When possible, the designer should attempt to optimize the AP placement plan such that unfrequented areas are more likely to have fewer APs and frequented areas are more likely to have more APs.

Part of capacity planning is throughput analysis. ESS offers a special view showing throughput when an active survey was performed. This feature is useful in site surveys and validation surveys. Figure 3.10 shows the throughput heat map.

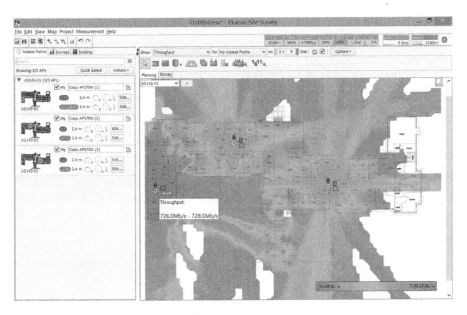

Figure 3.10—ESS Showing a Throughput Heatmap

An additional feature of ESS related to capacity planning is the ability to view metrics based on number of clients per AP (see Figure 3.11). With the estimated number of clients per AP and the types of clients (802.11ac laptops vs. smartphones, 802.11n vs. 802.11ac, etc.) the software can better represent capacity demands expected in areas and allow the WLAN designer to provision the appropriate APs and number of APs to all areas. For example, if an area will have 100 clients connecting, that area should be serviced by more than one AP in all but the most extreme high-density deployments (such as a sports stadium, which may still have fewer than 100 clients per AP).

Note that the view in Figure 3.11 also shows 2.4 GHz vs. 5 GHz clients. This comparison is very important as the designer's ability to implement multiple APs in 5 GHz within a coverage area is much greater than the implementation of multiple APs in 2.4 GHz. For example, deploying an AP on channel 48 and another AP on channel 153 can be performed easily without requiring much separation between the APs. In the 2.4 GHz band, no such options exist.

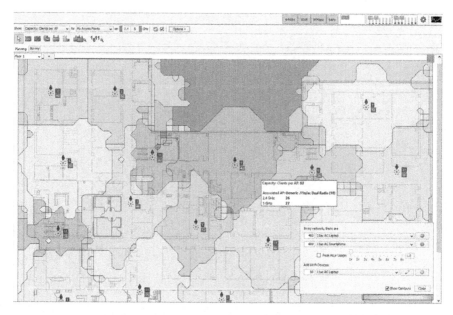

Figure 3.11—ESS Showing Clients per AP

An additional feature of site survey software is the ability to select different antennas, which is particularly useful for predictive modeling. Figure 3.12 shows the antenna selector on the ESS software. Note that the selector shows the antenna model, but also elevation and azimuth charts, which you learned about in your CWNA studies.

EXAM MOMENT: This study guide does not repeat all information covered in your CWNA studies. However, it is important to remember that the CWDP exam will test your knowledge of new CWDP topics (covered in this study guide) and your existing CWNA knowledge, which is a prerequisite to the CWDP exam.

As a final example, site survey software may provide detailed information on channel overlap. Channel overlap is essential for proper roaming. For example, if users must be mobile while connected with real-time applications, such as VoIP, multiple APs should be visible to the client at each location. This allows the client to roam from one AP to another and also enables redundancy should a single AP fail. Many designs call for the visibility of at least two APs at each location in 2.4 GHz and three APs at each location in 5 GHz when 20 MHz channels are used.

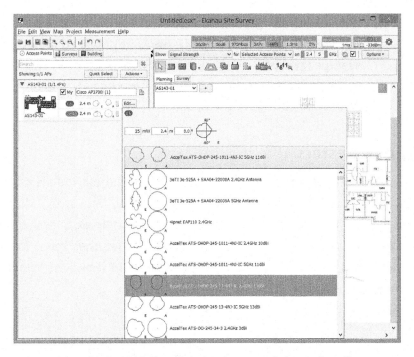

Figure 3.12—ESS Showing the Antenna Selector Interface

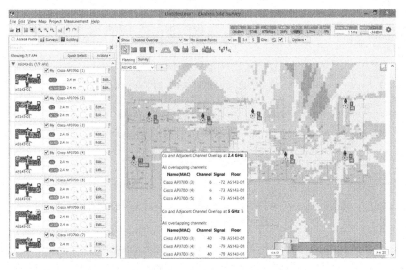

Figure 3.13—ESS Revealing Overlapping APs within an Area

Note: **When using the predictive modeling features of site survey software, be sure to set the AP transmit power to the estimated average level of a client, such as 20 mW or 25 mW. This is particularly important when Radio Resource Management will be used to configure the APs.**

Throughput Testers

The final piece of software that will be used in site surveys (both the manual site survey, when active, and the post installation survey (validation survey)) is the throughput tester. Throughput testing can be simple or complex. Simple throughput testing can be implemented using basic features such as returned metrics from common client tools, like FTP download clients. Figure 3.14 shows the Windows FTP client reporting the speed of a download.

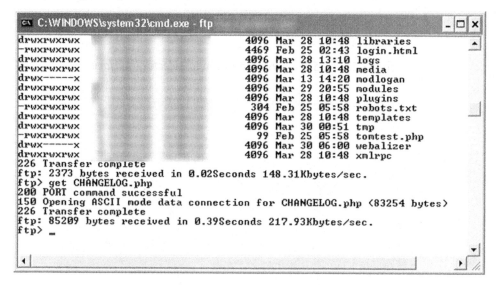

Figure 3.14—FTP Used to Report Throughput Metrics

More advanced software, coming as command line tools or graphical engines, add capabilities beyond the basic metrics of file transfer programs. For example, they may offer the ability to choose statistics for UDP or TCP. They may be able to simulate particular traffic types, such as VoIP, streaming video, or large file transfers. Having these features is a great advantage of true throughput testing software.

Throughput testing software is available from the open source community and also in the form of commercial products.

A basic commercial testing product, which is available for free, is the TamoSoft Throughput Test software. This software can be downloaded from Tamos.com. Figure 3.15 shows the single screen of the Throughput Test software. It is comprised of a client and server. The server runs on one computer and the client on another. Each computer is connected on either end of the link you desire to test. The test can be against Wi-Fi only (both computers connected to the same AP) or include the network infrastructure (one computer connected to the AP and the other connected at the desired point on the wired network).

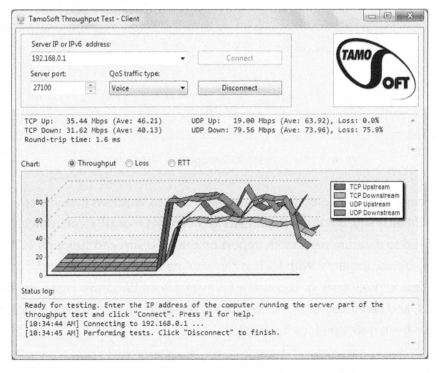

Figure 3.15—TamoSoft Throughput Test Client View

Unlike iPerf, discussed next, Throughput Test sends data in both directions during the test. Therefore the uplink (upstream) and downlink (downstream) traffic can be measured across the wireless connection. Figure 3.16 shows the server view of the Throughput Test utility.

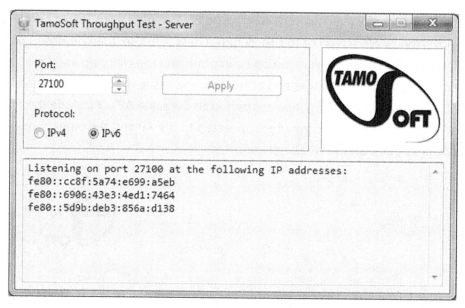

Figure 3.16—TamoSoft Throughput Test Server View

iPerf, originally developed on Linux and now ported to Windows systems as a command line utility, is a throughput testing tool for TCP or UDP communications. It can be used to measure bandwidth, report on the MTU size and supports TCP windows size adjustments. With UDP, it can also measure packet loss and jitter, which is important for VoIP testing. Today, iPerf is available on Windows, Linux, Android, Mac OS X, and several other platforms. As a command line tool, several GUI front ends have been developed for it as well.

Figure 3.17 shows a basic iPerf test run on Windows. The iPerf client pushes data to the server. Therefore, to test download data, you must make the wireless client the server and use a wired client as the actual iPerf client. Alternatively, with supporting versions of iPerf, you can use the -d option to perform bi-directional testing. This mode is not always accurate.

```
Microsoft Windows [Version 6.1.7601]
Copyright (c) 2009 Microsoft Corporation.  All rights reserved.

C:\Windows\System32>cd c:\iperf-2.0.5

c:\iperf-2.0.5>
c:\iperf-2.0.5>
c:\iperf-2.0.5>iperf -c 10.0.0.4
------------------------------------------------------------
Client connecting to 10.0.0.4, TCP port 5001
TCP window size: 64.0 KByte (default)
------------------------------------------------------------
[  3] local 10.0.0.3 port 11164 connected with 10.0.0.4 port 5001
[ ID] Interval        Transfer      Bandwidth
[  3] 0.0-10.0 sec   768 MBytes   644 Mbits/sec

c:\iperf-2.0.5>
```

Figure 3.17—iPerf Testing

Another commercial product, used heavily by vendors, is the IxChariot software suite. IxChariot can be used to perform network diagnostics with detailed statistical information about network performance. Included support for application emulation aids in the testing process. For example, the following applications can be emulated through the software:

- Facebook
- Google search
- Google mail
- SQL Server
- Gnutella
- VoIP calls

Metrics gathered from IxChariot include bitrate, loss, jitter, and delay, among others.

Hardware

The final components that will be included in a site survey toolkit are hardware items. These include laptops, tablets, mobile phones, adapters, Aps, and more. This section provides an overview of these hardware items and how they may be used in the site survey process.

A lightweight laptop is invaluable when performing a site survey. You can work with site survey documentation in digital format and even begin the process of creating your site survey documentation on-the-fly while you perform the work. Many of these newer laptops have batteries that allow them to operate for 5 to 8 hours. However, the heavy use of the WLAN device during the site survey will reduce the battery life significantly. For this reason, you should consider purchasing one or two extra batteries if you are going into another organization to perform the site survey. If you are performing the site survey within your own organization and your office is within the same facilities structure, you may be able to pause for battery recharges between uses. The reality is that, if you are an employee of the organization for which the site survey is being performed, you probably do not have the luxury of doing nothing but the site survey for an entire day or more.

The most important feature of the laptop that you will be using for the site survey is the ability to install various WLAN cards. You may want to test with HR/DSSS cards (802.11b) as well as ERP (802.11g), OFDM (802.11a), HT (802.11n), and VHT (802.11ac). If you are implementing an 802.11n or 802.11ac network using the HT or VHT PHYs, you should test with 802.11n or 802.11ac devices. By swapping cards in and out of the laptop, you can test with all of these various PHYs using one laptop at one location. Some engineers, however, find that it is much easier to have a different laptop for each of the PHYs so that the testing at each location is faster. Most modern site survey engineers, use only one adapter for the testing as site survey software typically provided sufficient data from that one adapter for all needed calculations.

Many wireless network interface cards (NICs) come with site survey utilities that report signals detected, signal strength, channel, noise level, signal-to-noise ratio (SNR), and the MAC address of the AP. These utilities can be utilized to perform many of the same analysis steps performed with spectrum and protocol analyzers. This software may be useful for small deployments with one through five APs. Any more than this and you will want to utilize real site survey software.

Some wireless NICs will even allow you to change the output power of the device. This feature will allow you to easily test for near/far type scenarios, which commonly occur in wireless networks and can cause performance problems for nodes at greater distances from the AP. You could place one laptop with a high-output power setting closer to the AP and then place another laptop with a lower output power setting at the same location or at a greater distance to test for the existing of a near/far scenario. While you would never intentionally implement such a scenario in a production environment, it is useful to experience the phenomenon and it will also make you a better troubleshooter for later problems. In production settings, this problem is more commonly caused by using different wireless NICs from different vendors that have different power output settings. Figure 3.18 shows such a variable output power client utility.

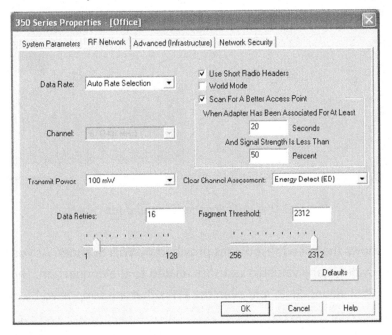

Figure 3.18—Wireless NIC Client Utility with Variable Output Power

In addition to the client utilities that come with WLAN NICs, you can use freeware and commercial tools like inSSIDer, Kismet, and Xirrus Wi-Fi Inspector to discover the metrics such as signal strength, noise floor, SNR, and MAC addresses. These tools are useful when you either do not have good NIC client utilities or when you want to have a similar interface regardless of the NIC that is installed in your laptop.

WiFi Scanner by Access Agility is a Mac utility that can display details such as SSID, network mode, encryption type, RSSI, frequency, and channel along with other details for a complete picture of the environment. With a combination of additional features like signal graphing, WiFi Scanner can also be used for additional tasks like detecting channel congestion. Figure 3.19 shows WiFi Scanner scanning for WLANs.

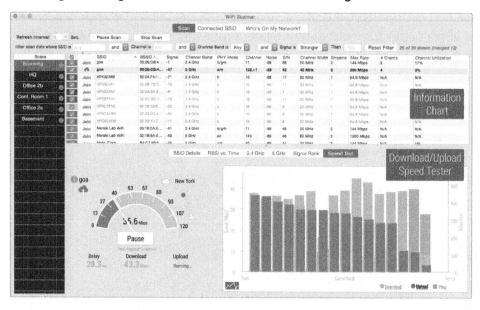

Figure 3.19—WiFi Scanner Scanning for WLANs

Figure 3.20 shows the speed test details provided by WiFi Scanner. As you can see, this utility provides many valuable statistics related to the connection. This data includes the RSSI values, SNR, and even the PHYs that are supported by name.

APs are essential for manual site surveys as well. You will use the AP as the RF and signal generator during the site survey. This AP needs to be equipped with output power settings and external antenna connectors so that you can test different power levels with different antennas to achieve the desired coverage. Of course, if you only perform site services for internal networks and you only deploy APs with internal antennas, the external antenna requirement can be ignored.

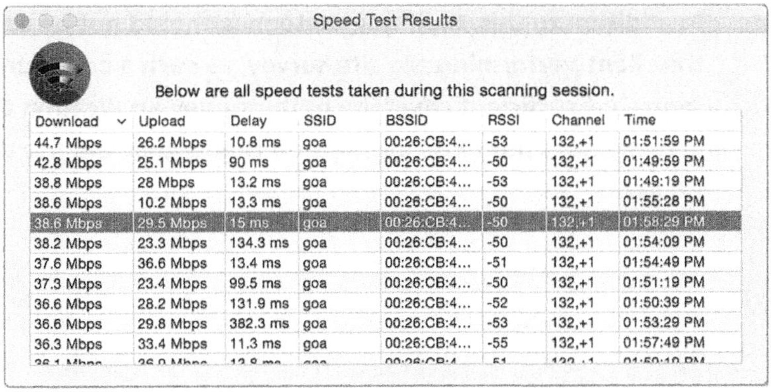

Download	∨	Upload	Delay	SSID	BSSID	RSSI	Channel	Time
44.7 Mbps		26.2 Mbps	10.8 ms	goa	00:26:CB:4...	-53	132,+1	01:51:59 PM
42.8 Mbps		25.1 Mbps	90 ms	goa	00:26:CB:4...	-50	132,+1	01:49:59 PM
38.8 Mbps		28 Mbps	13.2 ms	goa	00:26:CB:4...	-53	132,+1	01:49:19 PM
38.6 Mbps		10.2 Mbps	13.3 ms	goa	00:26:CB:4...	-50	132,+1	01:55:28 PM
38.6 Mbps		29.5 Mbps	15 ms	goa	00:26:CB:4...	-50	132,+1	01:58:29 PM
38.2 Mbps		23.3 Mbps	134.3 ms	goa	00:26:CB:4...	-50	132,+1	01:54:09 PM
37.6 Mbps		36.6 Mbps	13.4 ms	goa	00:26:CB:4...	-51	132,+1	01:54:49 PM
37.3 Mbps		23.4 Mbps	99.5 ms	goa	00:26:CB:4...	-50	132,+1	01:51:19 PM
36.6 Mbps		28.2 Mbps	131.9 ms	goa	00:26:CB:4...	-52	132,+1	01:50:39 PM
36.6 Mbps		29.8 Mbps	382.3 ms	goa	00:26:CB:4...	-53	132,+1	01:53:29 PM
36.3 Mbps		33.4 Mbps	11.3 ms	goa	00:26:CB:4...	-55	132,+1	01:57:49 PM
36.1 Mbps		26.0 Mbps	12.8 ms	goa	00:26:CB:4...	-51	132,+1	01:50:19 PM

Speed Test Results

Below are all speed tests taken during this scanning session.

Figure 3.20—WiFi Scanner Showing Connection Speeds

The AP feature of variable output power will allow you to reduce and enlarge service area cell sizes without changing antennas. This ability is essential for density deployments. For example, you will achieve a very different coverage pattern with an output power of 50 mW and a 7 dBi omni antenna than you will with an output power of 100 mW and a 7 dBi omni antenna. Additionally, you may be able to adjust the output power from your testing client laptop and then restart the AP without having to physically go to the location of the AP. This can save you time during the survey.

When selecting APs for manual site survey, two factors are important: they should be the same APs you plan to implement and they should be configured, in general, as you plan for them to be configured. You want to configure an average output power, even if you plan to use RRM. For example, for a standard density deployment, you may set it to 20 or 25 mW. For a high-density deployment, you may set it to 10 or 15 mW. The point is that you should survey and measure the environment with APs configured similarly to what you plan to deploy.

If, for example, you survey using an AP with 100 mW output power and 2.8 dBi gain antennas, but then you implement APs with a maximum of 50 mW output power and 2.2 dBi gain antennas, the coverage will be wildly different than the survey results. In fact, many gaps in coverage are likely to exist.

 Note: **In addition to this, high-gain antennas should not be used on the client performing the site survey, as such a configuration will represent sufficient coverage in the survey application that actually does not exist for the true clients that will use the WLAN.**

In addition to AP selection, you will want to include at least two of the three primary antenna types including:

- Omni-directional
- Semi-directional
- Highly Directional

The two to include, at a minimum, are omni- and semi-directional antennas. Highly directional antennas are more likely to be needed for outdoor site surveys, but you may wish to include this antenna type in any site survey kit just to be certain you are prepared. Including multiple omni-directional antennas with different levels of gain may also be beneficial. For example, you could include a standard omni, which is usually around 2.2 dBi, along with 7 and 12 dBi gain antennas.

By providing different antenna types, you can test AP installation with patch or panel antennas against omni antennas. This can help you provide the right coverage in the right place instead of simply allowing RF energy to be leaked into unneeded areas and, therefore, be wasted. Such antennas are more likely to be used in manufacturing or warehousing environments than in standard offices, which most often use standard omni-directional antennas. However, situations may arise where you can prevent or at least minimize Co-channel interference (CCI) in some areas of your network by using directional antennas in other areas. Such decisions can be simulated in most site survey software today.

Any device that uses electrical power must have a power source. Laptops and handheld protocol or spectrum analyzers may already have a battery; however, APs do not come with batteries so you may need to provide power to them. You can use a charged Uninterruptable Power Supply (UPS) unit to power the AP. A UPS that is able to power a standard desktop-class server or computer for 5 to 10 minutes can often power an AP for hours. Since UPS units are often very heavy, this is one of the components that you will likely place on your rolling cart as you move around within the facility.

 Note: **As you are beginning to see, the equipment that you use in a site survey may appear ominous to onlookers. This is why you need a contract clearly stating your purpose for being there. You also need to ensure you have all the proper clearance, and to avoid time wasting interruptions you may even ask for a security escort if the organization has onsite security staff.**

In many cases, you will desire to test an AP at a location where AC power is not available. For these scenarios, having a PoE injector is essential. Even with passive surveys, the AP must be powered on to transmit a beacon from so that the minimum signal for the configuration can be detected. For example, a PoE injector plugged into a wall outlet 100 feet away can be used to power the AP at the desired location through a CAT5 or CAT6 cable.

It might seem odd to think that binoculars should be in an indoor site survey kit, but large auditoriums can be very difficult to see across. Large warehouses may also introduce difficulties in visually locating devices residing on the other side of the building. The binoculars can help you see if your assistant is placing the AP antennas as desired without having to make the journey across the open space yourself.

If you are using an assistant, you may not always be in her or his visual line of sight and you cannot signal them to indicate that they have placed an object where you want it and you cannot get any other visual feedback from them. In these scenarios, some other form of communication is necessary. You could use cell phones or walkie talkies, but something will be needed.

Here's a great idea: how about using a tablet or mobile phone with a built-in webcam. Now you can communicate using any video conferencing software (even free software like Skype) and the assistant can even turn the camera away from himself and toward the installed device so you can see it. That's using modern technology to your benefit.

As you determine the proper locations for APs, PoE injectors, power plugs, switches and more, it is important to document these locations. With the help of a digital camera (like the one in most mobile phones today), you can remove all doubt from your documentation. If you will not be the person implementing the WLAN, digital photos of the recommended locations can be very helpful. You can open the photos in graphics editing applications, such as Paint Shop Pro or PhotoShop, and add comments and markups to the images. These images can then be inserted directly into your implementation plan documents so that the install techs can use them as a reference. Alternatively, you can markup the digital images directly in Microsoft Word with drawing objects.

A tape measure is a very important part of your site survey kit, but you should also include a measuring wheel. The tape measure can be used to determine smaller distanced such as ensuring enough clearance in a storage closet for a switch or other device. The measuring wheel allows for fast measurements of distances across large room floors or outdoor spaces. Laser-based measuring devices can also be useful for estimating large distances. These devices, such as the one picture in Figure 3.21, can often measure tilt as well as distance.

Figure 3.21—Laser-based Measuring Device (Leica - Disto A8)

Every site survey kit should include a long-lasting rechargeable drill with screw driver bit sets, as well as manual screw drivers. You will also want a rubber mallet and possibly a standard hammer as well as pliers and vice grips. These tools will help you access areas you could not otherwise access.

Additionally, you should include fastening ties, ropes, and duct tape in your kit. These items can be used to temporarily position APs and other devices at nearly any location.

Multi-color marking tape is also very useful. These tapes (electrical or bag tape will usually do) can be used for color-coded marking. For example, red tape could indicate the location of one type of AP while green tape could indicate that another type should be placed there. Alternatively, you could say that red tape indicates that the output power of the AP should be at 100 mW and green tape could indicate that it should be at 50 mW. You get the picture. The point is that color-coded tape can help you mark the areas and ease the actual implementation of the WLAN.

With all this equipment, and the fact that you have to move around within the facility while performing the site survey, it becomes clear that you are going to need some method for easily moving the items. A standard rolling cart or multimedia cart will usually serve the need. One such cart is shown in Figure 3.22.

Figure 3.22—Lightweight Rolling Cart

The cart in Figure 3.22 is a good example of the way site survey equipment can actually change the environment. While a metal cart like this should not have a major impact, due to the high reflectivity of the metal and the mesh-type structure of the base, you should be careful to either keep a cart like this out of the general testing area or use a different cart altogether. It is probably best to use a cart made of plastic materials instead.

> **EXAM MOMENT:** Make sure you understand the basic components needed for a WLAN site survey and their uses. Consider creating a list in your notebook of all the devices you would need to take with you if you were to perform a site survey for your local library or even your downtown area. This exercise can help you better comprehend the needed items for such an endeavor.

A variable-loss attenuator gives you the ability to impose signal loss on the signal before it is transmitted by the antenna. Such devices can be used to simulate using different cable lengths or types when testing outdoor bridge links. They can also be useful for indoor site surveys. For example, you may have the AP connected directly to the antenna during the indoor site survey; however, you may plan to mount the antenna in one place and the AP in another when you actually setup the WLAN. In this scenario, you can install a variable-loss attenuate between the antenna and the AP in order to simulate more closely the behavior you should expect after actual implementation. Figure 3.23 shows an example of a variable-loss attenuator. When purchasing these devices, be sure to select one supporting the frequency with which you are working.

Figure 3.23—Variable-loss Attenuator

Global Positioning System (GPS) units can be very handy when performing either outdoor site surveys for bridge links or site surveys for outdoor WLANs. The GPS unit can be used to document fairly exact locations for device placement or signal strength measurements. Today, the majority of smartphones have exceptionally accurate GPS systems in them for use in such scenarios.

The final part of the site survey toolkit is the cabling. Today, a WLAN designer should include CAT6 or CAT6e cabling in his kit. This will be used to connect APs to the infrastructure and to power APs with PoE. A 100 foot cable is an essential part of the kit for those areas away from AC power. Shorter patch cables should be provided for connecting APs as well as other test equipment, like laptops running the server for throughput testing software.

Site Survey Procedures

Site survey procedures must be followed to ensure that the site survey is performed properly and that all access needs are met for the WLAN designer. This includes acquiring floor mappings with information about applications used and user needs, when possible. It also includes access clearance and gaining permits.

Acquiring Floor Mappings

Among the documents that you should gather related to the physical building are:

- Floor plans/Blueprints/Site maps
- Building inventories
- Building construction plans
- Office layout/People densities

While many of the benefits of these documents are quickly evident, some of the beneficial uses are not quite as obvious. In this section, you will learn how you can use these documents to prepare for and perform a site survey.

Whether they are called floor plans, blueprints, or site maps, drawings like the one in Figure 3.24 are priceless to the RF site surveyor. They reveal the location of internal walls, external walls, closets, elevators, and more. If they are scaled and show that scale, you can even estimate how far you can go from an access point before the detectability of the signal is so degraded that you will lose acceptable performance.

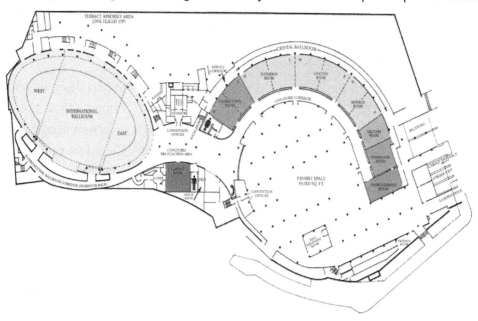

Figure 3.24—Sample Hotel Floor Plan

These floor plans can be strategically used in your documentation of the site survey to show where you will place access points and the expected coverage patterns of those access points based on your survey findings. For example, Figure 3.25 shows the same sample hotel floor plan as Figure 3.24 faded and modified to show how the International Ballroom will be covered by the WLAN.

If you know the building materials used to construct the facility in which you are installing a WLAN, you will have an advantage in that you can estimate the impact these materials will have on RF propagation. An area that is commonly overlooked is the actual items that are in the building. Everything from a filing cabinet to storage shelves and furniture can have an impact on the RF coverage within the facility. For this reason, it is useful to inventory the contents of the area. While you may not take the time to consider every piece of furniture, you should at least consider items like elevators, metal storage racks, metal filing cabinets, microwave ovens, special walls (such as lead-lined walls in hospitals) and walls lined with metal filing cabinets. These items can impact the RF signal's ability to reach certain areas.

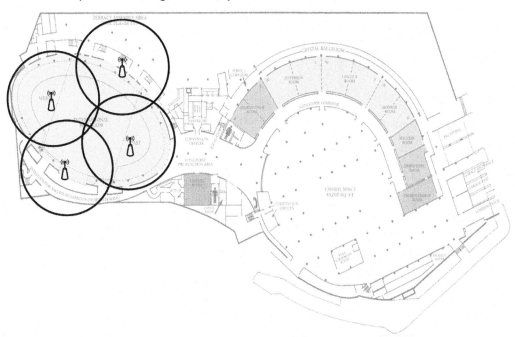

Figure 3.25—Sample Hotel Floor Plan with APs

EXAM MOMENT: In environments such as warehouses with highly-reflective materials, it is sometimes useful to test the WLAN with short guard intervals disabled. While most environments can handle the short guard intervals, some environments may benefit by disabling this feature first introduced with the 802.11n amendment.

As an example, consider the floor plan segment represented in Figure 3.26. Here you see meeting rooms that are behind a row of wall-to-wall and ceiling-to-floor metal filing cabinets. Due to the placement of the access point and the barrier presented by the filing cabinets, there are sure to be dead spots (areas without RF coverage) within the meeting rooms and particularly within Meeting Room A. Of course, a simple relocation of the access point may resolve the issue, but depending on placement it could introduce others problems like hidden node issues.

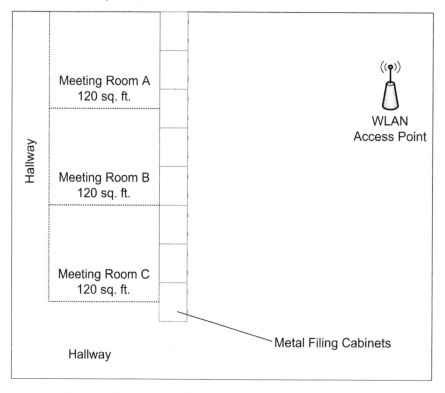

Figure 3.26—Impact of Inventoried Items on RF Coverage

Because buildings are constructed from different material types in different parts of the world, it is important to gain an understanding of the materials used in construction. For that matter, there are different building materials used in buildings within the same city or even the same city block. If construction plans are available, they can reveal the materials used. Are the walls concrete or wood framed? Are they metal framed (metal studs)? Do they contain insulation and, if so, what type? Are there different materials, as is likely, in the internal walls than those used in the external walls?

Some multi-floor buildings have concrete floors that are reinforced with rebar and other metal materials that, while they cause attenuation of the RF signal, will likely allow the signal to pass through floors. Other multi-floor buildings have a steel or metal sheet or pan on which the concrete floor is poured. In these cases, the metal pan—after the concrete attenuation—will often cause enough reflection so that the RF signal cannot pass through cleanly with sufficient signal strength for association. It should be noted that different building code standards require different amounts of rebar or steel to be used in concrete reinforcement. Depending on the amount of rebar or steel used, the attenuation of the RF signal as it passes through the concrete can be so great that the signal is too weak for utilization on the other side.

Internal walls can pose similar problems. They may be constructed with wood or steel frames (studs) that are covered with drywall. In these cases, the RF signal will likely pass through with no problem or with only minimal attenuation. It is not uncommon for first floor (or higher floor) walls to be poured concrete or prefabricated concrete. The same issues exist in that the amount of supporting rebar or steel used will impact the attenuation caused by the walls. In certain scenarios, reflection of the RF signal throughout the internal space may allow for coverage on both sides of a highly reinforced wall, but this must be tested for accuracy – usually by doing a physical site survey.

Additionally, some walls are intentionally shielded to prevent the exit of electromagnetic energy. An example of this would be in a hospital x-ray room. These walls are usually shielded to prevent the electromagnetic energy of the x-ray machine from escaping the room; however, the design also prevents RF energy from entering the room. It is also possible, though uncommon, that a building once used for testing wireless equipment may later be used for other purposes. The design of the testing rooms will probably be such that electromagnetic waves are trapped in the testing rooms. This could cause the same problems as the hospital x-ray room when implementing a WLAN.

The point is this: you never know what you're going to encounter unless you are building a building from scratch. Even then, you may be surprised at the twists and turns that happen during building projects. In the end, you need to know what materials are in the building and not what materials were planned for use.

Another topic of importance is the layout of offices and work areas within the facility. You can only determine proper placement of access points for effective coverage when you know where the users needing wireless access are to be located. It would be convenient if you could verify that the RF signal was detectable at an acceptable data rate in a given location and then move on; however, reality dictates that you divide this coverage among multiple users. These users will have minimum throughput demands that vary based on the usage of VoIP solutions, applications in use and more. This minimum throughput will dictate that you install more access points in a coverage area than are actually needed to provide "just coverage" in that area. The end result may be that you install two or three access points in small cells (lower output power settings) on different channels (1, 6, and 11 are common in 2.4 GHz) and then limit the number of users on each access point to ensure each user is able to have his or her minimum throughput provided.

In addition to throughput, you must consider latency issues. Certain applications, such as VoIP, require faster response times than others. If an access point is serving too many users, the DCF routines may cause the response time to grow to a point where the application either fails or provides less than acceptable quality. In these cases, QoS mechanisms may be used and multiple access points may also be implemented. As you can see, there is more to planning a WLAN than simply installing a sufficient number of access points to provide RF signal coverage throughout the service area. Capacity and capability are essential as well.

Gaining Access Clearance

It is essential to ensure you have access to all required areas to perform the site survey. Many organizations have areas within the facility where it is required that you have special access to get into those areas even if you have access to the larger facility. You may be granted access to these areas with an access card or you may have to have a guide who assists you in gaining access to these areas. During the interview with onsite staff, be sure to verify such locations. Ensure that you have the proper access and that it is documented that you should have that access.

Gaining Permits

Depending on the scenario, government permits may be required. For example, the FCC requires that you notify the FAA any time a tower will be more than 200 feet or 60.96 meters above ground level in the United States. Additionally, structures placed on top of existing buildings that cause the total height to exceed 200 feet will require the notification of the FAA. The proper forms and where they should be sent can be found in the Code of Federal Regulations, title 47, part 17. Simply search the web for "47 CFR Part 17" and you will find it.

The exception to this rule is when a tower or building plus tower that is more than 200 feet is shielded by other existing structures. For example, if you were to place a tower right next to the Empire State Building in New York City, it would not require the notification of the FAA, though it is certain other city regulators would be involved. This exception is granted based on the logical reality that the new tower is not likely to cause a problem for aircraft seeing that it is shielded from aircraft by the other buildings or structures of equal height or greater.

Additional algorithmic calculations are required to determine the maximum height of a tower or structure when it is closer to an actual airport. These special calculations only need to be made if the structure is being placed within or at 20,000 feet of an airport. The measurements are different at 20,000 feet than they are at 10,000 feet and they are different at 10,000 feet than they are at 5,000. You can read the details in 47 CFR Part 17.7.

Special painting and lighting rules may also apply to towers that exceed 200 feet in height. These rules vary according to FAA advisory circulars and at times you may be required to paint or light the tower in a different way than that which is stated in the circulars. This is usually due to unique issues in the construction area that demand unique lighting or painting in order to provide for safe flight passage by or near the tower. The tower issues presented here are just an example and will not be tested on the CWDP exam as they are specific to a regulatory domain.

In addition to tower issues, some cases may demand building permits when building outside enclosures to house wireless equipment. Since these enclosures are usually small, they may pose no problem; however, electrical and other inspections may be required.

Defining Metrics

Metrics are the data values gathered that represent effective or ineffective operations of a WLAN. They are used to establish minimum expectations for particular data rates and other WLAN expectations. The following metrics should be defined at a minimum:

RSSI—Received Signal Strength Indicator (RSSI) is a measurement of the signal strength at a given location. Devices have receive sensitivity ratings and must have a signal at a particular level to receive transmissions at a particular data rate. RSSI is a relative number as each vendor calculates it using a different range. But higher numbers mean a better signal up to some maximum and lower numbers mean a worse signal down to some minimum.

Noise Floor—Noise is effectively any signal or RF energy other than the signal being monitored. The noise floor is the level of energy in the environment without the introduction of local intentional signals, typically measured in dBm. For example, -94 dBm is a common noise floor reading.

SNR—The signal-to-noise (SNR) ratio is not so much a ratio as simply the difference between the noise floor and the desired signal's strength. For example, if the noise floor is -94 dBm and the signal is -53 dBm, the SNR is 41 dB. The ability to properly interpret (demodulate) signals is directly related to the SNR. When SNR values are higher, more complex modulations may be used that result in higher data rates. The reality is that SNR is the key factor in getting a data rate, assuming CCI is not a problem. RSSI is relative, SNR is actual and real.

 Note: **Technically, if the signal is greater than the noise then the SNR is a ratio higher than 1:1, but we measure it in dB for practical usability in WLANs.**

Interference Levels—Interference levels can be higher in some channels than in others. For example, video cameras and other devices may be operating on channel 6 in an area, but not on channel 11. The result is that the interference levels are higher on channel 6. Effectively, the interference level can be thought of as the noise floor on that channel as it is a measurement of signals on the channel and the strength and duty cycle of those signals.

Cell Coverage—Cell coverage is a reference to the size of a single AP cell. That is, how much physical space should an AP cover? This is typically defined as a signal strength metric and then the actual size is simply accepted given some output power level determined for the APs, such as 10 mW for high density or 25 mW for standard density or even 50 mW for low density.

Cell Overlap—Cell overlap is the measurement of overlap among cells, which allows for effective client roaming. Vendors sometimes encourage 25 percent or more overlap, but of course this is not possible to measure. Instead, the goal should be two or more APs (depending on density) at each measurement location. This suggesting is particularly true for 5 GHz WLANs, though a bit harder to achieve for 2.4 GHz WLANS, where accepting that two APs should be visible to a client for an acceptable distance to allow roaming while mobile, for example, for 20–40 feet, is more realistic.

Data Rates—The speed at which bits can be send across the RF medium is the data rate. The data rate is determined based on several factors, including, signal strength, channel width, guard intervals, modulation, and coding methods.

Throughput—A measurement of the usable data passed through the network. For example, the speed at which a file is transferred as opposed to the data rate. On WLANs, the data rate is always significantly higher than the throughput. To ensure application functionality, throughput, and not simply data rates, should be used to test for achieved capacity.

Latency—Latency, also called delay, is a measurement of the time it takes to move data from one point to another. That is to say, how long does it take for data to get from a VoWLAN phone to the other VoWLAN phone in the conversation. This value should typically be less than 150 ms unidirectionally for VoIP implementations.

Jitter—Jitter is the variance in delay (latency). If one packet takes 130 ms to get from point A to point B and the next packet takes 80 ms, it can cause problems in VoIP communications. Jitter buffers are typically used to circumvent this problem.

Loss—Loss is a generic term used to reference packets that do not reach their destination for any reason. Packet loss is typically measured in percentages.

Retries—With connection oriented protocols and the 802.11MAC, when frames are lost (or packets with TCP), they are resent. This resending is called a retry. High retry rates indicate a problem in a WLAN.

With all of these metrics, clear definitions of expectations should be set in requirements analysis so that the site survey can be performed such that the resulting network design accommodates the expectations. What is an acceptable loss rate? What is the acceptable delay in communications? What SNR must exist (or RSSI)? How many APs should cover each area? Clearly defining these metrics gives you something to measure in the site survey. Without their definition, you are simply designing for coverage and, sometimes, not even that.

 Note: **Some site survey software applications will allow you to simulate a network adapter other than the one you actually use to capture WLAN metrics. It is important to know that, while this feature may show the results in a manner that is closer to**

the simulated card, the only way to ensure you are capturing data as that card would see it is to capture with that card.

Meeting Scenario-Specific Requirements

Some WLAN implementations are different than the normal get requirements, do a survey, design the network, implement it, and test it. They have additional requirements. The following scenario specific requirements may have to be considered:

Meeting Access Requirements (Clearance and Badges)—To access controlled areas, you may require key cards, traditional lock keys, or access codes. Ensure that this information is gathered before entering the facility to perform the site survey. Clearance is granted through authorization, which can be as simple as a list with your name on it or as complicated as requiring a smart card and access code to gain entry. Badges can be person-specific, with name and photo, or generic guest badges.

Figure 3.27—Typical Visitor Badge for Access

Arranging Escorts—In many environments, you cannot access restricted areas alone, but must have a guide or escort with you at all times. This requirement should be planned so that your survey is not delayed while waiting on an escort to arrive.

Single Floor vs. Multiple-Floor Installations—The difference between single floor and multiple-floor installations is significant. In single-floor installations, you are concerned only about the signals propagating horizontally through the space. In a multiple-floor installation, you must also consider the signals propagating vertically between floors. Attenuation levels must be calculated for walls and floors to properly perform the survey and/or to perform a predictive modeling survey. APs should be placed so that channels do not cause CCI, as much as possible, with the floors above and below as well as horizontally dispersed cells.

Industry-Specific Requirements—Some industries have unique requirements. For example, it may be required that union workers assist with certain tasks or in healthcare scenarios patient privacy becomes paramount. As a WLAN designer, you may be required to work with a union employee to meet union requirements. This employee may assist with ladders, mounting APs, and performing other non-technical tasks, if he is not trained in Wi-Fi installations. When operating within healthcare environments, it is essential that you honor patient privacy. This is both an issue of respect and legal compliance. Additional industry-specific requirements include OSHA regulations, PCI DSS security guidelines, SOX guidelines, and more.

Training Requirements—The final specific requirement is training in safety and operations. Safety training may be required for installation engineers. This includes OSHA-type compliance training (or additional local safety regulations) as well as training in electrical safety. Operations training is offered to administration staff and users. Administrators require training in configuration and management of the WLAN and infrastructure support services. Users require training, in some instances, on WLAN access methods and acceptable use policies.

EXAM MOMENT: A special equation is used to calculate RF path loss in free space and can impact requirements for outdoor bridge links. It is called Friis transmission equation and is LdB = 20log(d)-27.55. LdB stands for loss in dB. The most important thing to know is that this equation is used to calculate the loss in dB as RF travels its path through free space.

Surveying for Applications and Architectures

Surveying for specific applications and architectures is about understanding unique requirements they impose on the network. This section provides an overview of common applications and architectures, and their requirements.

Voice over IP (VoIP)

Surveying for specific applications has become much easier in recent years. Major site survey software providers have included configuration templates for site surveys aimed at VoIP and other common application and architecture installation types. Vendors provide recommendations ranging from providing coverage at a minimum of -65 to -70 dB signal strength to ensuring that three APs are available at all times to all users. Ultimately, the system must meet your needs and these needs may allow for some variance from vendor recommendations, but be sure to understand if the vendor's recommendations are just that, recommendations and not requirements for support.

Today, with VoIP, you are dealing with several Wi-Fi client types. You have the laptop or tablet user using softphone software. You have the true Wi-Fi VoIP phone or handset. And you also have to consider custom designed smartphones or communications devices, like the ASCOM MYCO, which is effectively an Android smartphone with a design to accommodate healthcare professionals. Figure 3.28 shows this device.

Many VoIP devices support push-to-talk features so that dialing a number is not required and faster communications can be achieved. This is usually implemented in healthcare and emergency response scenarios. Note that push-to-talk features of many systems require multicast packet delivery to work. The WLAN should be planned to support multicast delivery for such applications.

Figure 3.28—ASCOM MYCO Smartphone/VoIP Device

Video

Video is a high-bandwidth application. Video comes in two primary forms: live and streaming. Live video has real-time requirements and often requires multicast support as well. Streaming video typically uses buffering to reduce the latency demands on the application. For example, the player may buffer anywhere from five seconds to one minute of video so that network delays do not prevent smooth play of the video. When designing for video, be sure to consider the kind of video being implemented.

Both voice and video use codecs (coders and decoders). Codecs are used to encode and compress (in most cases) the data so that network throughput requirements are reduced. Table 3-2 lists common audio codecs and their characteristics. Table 3-3 lists common video codecs and their characteristics.

Codec	Bitrate	Compression (Yes/No)
G.711	64 Kbps	No
G.722	64, 56, 48 Kbps	Yes
G.723/723.1	5.4, 6.3 Kbps	Yes
G.729/729A	8 Kbps	Yes

Table 3.2—VoIP Codecs

Codec	Bitrate	Compression (Yes/No)
MPEG Basic	Varies by profile (96 Kbps to 135 Mbps)	Yes
H.263	384, 768 Kbps	Yes
Uncompressed	1.5 Gbps for 1080p	No

Table 3.3—Video Codecs

For applications like voice and video it is essential to implement QoS. Figure 3.29 shows the QoS management interface in the Aerohive HiveManager solution.

Multimedia data packets come in varying sizes. We generally speak of a long packet or a short packet, and each packet type has its benefits and drawbacks. Since management information is related to each frame or packet, longer packets incur less overhead. This conclusion is simple math. If you have a total amount of data that you wish to transmit and you transmit that data with short packets, you will incur more overhead. That exact same amount of data sent with long packets incurs less overhead, since there are fewer packets. To clearly understand this concept, consider the fictional packet sizes in Table 3-4.

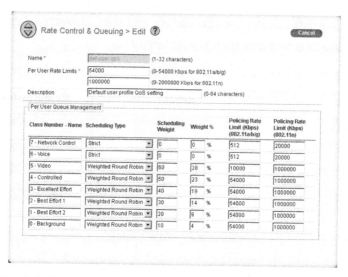

Figure 3.29—Aerohive HiveManager QoS Administration Screen

As the table shows, a packet size of 10k results in 10k of management overhead, assuming a 1k measurement for management data per useful data packet. However, a 2k packet size increases the management overhead by five times (interestingly, the same factor by which it reduced the packet size). The resulting principle is that long packets usually incur less management overhead than short packets.

Total Data	Packet Size	Management per Packet	Total Packets	Total Management
100k	10k	1k	10	10k
100k	2k	1k	50	50k

Table 3.4—Management Overhead and Packet Size

Long packets also reduce the packet processing load. The devices that forward the packets on the network must de-encapsulate the packets from the frames and re-encapsulate them to send them on to their destination. The result of using long packets is that there are fewer iterations of the de-encapsulation and re-encapsulation process per total data payload. Think back to the table that listed management overhead for a long packet as opposed to a short packet (Table 3-4).

The same factor applies here. The long packet configuration would demand only 10 iterations of the packet processing, and the short packet would require 50 iterations.

Another possible benefit of long packets is that you achieve greater network loading. More time is spent sending data as opposed to determining where to send data. This greater loading capability means that the network bandwidth may be more evenly consumed and the network performance may be more predictable.

The negative aspects of long packets become the positive benefits of short packets. Long packets do create more problems when packets are lost. Since there is so much data in an individual packet, the loss of just one packet can greatly impact the quality of a video or audio stream. Shorter packets are less detrimental in such situations. In fact, some scenarios where a packet is lost will hardly be noticeable to the user.

When longer packets are used, latency is increased. Latency is a measure of the difference in time from when a packet is transmitted to when the same packet arrives. Most streaming video and audio technologies, as well as VoIP in general, have upper boundaries that must be imposed on latency variables. One way to reduce latency is to shorten the packet size. Smaller packets move through the network faster due to the fact that there are simply smaller bits to transmit and Quality of Service processing can "fit" the smaller packets in more easily.

Finally, short packets have less need for fragmentation. Upper-layer (OSI) data must be chunked or fragmented if it is too large for the lower TCP, UDP, or IP layers or MAC layers like 802.11. Fragmentation incurs extra processing for both the sender and the receiver and can cause unnecessary extra delay. A simple method for removing much of the fragmentation is to set your application to send data chunks that result in smaller packets and, therefore, less fragmentation.

Data

Standard data networks are much easier to design than real-time data networks. However, unless you are implementing separate WLANs for real-time applications and standard data applications, you will need to accommodate for QoS configuration in all modern enterprise WLANs. This is because applications such as Skype,

FaceTime, and additional real-time applications will be used even if VoWLAN is not implemented.

Even when planning for standard data, you must ensure that the required throughput demands (part of capacity) are met. For example, if the average user will require 2 Mbps and 25 users will be connected to each AP, the APs must provide 50 Mbps data throughput. Given that throughput is often 50 percent of the data rate, the users will require a data rate higher than 100 Mbps to ensure throughput demands are met.

Location Services

Location services are implemented, in WLANs, in two ways: 802.11-based or non-802.11. With non-802.11 systems, RFID or some other RF mechanism is used to track the device and the systems may use Wi-Fi to communicate with central servers, but the actual location tracking is performed using non-Wi-Fi tags or devices. 802.11-based uses various triangulation techniques, such as those covered in your CWNA studies, to locate devices. When designing for location services, it is important to ensure that multiple APs, three for best results, can see each possible location. This will allow for the most accurate location processing.

Multiple-Channel Architecture (MCA)

Standard WLANs are MCA in design. This simply means that each AP is configured for a different channel so that same-channel APs are significantly separated. The goal of separation is often -85 dB. That is an AP on channel 1 can only hear the next AP on channel 1 at -85 or -86 dB or lower. This is actually quite difficult to achieve in 2.4 GHz, but much easier to achieve in 5 GHz because more channels are available in that frequency range.

You may wonder where the -85 or -86 dB number is sourced. The answer is from the Clear Channel Assessment (CCA) threshold. For example, for all 5 GHz PHYs, the threshold is -82 dBm for the primary channel and -62 dBm for 802.11n secondary channels and -72 dBm for 802.11ac secondary channels. Going with -85 or -86 provides a bit of buffer in the boundary for fluctuations in the RF environment.

An additional requirement before a client can transmit is the clearance of Energy Detect (ED), which is typically 20 dB above the minimum receive sensitivity for a given PHY (this is the CCA threshold just referenced in the preceding paragraph).

 Note: **In the real world, it is very difficult to measure and design for this CCA analysis. In most cases, a quick look at the APs that can be seen from an AP is sufficient to discover the likely CCI. However, CCI is a factor, not only of the visibility of the AP, but the actual communications that happen between that AP and associated STAs. A relatively quiet, but clearly visible, cell will cause less CCI than a cell that is very active though it may present a weaker signal in the other same channel cell.**

Single-Channel Architecture (SCA)

SCA is implemented based on density requirements. That is, because the APs are configured by the controller and are all operating on the same channel, SCA surveys are usually determining the number of clients and types of applications to be used. Once this is known, an appropriate number of APs may be selected for the deployment. For more information on SCA design, which is not heavily tested on the CWDP exam, see the Meru website at www.merunetworks.com.

Outdoor Surveys

When creating outdoor wireless bridge links, you will be implementing one of two primary types: point-to-point and point-to-multipoint. In a point-to-point implementation, two wireless bridges are configured to communicate with each other and provide the link across which network traffic is routed as seen in Figure 3.30.

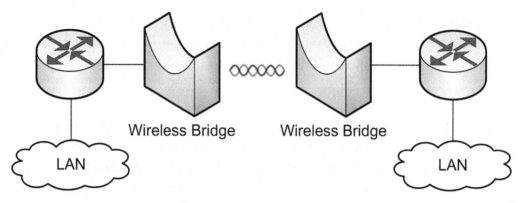

Figure 3.30—Point-to-Point Bridge Link

When creating a point-to-multipoint bridge link, you will configure one bridge to act as the centralized bridge and the other bridges to act as remote bridges. The remote bridges will communicate with each other through the centralized bridge and users from all LANs may be allowed to communicate with all other LANs through some link pathway. Figure 3.31 shows a point-to-multipoint bridge link.

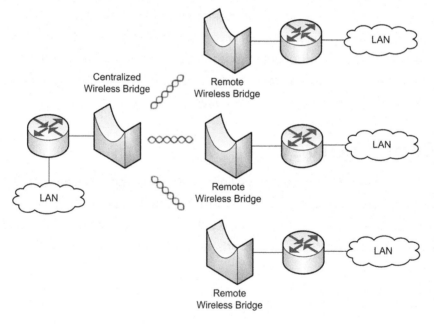

Figure 3.31—Point-to-Multipoint Bridge Link

When creating these bridge links, you must ensure that proper LOS exists and that the first Fresnel Zone is acceptably clear. This may mean gathering terrain maps from online and local government sources. It may also require that you photograph the surrounding areas to document buildings, trees, and other structures that may factor into your link configuration. You may also benefit from local weather information that can be used to predict the amount of fog, smog, and other weather factors common to the area in which the link is expected to operate.

With this information gathered, you can begin to plan the links. You will need to determine the optimum height and directionality in order to overcome obstacles that were discovered in the information gathering phase. You may need to obtain permits for towers of greater than 200 feet in the United States, as was noted earlier. Check with your local flight regulatory agency to determine the constraints imposed on towers and tall construction projects in your regulatory domain.

> **EXAM MOMENT:** When creating outdoor bridge links, due to the distance the signal must travel in links over 10 miles or 16 kilometers, increasing the acknowledgement timeout threshold may be useful in avoiding unneeded frame retransmissions.

Not all outdoor WLAN implementations are intended to act as bridge links. In fact many outdoor WLANs are being implemented today that are intended to provide direct client connectivity for network access. There are two primary implementation models that use 802.11 technologies: hotspot-type WLANs and mesh networks.

Outdoor WLANs that implement standards-based IEEE 802.11 equipment are sometimes called hotspots as well. Most people think of a hotspot as a location that provides wireless network access to the Internet for the public. These hotspots may provide Internet access for free or for a charge. The term hotspot has more recently been used to mean a location when authorized users can gain access to a private network as well. In this case, the WLAN is simply taken outdoors and provides client-to-access point connectivity.

In most outdoor WLAN implementations, a wire is run to the location where the access point is placed. The access point acts as a bridge between the wireless clients and the wired network and the wired network may or may not provide a gateway to the Internet. Some outdoor WLANs may use a wireless bridge to connect back to the private network and then connect one or more access points to this wireless bridge via a small switch. Electrical power is all that is required at the location to implement such an outdoor WLAN. This type of implementation could still utilize all IEEE 802.11-compliant hardware and is represented in Figure 3.32.

Mesh networks are newer wireless networks that are sometimes called self-healing and self-forming. Both infrastructure and client meshing may be supported. Infrastructure mesh networks usually consist of wireless links between remote sites with built-in redundancy provided by the mesh infrastructure. They may not allow clients to connect and, in these cases, only provide a series of links across which data may be routed. Client mesh networks may consist of wireless client and infrastructure devices and some devices may be both. These devices may be self-configuring in that they automatically determine if they are acting as a client or an infrastructure device and the network is self-healing in that new routes can be determined when a device that was involved in routing becomes unavailable. This self-configuration is called automatic topology learning and the self-healing is called dynamic path selection in the IEEE 802.11s amendment.

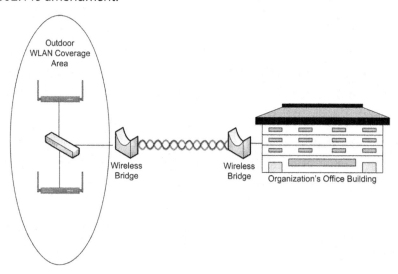

Figure 3.32—Outdoor WLAN across Bridged Connection

Security may be a concern in mesh networks. Due to the somewhat open nature of mesh networks, they are not always configured with the best security. Additionally, the mesh network devices are not currently standards based, although the IEEE is working in an amendment to the IEEE 802.11 standard as task groups. Table 3-5 compares mesh networks to outdoor WLAN networks.

Outdoor WLANs	Mesh Networks
Less tolerant to failures.	More tolerant to failures.
Usually completely standards based.	Standards based with implementations outside the standards until IEEE 802.11s (Clause 11A) is ratified.
May require wired line or dedicated bridge links.	Does not require wired line or dedicated bridge links throughout the mesh network, but will be connected to a wired network at one or more points.
No standard for self-configuration though it is implemented by many vendors' WLAN controllers and management software.	No standard for self-configuration at this time though vendors have implemented proprietary protocols for this. IEEE 802.11s (Clause 11A) does specify procedures for neighbor discovery and automatic configuration.

Table 3.5—Outdoor WLANs versus Mesh Networks

Chapter Review

In this chapter, you learned about site survey tools, procedures, and scenarios. This information will help prepare you for the CWDP exam and in preparing to perform site surveys in real-world scenarios.

Facts to Remember

Be sure to remember the following facts as you prepare for the CWDP certification and be sure that you can explain the details related to them:

- Manual site surveys are also called AP-on-a-stick and involve placing APs in the physical environment and then testing the signal propagation throughout that environment.

- APs used in site surveys should be the same APs being deployed.

- Predictive modeling surveys use software to simulate RF behavior on a floor plan of the environment.

- Calibration of site survey software is essential.

- Proper material definition is key to accurate predictive modeling surveys.

- Attenuation measurements should be taken in the RF environment both horizontally (walls, doors, etc.) and vertically (ceilings and floors).

- Protocol analyzers can locate WLANs and the configuration parameters of them which are revealed through the beacon frames.

- Spectrum analyzers can locate both Wi-Fi and non-Wi-Fi devices that may cause issues on specific channels.

- Co-channel interference (CCI), also called co-channel contention (CCC) is caused by two or more APs existing on the same channel in close proximity (from a signal strength perspective) to each other.

- Adjacent channel interference (ACI) is caused when a near cell is using an adjacent channel; for example, when a cell is on channel 1 and another near cell is on channels 2, 3, 4, or 5.

- CCI is related to the Clear Channel Assessment algorithm.

- ACI is related to the Energy Detect algorithm.

- VoIP requires low latency and low jitter with low packet loss of less than 1 percent.

- Throughput on a WLAN is often 50 percent or less than the data rate.

Chapter 4:

Enterprise WLAN Design

In this chapter:

- WLAN Architectures
- RF Management
- Channel Plans
- Infrastructure Services
- Selecting Access Points
- Configuring Access Points
- Designing for Client Devices
- Designing for Applications
- Planning for Quality of Service (QoS)
- Security Solutions
- Advanced Security Solutions
- Planning for Roaming
- Using Network Planning Tools

Objectives

3.1 Demonstrate a knowledge of WLAN architectures and solutions including management solutions, communication protocols, data forwarding models, scalability, redundancy, encryption methods, controller-based solutions, cloud-based solutions, autonomous solutions, centralized data forwarding, distributed data forwarding, and the advantages and limitations of various architectures.

3.2 Plan for RF management including channel usage, MCA and SCA, RRM, solutions for co-channel interference, non-overlapping adjacent-channel interference, overlapping adjacent-channel interference and non-802.11 interference all within regulatory constraints and including client station considerations (interference at client locations, high density of clients, and mobile and non-mobile clients).

3.3 Design appropriate 802.11 channel plans including channel widths, frequency bands, output power levels (including DFS and TPC requirements), channel reuse, 802.11n and 802.11ac channels and advanced channel features (80+80, RTS/CTS enhancements, etc.).

3.4 Select access points (APs) and define configuration and installation parameters for them including indoor APs, outdoor APs, internal antennas, external antennas, PoE-powered APs, wall outlet-powered APs, mounting solutions, and staging procedures.

3.5 Understand and explain the varied configuration processes for different AP deployment models including MCA, SCA, controller-based, cloud-based, distributed, autonomous, and additional models commonly used in modern WLANs.

3.6 Design infrastructure services and connectivity to existing services required to support WLANs including RADIUS services, LDAP connections, DHCP provisioning, PKI implementation, NTP availability, DNS services, firewall configuration, ACL management, RBAC implementation, VLAN management, BYOD/MDM, onboarding, and NAC integration.

3.7 Ensure availability of appropriate cabling and power provisioning including backhaul speeds, PoE, redundant connections, and connectivity to required services.

2.6 Understand the different methodologies used in site surveys for varying applications and architectures including VoIP, video, data, location services, multiple channel architecture (MCA), and single channel architecture (SCA).

3.11 Design for varied client devices including tablets, mobile phones, laptops, stationary devices, supported PHYs, data rates, channels allowed, channel widths, DFS support, and receive sensitivity levels.

3.12 Design for varied application types including roaming requirements, latency requirements, data throughput demands, specialty devices (barcode scanners, healthcare devices, ID badges, location tracking systems, wireless cameras), and voice/video.

3.13 Design end-to-end QoS solutions including 802.11 QoS, wired QoS, WMM, airtime fairness, band steering, load balancing, QoS markings, and queues.

3.14 Design standard security solutions including RADIUS server selection, EAP type selection, encryption solutions, passphrase-based implementations, and WPS.

3.15 Design advanced security solutions including Per-User PSK (PPSK), VPN implementation, endpoint security, Wireless Intrusion Prevention Systems (WIPS), BYOD/MDM/guest access and onboarding, captive portals, network segmentation, and content filtering.

3.16 Given a scenario, plan for secure roaming including 802.11-2012 roaming methods, Opportunistic Key Caching, SCA roaming, pre-authentication, PMK caching, and preshared key implementations.

3.19 Understand the use of network planning tools including site survey software design features, network diagramming tools, throughput testing tools and, link calculation software/spreadsheets.

After discovering network requirements and performing a site survey, the design of the WLAN can proceed. The output of the site survey should be a determination of AP locations and the configuration settings for those APs; however, much still remains. The WLAN architecture must be selected. The details of RF management must be considered. Ensuring that the channel plans suggested within the site survey software, or that are manually entered into the software, are effective is also important. This chapter begins the exploration of WLAN design practices and the next chapter completes it. The first topic is WLAN architectures.

WLAN Architectures

The WLAN architecture defines the way in which the WLAN operates and is managed. Does it send client data directly onto the network from the AP routed to the final destination, or does it pass all data through a controller within a tunnel? Is it managed onsite or from the cloud? Will you deploy an autonomous solution? These questions can be answered based on the information in this section.

Management Solutions

Management solutions typically fall into three categories:

- controller-based
- cloud-based
- autonomous

Controller-based solutions include virtual controller solutions where one of the APs acts as the controller for the other APs. Aruba's Instant AP solution is an example of this.

Controller-based solutions were really the first popular centralized management solutions (with the possible exception of some wireless network management systems (WNMS), which have all but fallen out of use today). They allow administrators to connect an AP to the network, have it receive updates and configuration settings appropriate for it, and go live on the network automatically. Of course, someone had to set up the controller, but the AP configuration was made much simpler.

Cloud-based solutions, from a configuration standpoint, work much like controller-based solutions. The APs are connected to the network, then they connect to the cloud management software, and finally they are either configured automatically or manually within the cloud then brought online. A key difference is that cloud-based solutions do not use centralized data forwarding in most cases so that the data can pass directly through the AP onto the local network.

Autonomous APs are directly configured by the WLAN engineer during installation. This model is still very popular in small businesses that require only a few APs. An engineer can typically configure four or five APs in the amount of time it would take to install a controller and configure the profiles and then connect the APs. Ongoing management may take more time, but the reality is that enterprise-grade APs often run for months without requiring maintenance resulting in the autonomous model continuing to thrive in very small WLANs.

The following sections provide more details about each of these three management solutions. Additionally, data forwarding models are explained so that the WLAN designer can make effective selections.

Controller-Based Architectures

Controller-based architectures are often called split MAC models because a portion of the MAC is managed in the AP and a portion is managed in the controller. These types of APs are often called thin APs or lightweight APs because they do not perform as many functions as the traditional APs (fat APs or think APs). The split MAC model is very popular in large networks today and is becoming more popular in smaller networks, as well. Again, the costs and benefits associated with the split MAC model must be considered.

Split MAC model costs:

- Possible single point of failure at the wireless LAN controller (WLC).

- Increased wired network traffic required to manage the wireless stations.

- Fewer features within the APs themselves when using truly thin APs.

Split MAC model benefits:

- Centralized administration may reduce ongoing support efforts.

- APs may or may not be less expensive since they can have less memory and processing power. The reality is that many APs today can operate either in autonomous or controller-based modes and, therefore, do not cost less or more depending on how you implement them.

- Each AP may be able to handle more client stations since the AP doesn't have to handle management processing overhead.

Controller-based architectures use Lightweight Access Point Protocol (LWAPP) or Control and Provisioning Wireless Access Point (CAPWAP) tunnels between the APs and the controllers. Traditionally, all data is forwarded to the controller, and then the controller passes the data onto the wired network. LWAPP uses UDP ports 12222 and 12223 by default. CAPWAP uses UDP ports 5246 and 5247 by default. So LWAPP or CAPWAP is the communication protocol between the AP and the controller. The 802.11 frame is tunneled to the controller so that the controller can see all of the 802.11 details and make appropriate decisions.

To understand what is typically performed in the AP, when using a split MAC model, and what is typically performed in the controller, consider the following AP responsibilities (based on Cisco documentation):

- Frame exchange handshake between a client and AP

- Transmission of beacon frames

- Buffering and transmission of frames for clients in power save mode

- Response to probe request frames from clients; the probe requests are also sent to the WLC for processing

- Forwarding notification of received probe requests to the WLC

- Provision of real-time signal quality information to the switch with every received frame

- Monitoring each of the radio channels for noise, interference, and other WLANs

- Monitoring for the presence of other APs

- Encryption and decryption of 802.11 frames

Now consider the following wireless controller responsibilities (based on Cisco documentation):

- 802.11 authentication

- 802.11 association and reassociation (mobility)

- 802.11 frame translation and bridging

- 802.1X/EAP/RADIUS processing

- Termination of 802.11 traffic on a wired interface, except in the case of REAP and H-REAP configured APs

Figure 4.1 provides the high-level comparative difference between autonomous APS and split MAC APs.

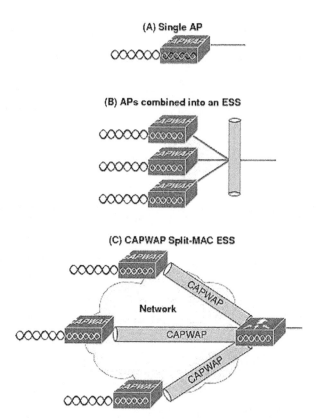

Figure 4.1—Single AP, APs in an ESS and CAPWAP Split-MAC ESS

In summary, as shown in Figure 4.2, a controller-based architecture depends on a wired network device called a controller (in the past they were actually called wireless LAN switches). The lightweight APs connect to the controller to update firmware, be configured, and then provision the radio for the WLAN.

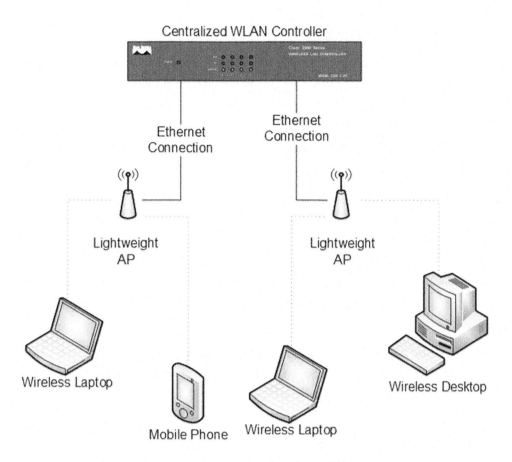

Figure 4.2—Controller-Based Architecture

Cloud-Based Solutions

Cloud-based solutions work across the Internet for device management. Modern cloud WLAN vendors provision APs, monitor APs, reconfigure APs, and provide other maintenance operations from the cloud; however, most APs work in a distributed edge manner such that they fully function as MAC stations without requiring access to the cloud. This provides for faster data communications and also allows for continued local operations if the Internet connection fails.

The advantages of cloud-based management include "anywhere access" to monitoring and configuration options and the lack of need for on-premise gear (WLAN controllers) to run the WLAN. The disadvantages of cloud-based management include consumption of Internet bandwidth, inability to manage the WLAN when the Internet is down (with the common exception of some basic console commands), and the monthly or annual service contract fees required to use the system.

 Note: Some cloud-based providers also offer on premise solutions so that their APs can be used without requiring cloud management.

Autonomous Solutions

Autonomous APs work in either a standalone deployment model where each AP is individually configured and managed or in a centralized configuration management model where they are configured from a centralized software application or server console, but other than monitoring and configuration they perform completely independent as WLAN APs.

Figure 4.3 shows the typical autonomous AP deployment. Such a deployment is still very common for smaller networks.

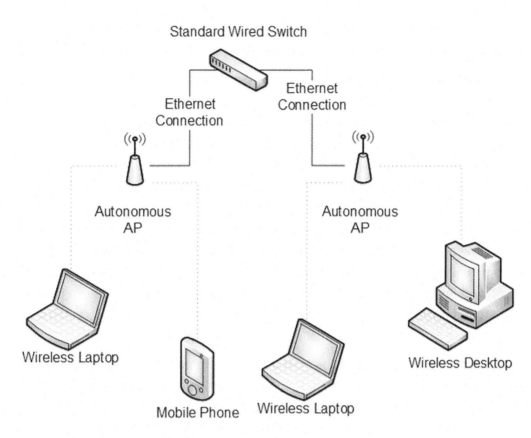

Figure 4.3—Autonomous AP Deployment

Data Forwarding Models

Data forwarding models are either centralized or distributed. Early WLAN controllers (switches) all used centralized data forwarding. And, Autonomous APs all use distributed data forwarding. Over the years hybrid models have arisen.

Cloud-managed WLANS mostly use distributed data forwarding, which means that the actual user data goes from the AP directly to the destination and need not go first to the cloud. This makes sense for cloud-managed WLANs because data destined for an internal server would not perform well when first going to the cloud provider network and then back into the local network to the server. Distributed data forwarding then indicates that the AP determines where to send the data next along the journey to its final destination rather than that WLAN controller.

Centralized data forwarding indicates that all data is tunneled to the controller, usually in a LWAPP or CAPWAP Layer 3 tunnel, and it is then forwarded from the controller to the actual destination. While most networks and most controllers are well able to keep up with such demands, it may not be a very efficient route. In many cases, the data is destined in the data center where the controller may well reside anyway, in many scenarios this results in great redundancy. For example, if the wired network is designed such that many services (printers, DNS, Internet proxy servers, etc.) are located near the access layer and not near the data center, it simply results in data traveling the path twice to reach the destination. The outcome is greater delay in communications. If the network has sufficient extra bandwidth to handle this, it will be no problem. If the network is already heavily loaded (for example, utilizing many 100 Mbps links instead of 1 or 10 Gbps links), the extra communications could cause performance issues for other time-sensitive communications.

Most modern controller-based solutions allow for the enabling of distributed data forwarding. However, it is important to read the vendor documentation closely. While they may support distributed data forwarding instead of centralized data forwarding, some features may be lost in such scenarios. For example, certain monitoring and alerting features may be lost if the data is no longer passing through the controller.

RF Management

RF management involves controlling the RF activity in an environment. Specific to WLANs, it involves choosing an MCA or SCA solution, understanding RRM and addressing interference. These topics are covered in this section.

MCA and SCA RF Management

RF management, in MCA, is about planning channel assignments. This will be discussed more in the next section, Channel Plans. With SCA solutions, RF management is automatic within the channel selected and more density or WLANs dedicated to additional purposes can be added by adding new channel blankets. For example, if you first implement SCA on channel 6, you can later add a network on channel 11 to use for VoIP only. The remainder of this section will address areas with a high density of clients and mobile and non-mobile clients and their needs.

WLAN clients can be either mobile or non-mobile. Non-mobile clients generally have consistent results because the AP does not move and neither does the client. Unless a significant change occurs in the environment, such as the addition of new walls, doors, or filing cabinets, the non-mobile client is likely to continue connecting to the same AP day after day.

Mobile clients will utilize many APs throughout their life. Mobile clients include laptops, tablets, barcode scanners, mobile phones, and VoWLAN handsets among others. These clients will have varying results depending on the signal strength and CCI and ACI in the area where they are used. The WLAN should be designed to provide a minimum level of service and the users should be trained to understand that varying levels of performance can be expected above that minimum level. Service Level Agreements (SLA) can be written to document the minimum level required of the WLAN.

Whether using MCA or SCA architectures, the WLAN designer will encounter areas with a high density of clients. Such high density (HD) and very high density (VHD) WLANs must be carefully engineered to provide the required coverage and capacity. In the later section, Selecting Access Points, you will discover a useful tool freely available that assists in capacity planning. But the general guideline for high density networks is more APs with lower output power settings. This allows for a greater density of APs in a physical space. In many cases, these APs will be configured at 5 or 10 mW of output power to accomplish the small cell size required. More information will be provided on cell size planning in the later discussions of co-channel and adjacent channel interference.

Radio Resource Management (RRM)

RRM is often defined as dynamic channel assignment and dynamic RF output power control and this definition is true. However, modern implementations of RRM evaluate additional factors and provide additional benefits because of this extra evaluation.

The basic features of all RRM solutions is dynamic channel selection or assignment and transmit power level management. Most RRM solutions use some kind of neighbor communications that provide information to APs about their neighbors and then this information is passed up the chain to a WLAN controller that uses the data to make decisions about channels and power levels. The basic process is as follows:

1. APs send neighbor communications.

2. APs listen on all channels for neighbor communications.

3. The information gathered is sent to the controller.

4. The controller adjusts AP configurations based on the information

However, there are additional features, such as coverage hole detection and interference detection. Coverage hole detection is focused on clients. When an AP hears from an associated client below a configurable dB threshold, it is assumed that the client has no better AP as a roaming option. The controller can either increase the output power of the AP (while hoping not to create a link mismatch) or alert an administrator of the potential problem.

Interference detection occurs by scanning all channels, including adjacent channels, and listening for communications. When detected, the controller is notified. When the frame is not recognized by the controller, it is identified as interference and the controller may adjust appropriate AP channels to avoid the interference and it may provide an alert to the administrator.

Note: **Some WLAN engineers are completely opposed to RRM and others feel it must be carefully managed. The CWNP position is a neutral position in that many WLANs benefit greatly from RRM and others can experience severe problems. It is a technology that provides exceptional value in the right environment.**

Co-Channel Interference

Co-channel interference has been defined in previous chapters. It occurs when two cells are close enough to each other and are operating on the same channel that some clients and often even the APs will be required to contend with each other to gain access to the medium. As was previously noted, for this reason, many are now calling it co-channel contention (CCC) as it is a more precise reference to what it is.

The mitigating solution to CCI is cell sizing. By adjusting cell sizes (and shapes with directional antennas) you can reduce CCI in 2.4 GHz and all but remove it in many 5 GHz deployments. To understand how this works, you should understand two boundaries of a cell: the association boundary and the CCI boundary. Additionally, you should be aware that every client associated to a cell (an AP) will have its own CCI boundaries, as well.

The association boundary is the edge of the cell where the minimum supported data rate can be achieved. If the lowest data rates of 1 and 2 Mbps have been disabled, for example, this will result in a smaller association cell (reduced association boundary) than when they are enabled. However, just because clients can no longer associate beyond that point does not mean that CCI cannot exist beyond that point.

The CCI boundary exists where the listening stations that are not part of the cell must be silent because they have detected a signal at a minimum threshold. This behavior is part of the CSMA/CA protocol used in 802.11 WLANs. Even when lower data rates are disabled, such as 1, 2, and 5.5 Mbps, 802.11 standard devices must still process and wait for 1, 2, and 5.5 Mbps signals that are heard in the 2.4 GHz band. The same is true in 5 GHz if low data rates like 6 and 12 Mbps are disabled. Therefore, CCI can occur based on low-data rate signals even though those signals are not enabled in the local cell.

Additionally, just because the signal cannot be fully processed does not mean that the signal cannot be detected and initiate a backoff based on the duration for a STA.

When considering association boundaries (also called data rate boundaries) and CCI boundaries, the AP perspective is almost always considered, and it should be. Additionally, the client perspective must be considered. The AP perspective is the simplest and is represented in Figure 4.4. The APs in the image have low data rates of 1, 2, and 5.5 Mbps disabled. Therefore, the association boundary is smaller than the CCI boundary by a significant amount. The image shows only a 2.4 GHz representation, but 5 GHz boundaries work in a similar manner. In Figure 4.4, the CCI boundary does not reach all the way into the space of the other AP, but this does not mean it will not cause problems. The client perspective will show that problems still occur in such scenarios.

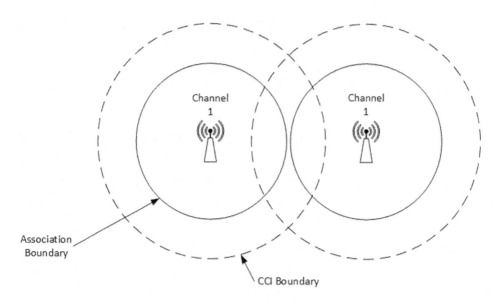

Figure 4.4—Association Boundaries for APs

The client perspective of the association boundary, remember, is also called the data rate boundary and the CCI boundary is much different. Like APs, the clients transmit, typically, in an omni-directional manner. Therefore, they both see the boundaries of other nearby APs and create their own. That is, they see cells and they also create a cell of RF energy of their own. Figure 4.5 illustrates this.

Notice in Figure 4.5 that the signals from the client station, that are associated with the AP on the left, are reaching the AP on the right. The client is causing CCI for the AP on the right and the AP on the right is causing CCI for the client even though the APs are not causing significant CCI for each other directly. Therefore, the cells created by the two APs are causing CCI for each other. Again, remember, that CCI is the normal contention process defined in CSMA/CA. The client station in Figure 4.5 must be silent for the duration of any frames it sees from the AP on the right, or any stations associated with the AP on the right, that it can see. Additionally, the AP on the right must be silent for the duration of any frames it sees from the client, or any other clients it can see, that are associated with the AP on the left. Therefore, CCI is not an AP-only issue, but it is an issue impacting clients and created by clients, as well.

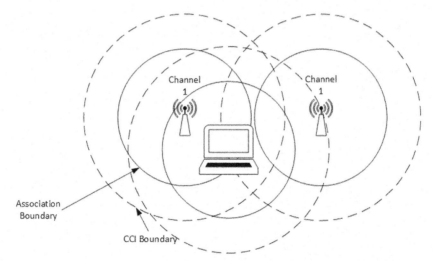

Figure 4.5—Association Boundaries for Clients

Adjacent Channel Interference

Adjacent channel interference is caused when channels overlap intentionally, such as 2.4 GHz channels, or when non-overlapping channels cause side-lobe interference, such as 5 GHz channels. 2.4 GHz channels are 5 MHz apart and 20 or 22 MHz wide; therefore, it is a certainty that adjacent channels will overlap and cause interference. For example, Figure 4.6 shows the overlap of channel 1 and channel 2 in the 2.4 GHz band.

In Figure 4.6, the spectral mask for an OFDM channel is shown with an overlay of the center frequency for channel 1 and channel 2. Given that the spectral mask would be that of channel 1, it is obvious that channel 2 would overlap with it if its spectral mask were in view. When adjacent channels overlap they cause ACI, which can manifest as corrupt frames or simply prevent communications due to energy detect in 2.4 GHz. In 2.4 GHz, ACI can be prevented within your controlled networks by using channels 1, 6, and 11. However, in areas where neighbor WLANs can be seen, if they are using channels 2-5, 7–10, or 11–14, ACI may exist regardless of your network settings. This can be mitigated by carefully planning channel selections nearest to these neighbor WLANs.

In 5 GHz, ACI is caused by side-lobes when the adjacent channel is either implemented very close to the AP or with high-output power or a client associated with the other channel AP is near the interfered AP/cell. 5 GHz ACI is typically manifest as corrupt frames. In 5 GHz it can be prevented with proper channel plans that do not place adjacent channels near each other.

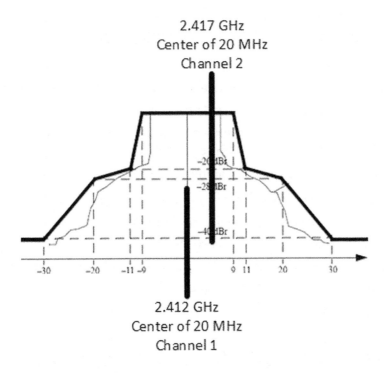

2.417 GHz
Center of 20 MHz
Channel 2

2.412 GHz
Center of 20 MHz
Channel 1

Figure 4.6—Channel Overlap in 2.4 GHz

Channel Plans

With an understanding of CCI and ACI, it is clear that channel planning is essential. This section provides information to help the WLAN designer in the channel planning process. Channel planning involves selection of channels, power levels of APs, and planning for channel reuse.

802.11 Channels

The channels available for use in WLANs are defined in the 802.11 standard and constrained by local regulatory agencies. For example, in the United States, only channels 1–11 may be used in 2.4 GHz, but in other regions of the world channels 12–13 and even 14 may be used. The first thing you must ensure is that you are in compliance with local regulations related to channel usage. Most enterprise APs can be configured for operation in a regulatory domain, and they will automatically remove the option to use channels not allowed in that domain.

However, the regulatory domain is only part of the picture. After you have determined the channels that you can use, you must then determine how to use those channels. Later portions of this section will address channel widths, reuse patterns, and advanced channel features. Here, you will find detailed information on the channels available in frequency bands (2.4 GHz and 5 GHz), automatic channel selection, and output power level requirements (like Dynamic Frequency Selection (DFS) and Transmit Power Control (TPC).

Figure 4.7 shows the channels available, with center frequencies, in 2.4 GHz. Channels are either 22 MHz wide (802.11-prime and 802.11b) or 20 MHz wide (802.11g and 802.11n). 802.11ac does not operate in the 2.4 GHz band even though some consumer-grade products have implemented 256-QAM modulation in 2.4 GHz, it is not part of the standard.

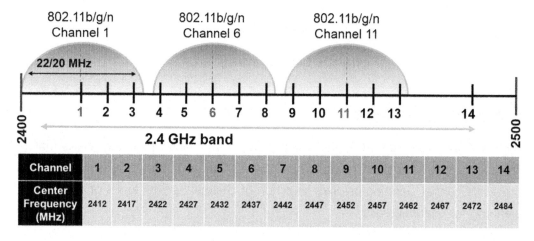

Figure 4.7—2.4 GHz Channels

EXAM MOMENT: Remember that 802.11ac does not operate in 2.4 GHz. Any time a scenario references 11ac, it should be assumed that 5 GHz is in view for enterprise WLANs.

Table 4.1 shows the channels available in 5 GHz. Many more channels are available in the 5 GHz frequency band with a total of 25 available and more coming in 2016 and later years. Not all channels are available in all areas due to DFS requirements in some regulatory domains, and Terminal Doppler Weather Radar (TDWR) also constrains the use of some channels. However, even if the lower and higher ranges alone are used, this provides nine 20 MHz channels and the channels do not intentionally overlap like 2.4 GHz channels. For this reason, channel reuse plans are much simpler in 5 GHz than in 2.4 GHz. Additionally, because there are so many channels and fewer devices (as of 2015) in the space, 5 GHz is far less busy (congested) than 2.4 GHz.

Frequency Range	Number of Channels	Channel Number	Center Frequency (MHz)
5.17–5.23	4	36	5180
		40	5200
		44	5220
		48	5240
5.250–5.330	4	52	5260
		56	5280
		60	5300
		64	5320
5.490–5.730	12	100, 104, 108, 112, 116, 120, 124, 128, 132, 136, 140, 144	5500, 5520, 5540, 5560, 5580, 5600, 5620, 5640, 5660, 5680, 5700, 5720
7.735–5.835	5	149	5745
		153	5765
		157	5785
		161	5805
		165	5825

Table 4.1—5 GHz Channels with Only Used Frequency Ranges Listed

Note: **Channel 144 was introduced with 802.11ac. It is unlikely that 802.11n and earlier gear will ever implement this channel.**

When selecting channels, you must also select the output power for the channel or allow RRM to automatically configure the output power. Output power selection is driven by three factors:

- Capabilities of the AP
- Desired cell size
- Regulatory requirements

APs have output power capabilities ranging from 5 mW to 1 W. As a WLAN designer you will need to select APs that have the output power capabilities you require, and then you can adjust the output power to create the desired cell size. However, at the same time, you must ensure that you are operating within regulatory requirements. Again, assuming the AP allows you to select a regulatory domain or region of the world setting, it will likely do this part for you. The software will ensure that the AP does not transmit on disallowed channels or at power levels beyond the allowance. This is good for operations, but it does not always help you during design. During design, you must still select the proper channels and power settings, and you must know the regulatory requirements so that your design can actually be implemented.

EXAM MOMENT: The CWDP exam does not test on specific requirements of regulatory domains; however, you should know that DFS may be required and that the regulatory domain requirements must be considered when creating channel plans.

Selecting Channel Widths

After selecting the channel on which an AP will operate, you must select the channel width. 802.11n APs will support either 20 MHz or 40 MHz channel widths using the bonding of two 20 MHz channels. 802.11ac APs will support 20, 40, 80, or 160 MHz channels. 160 MHz channels are not likely to be used in enterprise networks for the foreseeable future due to insufficient spectrum availability. 80 MHz channels may be used in some installations, but it will likely only be used in specific sections of the

WLAN based on the demand for very high throughput levels in that area. For example, if used as a connection in the network operations center or between two network operations centers, the justification may be made. But for links to individual clients, with today's application demands, 80 MHz channels are simply not warranted on a universal basis across an entire WLAN.

In the end, 20 and 40 MHz channels will be used for most 802.11n/ac deployments. The 20 MHz channels are used in 5 GHz for high-density deployments, and 40 MHz channels may be used for medium or low-density deployments. However, even in medium or low-density deployments, the throughput levels offered by a 40 MHz 802.11ac channel may not be required, and the decision must be made on a case-by-case bases. The decision is made based on the aggregate throughput requirements in a cell. In the later section on selecting APs, you will learn to use a free tool that helps in determining capacity requirements and discovering the difference between 20 and 40 MHz channels in an implementation.

Channel Reuse Patterns

Channel reuse patterns are used to diminish or remove CCI and ACI. In 2.4 GHz reuse patterns help to mitigate the CCI, but in 5 GHz reuse patterns properly implemented can remove it. The concept of a channel reuse pattern is simply to avoid placing APs near each other that are on the same channel or, in 5 GHz, on an adjacent channel. Figure 4.8 shows an example channel reuse pattern in 2.4 GHz.

Figure 4.9 shows more realistic patterns, though still not close to what is actually seen in physical spaces. The point is that APs do not generate cells that are circular or hexagonal. The most important thing to know is that such reuse patterns are essential in avoiding CCI and ACI. Notice in both Figure 4.8 and 4.9, the plans separate all APs on the same channel from other APs on the same channel by an entire cell. This is all that can be accomplished in 2.4 GHz due to that fact that there are only three non-overlapping channels. In 5 GHz, you can often separate APs on the same channel by two cells because so many more channels are available.

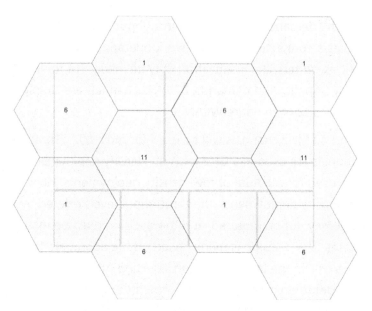

Figure 4.8—Channel Reuse Patterns

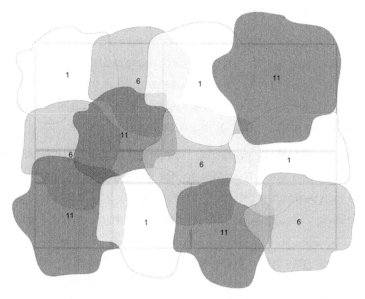

Figure 4.9—Realistic Channel Reuse Patterns

Advanced Channel Features

802.11ac added some channel operational features that should be understood and planned for by the WLAN designer as well. These include 80+80 channels and RTS/CTS enhancements.

The 80+80 channels use two 80 MHz channels that are not adjacent in the 5 GHz frequency band. This allows for the use of a 160 MHz configuration even if two adjacent 80 MHz channels are not available. This features is not likely to be used in enterprise deployment in the near future due to that fact that such high-data rate client connections are not typically essential, and currently there is insufficient frequency space available to use 160 MHz of bandwidth for a single channel and still have enough bandwidth for additional APs in the area.

The RTS/CTS enhancements have been made to 802.11ac to allow two cells to share the same space. That is, one cell can use channels 36, 40, 44, and 48 for an 80 MHz channel, and another cell in the same area can use channels 44, 48, 52, and 56 for an 80 MHz channel. The process works such that RTS frames are sent out on all four 20 MHz channels and the 80 MHz of bandwidth is only used to transmit a data frame if all four channels respond with a CTS frame. Therefore, at times, the cell will communicate as a 40 MHz channel and at times as an 80 MHz channel when the other sharing cell is not using the top or bottom two 20 MHz channels. Testing in implementations has not yet been performed on such a configuration and it is, as yet (in 2015), unknown if the operation will be efficient enough to warrant the utilization.

Infrastructure Services

WLANs do not stand alone. Instead, they depend on several infrastructure services to operate effectively. These services include DHCP, DNS, NTP, Firewalls, and the management of additional settings and services. This section provides guidance in implementing these settings and services to support the WLAN.

Dynamic Host Configuration Protocol (DHCP)

DHCP is used to provide IP configuration sets to computers on the network. It is sometimes said that DHCP provides IP addresses to computers, but this is an over simplification. In actuality, DHCP can provide the following and more:

- IP addresses
- Subnet masks
- Default gateways (routers)
- DNS servers
- Lease durations
- Configuration options

When planning for DHCP support of the WLAN, at least three things should be considered:

- Will you use an existing scope or create new separate scopes for the WLAN operations?

- What options should be provided by the DHCP server for proper WLAN functionality?

- How long should leases endure?

The selection of a DHCP scope for the WLAN is actually very important. It can impact roaming capabilities and result in a large subnet if you're not careful in your planning. For this reason, vendor recommendations should be considered when answering the first question. In general, it is best to place WLAN traffic on a separate IP subnet from wired traffic so that it can be managed accordingly. IPv4 is still the most commonly used IP solution, with IPv6 very slowly gaining momentum.

As you can imagine, a private network that uses the "ten space" (a phrase for referencing the private IP addresses that are in the 10.x.x.x range) can be rather large. In order to reduce network traffic on single segments, we can subnet our network and increase performance. To do this task, you will need to implement the appropriate subnetting scheme with subnet masks.

A subnet mask is a binary-level concept that is used to divide the IP address into a network identifier (ID) and a host ID. The network ID identifies the network on which the host resides, and the host ID identifies the unique device within that network. There are two basic kinds of subnetting: classfull and classless.

Classfull (also written classful) subnetting simply acknowledges the class of the IP address and uses a subnet mask that matches that class. For example, a class A IP address would use the first eight bits for the network ID, and therefore the subnet mask would be:

11111111.00000000.00000000.00000000

Notice that the portion of the IP address that is the network ID is all 1s, and the portion that is the host ID is all 0s. For example, if the IP address were 10.12.89.75 and we were using classfull subnetting, the subnet mask would be 11111111.00000000.00000000.00000000, which is represented as 255.0.0.0 in dotted decimal notation. As one more example, consider a class C IP address of 192.168.14.57. What would the classfull subnet mask be? Correct. It would be 11111111.11111111.11111111.00000000. This difference is because a class C IP address uses the first 24 bits to define the network ID and the last 8 bits to define the host ID. This network ID would be represented as 255.255.255.0 in dotted decimal notation.

Most configuration interfaces allow you to enter the IP address and also the subnet mask in dotted decimal notation. This notation makes configuration much easier; however, if you want to perform classless subnetting, you will need to understand the binary level where we now reside in our discussion.

Classless Inter-Domain Routing (CIDR) is the standard replacement for classfull addressing and subnetting. Classless subnetting allows you to split the network ID and the host ID at the binary level and, therefore, right in the middle of an octet. For example, you can say that 10.10.10.1 is on one network and 10.10.10.201 is on another. How would you do this separation? Let's look at the binary level.

Here are the two IP addresses in binary:

00001010.00001010.00001010.00000001 (10.10.10.1)

00001010.00001010.00001010.11001001 (10.10.10.201)

In order to use CIDR and indicate that the final octet should be split in two so that everything from 1 to 127 is in one network and everything from 128 to 254 is in another, we would use the following subnet mask:

11111111.11111111.11111111.10000000

You might be wondering how this subnet mask works. In order to understand it, consider it in Table 4.2. The first row (other than the bit position identifier row) of the table is the IP address of 10.10.10.1, and the third row is the IP address of 10.10.10.201. The second row is the CIDR subnet mask. If you count the columns carefully, you'll see that the first 25 positions have a 1 and the last 7 positions have a 0. Where there is a 1, the IP addresses must match or they are on different network IDs. As you read across the rows and compare the first row with the third row, you'll notice that they are identical until you read the 25th bit position. In the 25th bit position, the first row has a 0 and the third row has a 1. They are different and therefore are on different network IDs. This is CIDR in action.

B1	B2	B3	B4	B5	B6	B7	B8	B9	B10	B11	B12	B13	B14	B15	B16	B17	B18	B19	B20	B21	B22	B23	B24	B25	B26	B27	B28	B29	B30	B31	B32
0	0	0	0	1	0	1	0	0	0	0	0	1	0	1	0	0	0	0	0	1	0	1	0	0	0	0	0	0	0	0	1
1	1	1	1	1	1	1	1	1	1	1	1	1	1	1	1	1	1	1	1	1	1	1	1	1	0	0	0	0	0	0	0
0	0	0	0	1	0	1	0	0	0	0	0	1	0	1	0	0	0	0	0	1	0	1	0	1	1	0	0	1	0	0	1

Table 4.2—Subnetting with CIDR

Because of the fact that CIDR subnetting allows subnet masks that mask part of an octet, you will see subnet masks like 255.255.255.128 (which is the decimal equivalent of the subnet mask row in Table 4.2). Instead of representing the subnet mask in decimal notation, it is often simply appended to the end of the IP address. For

180

example, the IP address and subnet mask combination in Table 4.2 could be represented as 10.10.10.1/25. This representation, which is sometimes called Variable Length Subnet Mask (VLSM) representation or CIDR representation, is becoming more and more common. It indicates that the IP address is 10.10.10.1 and the network ID (sometimes called the subnet or subnetwork) is the first 25 bits of the IP address.

When designing a WLAN, you must determine how subnetting will be performed and the networks on which WLAN clients will operate. Will the clients operate on the same subnet whether they are internal users or guest users? Will VLANs be used to separate them, separate subnets or tunnels to the DMZ? These decisions should be made and specified in the WLAN design documentation.

Lease durations or timeouts should also be considered relative to DHCP. This is particularly important in networks where users come and go, such as guest WLANs or mobile areas of the WLAN like a lobby. Setting the lease duration to a few hours instead of a few days can reduce DHCP pool (scope) exhaustion and allow the DHCP operations to continue.

 Note: DHCP Option 43 can be used to provide the WLAN controller IP address so that IPs can locate the controller when they first connect to the network.

Domain Name System (DNS)

DNS is used to resolve domain names to IP addresses. It is used in WLANs to service clients for host name resolutions, but it is also used for specific WLAN functions including locating controllers. For example, when a Cisco AP receives its IP configuration from the DHCP server, if option 43 is not specified, the AP will try to resolve the DNS hostname *CISCO-CAPWAP-CONTROLLER.localdomain*, where *localdomain* is the domain configured by DHCP.

EXAM WATCH: When using CAPWAP, four controller discovery methods are available: 1) Layer 3 subnet broadcast looking for a controller, 2) NVRAM stored addresses from past controller connections, 3) DHCP option 43, and 4) DNS resolution as referenced here.

Network Time Protocol (NTP)

NTP is used to configure the time on a device using a network time server. Accurate time configuration is important for logging and other operations. Most WLAN controllers and APs can have their internal clock set using a network time server. Figure 4.10 shows the configuration of NTP in a Ruckus Wireless solution.

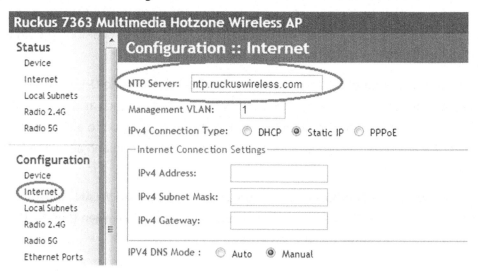

Figure 4.10—Configuring NTP Server Settings

Firewall Configuration

Firewalls may require configuration to support the WLAN. If a firewall resides between the APs and controllers, modifications may be required. The firewall should allow the LWAPP or CAPWAP ports through. LWAPP uses UDP ports 12222 and 12223 by default. CAPWAP uses UDP ports 5246 and 5247 by default.

Additional firewall configuration settings may be required. Check the vendor literature for the ports (both UDP and TCP) used for various communications and ensure that the appropriate firewall rules are in place.

ACL Management

Access Control Lists (ACLs) are used on network routers to control the traffic that is enabled for pass-through to other networks. Like a firewall, the routers must allow the communications to go through that is required by the WLAN. In fact, ACLs on routers are more likely to cause problems than firewall rules as the controllers and APs are more frequently inside the firewall. Check the vendor literature for the ports (both UDP and TCP) used for various communications and ensure that the appropriate ACLs are configured.

VLAN Management

Virtual LANs (VLANs) are used to segregate network traffic into separate broadcast domains even when they traffic originates in the same physical switch or switch aggregate. Additionally, VLANs, through tunnels can span multiple physical subnets. In WLANs, VLANs are used to separate wireless traffic from wired traffic, and they are used to separate one wireless network from another, such as separating an enterprise WLAN from a guest WLAN using the same APs.

The VLAN can be configured in relation to the SSID within the AP configuration profile. It can also be configured through information provided by the RADIUS server at the time of authentication. Additionally, VLANs can simply be assigned based on the switchport configuration to which the AP is connected. That is, with an autonomous or cloud-managed AP, the switchport can determine the VLAN on which all traffic coming from the AP is placed.

RADIUS and LDAP

RADIUS is used for authentication, and LDAP is a protocol used to access a directory service. A directory service contains network objects like user accounts and groups. In many deployments, RADIUS servers are used for authentication, but they often depend on large-scale directories for account information such as Microsoft Active Directory. LDAP is used to make the connection from the RADIUS server to the Active Directory Domain Controller.

From a design perspective, you can recommend the use of a RADIUS server that fits well with the existing network solutions. For example, in a Microsoft Active Directory environment, using the Microsoft RADIUS server makes sense. In a Linux/Unix environment, FreeRADIUS or a commercial RADIUS product may be recommended, or the organization may choose to use a RADIUS server from the network infrastructure provider like Cisco.

Public Key Infrastructure (PKI)

Because many EAP types rely on certificates and some depend on client certificates a PKI may be required. A PKI is comprised of certificate authorities (CAs) that either authorize other CAs to distribute certificates or generate and distribute (issue) certificates themselves. As a WLAN designer, you will have to determine whether a PKI will be available or not so that you can select the appropriate EAP type. If a constraint is in place requiring an EAP type that must have client certificates, you should be sure to document the requirement of a PKI in the design plans, though the details of the PKI can be left up to the individuals who will implement that project.

RBAC Implementation

Role-Based Access Control (RBAC) is another security solution of worth. This solution allows for the implementation of authorization based on roles (or groups). Rather than manually authorizing each users, the users can be assigned roles and then perform any function the roles allow.

> **EXAM MOMENT:** As vendor implementations of RBAC vary greatly and many depend on wired-side solutions for this capability, it is not covered in detail on the CWDP exam. For the exam, be sure to remember that RBAC organizes users into groups or roles and assigns capabilities or authorizes users based on those groups or roles.

BYOD and MDM Solutions

When designing for Bring Your Own Device (BYOD), Mobile Device Management (MDM) becomes an important factor. MDM is used to onboard, manage, and decommission mobile devices (both organization-owned devices and BYOD units). An MDM solution may be cloud-based (sometimes called Software as a Service (SaaS) or on-premise. Both have pros and cons.

The cloud-based solution can be used without requiring the installation of software or hardware within your organization. It will include robust features from the start and enhanced features may be added by simply expanding your subscription. However, the downside of cloud-based MDM is that the Internet connection must be working to onboard new devices and to manage the system.

On-premise MDM will work even if the Internet connection goes down. It is likely to have the same capabilities of a cloud-based service, but may require more time and effort to add features at a later time.

MDM solutions may integrate with Network Access Control (NAC) solutions to perform onboarding with security. For example, when a new device connects that should have antivirus but does not, it can be disallowed network access and placed into a quarantine network until it can be repaired.

As a WLAN designer, it is important to select an MDM solution that meets the needs of the organization. Consider the following questions:

- Must the MDM solution integrate with existing directory services?

- Is self-service onboarding required?

- What devices are supported and what operating systems and versions are used?

- Will containerization be required?

- Will features like remote wipe, remote lock, and encrypted storage be required?

Additional questions may be required in some installations, but the important thing is to ask the right questions and match the MDM solution to the organization's needs.

Selecting Access Points

When selecting APs, it is important to choose the right AP for the installation. You may be constrained to a specific vendor by the RFP or Project Charter, but vendors often have several models, and the appropriate model should be acquired and documented in the design. This section will provide information to help with this process.

Selecting APs

The first step in selecting an AP is determining the location of mounting. If the AP will be mounted indoors or in a weather-protected space, an indoor AP should be purchased. If the AP will be mounted in a weather-exposed area, an external AP should be purchased. The same basic AP in an external model is usually more expensive because costly materials are used to ruggedize the AP. Indoor APs usually use plastic covers with metal backing and outdoor APs often use either entire metal encasements with non-reflective coating and external antennas, or they use a more rugged plastic cover with internal antennas.

The last statement reveals another important decision about APs. Should you use internal or external antennas? In general indoor implementations, internal antennas with omni-optimized patterns are sufficient. In specific indoor scenarios, directional antennas may be used. For example, you might use a directional antenna mounted on the wall and aimed inward or an antenna aimed down a hallway in a warehouse. With these kinds of exceptions considered, most other indoor APs use internal antennas.

Outdoor APs commonly use external antennas. They will either use high-gain omni antennas or directional antennas. Just as APs that are weather-exposed must be designed with rugged enclosures, antennas intended for outdoor use should also be designed such that they can endure cold, heat, rain, and other weather factors.

In addition to choosing indoor or outdoor APs and internal or external antennas, selecting the right number of APs and the APs with the right antenna/radio options is important.

For example, an AP with one antenna using SISO can perform at a given level. But an AP with two antennas, using the same PHY and MIMO, can perform significantly better. This is not just true about data rates, but also about other features like Maximal Ratio Combining (MRC) and Transmit Beamforming (TxBF), which were introduced in your CWNA studies.

Using logarithmic math, you can calculate the maximum theoretical gains of signal reception and transmission techniques like MRC and TxBF so as to quantify their potential benefits. By adding a second antenna, the maximum theoretical gain is 3 dB (log2 x 10). By adding a third antenna, the maximum theoretical gain is 4.77 dB (log3 x10) or roughly 5 dB, and by adding a fourth antenna, the maximum theoretical gain is 6 dB (log4 x 10). In reality, MRC gains are much closer to the theoretical maximum than are TxBF gains. For that reason, MRC is generally a more useful feature. When TxBF with explicit feedback is standardized and well-supported by infrastructure and client vendors, the real-world gains may improve. Also note that some vendors advertise higher gains because the comparative reference (remember, dB is a reference against something else) is slightly misleading.

So how do you determine the number of APs you require and the number of radio chains that should be in the APs? You can use a freely available tool that can be downloaded from www.revolutionwifi.net/capacity-planner. This tool, currently in the form of an Excel spreadsheet, can be used to perform predictive WLAN design, scope a project, or even create a BoM based on the number of APs required.

The first items you configure in the Revolution Wi-Fi Capacity Planner is the Network Infrastructure options shown in Figure 4.11.

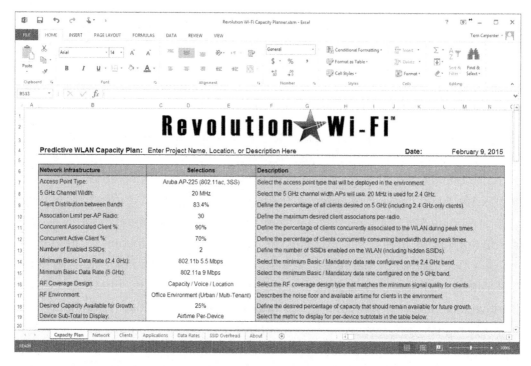

Figure 4.11—Configuring Network Infrastructure Options

Next, you will configure Client Devices and application profiles shown in Figure 4.12.

Finally, you will configure Capacity Distribution and calculate results ad shown in Figure 4.13. Network details, clients, applications, and more can be modified on additional tabs. The spreadsheets comes with a detailed 40+ page document explaining how to use it, and this free resource provides great value to the WLAN design industry.

Client Device	Application or Throughput SLA	Device Quantity	Which Concurrent Limits Apply?	Application Throughput	2.4 GHz Band			5 GHz Band		
					Assoc	Active	Airtime	Assoc	Active	Airtime
1 Laptop (11n, 2SS, 40 MHz)	1 Mbps per-device throughput SLA	56	Both	1 Mbps	4	3	1.54%	46	36	1.54%
2 Laptop (11n, 3SS, 40 MHz)	1 Mbps per-device throughput SLA	30	Both	1 Mbps	2	2	1.03%	25	19	1.03%
3 Laptop (11ac, 2SS, 80 MHz)	5 Mbps per-device throughput SLA	45	Both	5 Mbps	3	3	7.69%	38	29	6.41%
4 Tablet (11n, 1SS, 20 MHz)	1 Mbps per-device throughput SLA	120	Both	1 Mbps	9	7	3.46%	99	77	3.08%
5 Smart Phone (11n, 1SS, 20 MHz)	1 Mbps per-device throughput SLA	100	Both	1 Mbps	90	70	3.46%	0	0	0%
6 Smart Phone (11ac, 1SS, 80 MHz)	2 Mbps per-device throughput SLA	120	Both	2 Mbps	9	7	6.92%	99	77	5.77%
7 Cisco 7925G VoIP Handset (11ag)	250 Kbps per-device throughput SLA	240	Both	250 Kbps	17	13	1.6%	199	155	1.6%
8 Custom Device 1	2 Mbps per-device throughput SLA	360	Both	2 Mbps	26	20	2.31%	298	232	1.71%

Capacity Plan | Network | Clients | Applications | Data Rates | SSID Overhead | About

Figure 4.12—Configuring Client Devices and Application Profiles

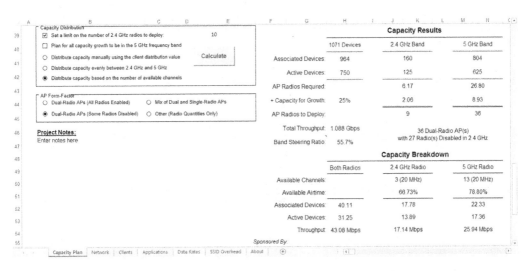

Figure 4.13—Configuring Capacity Distribution and Calculating Results

Choosing a Power Source

When selecting a power source for APs, you have two basic choices: PoE-powered APs and wall outlet-powered APs. PoE-powered APs receive their power through the same Ethernet cable as the network connection. PoE requirements come in two basic models: 802.3af and 802.3at. Both of these amendments are simply part of the 802.3 Ethernet standard at this point. The original difference between them was that 802.3af provided 15.4 watts of power at the power source (also called power sourcing equipment (PSE) and roughly 12.95 watts at the powered device (PD). 802.3at provided up to 30 watts at the power source and 25.5 watts at the PD. Therefore, APs requiring more power require 802.3at PoE sources, and APs requiring less power require only 802.3af PoE sources.

 Note: **802.3at defined up to 60 watts at the PSE; however, this is only over four pairs, which is not implemented in today's APs.**

When choosing PoE PSEs, you must select between endpoint and midspan PSEs. Endpoint PSEs are switches that also provide PoE. Midspan PSEs are usually single port injectors that sit between the switch and the AP; however, multi-port injectors are also available. Figure 4.14 shows these options.

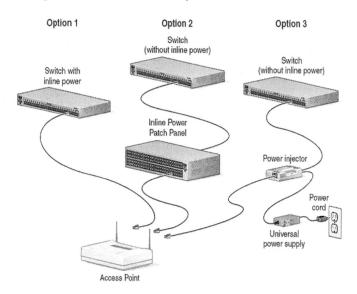

Figure 4.14—PSE Types (Option 1 is endpoint; Option 2 and 3 are midspan)

When designing a PoE solution for a WLAN, power budget is an important consideration. For example, endpoint PoE switches may have 24 ports that can be powered with PoE, but they may only have 300 watts of power to provide. If ten devices are connected requiring 30 watts, the entire power budget is consumed and the remaining 14 ports must be used as standard Ethernet ports without PoE or simply remain unused. Determining the power budget is not as simple as buying a PoE switch and assuming that all ports will work at the same time regardless of the PoE PD connected. One PD may require 12 watts while another requires 25 watts. Together, the two PDs have consumed 37 watts of your switch PoE budget. To calculate the PoE budget required:

1. Determine how many PoE devices will be deployed and what they require in power provisioning.

2. Determine the power provisioned by each switch.

3. Purchase the appropriate number of switches to provide the power.

AP Staging Procedures

After APs are selected, they must be appropriately prepared for installation. AP staging procedures should be clarified and even documented to ensure proper implementation. Staging procedures should answer the following questions at a minimum:

- Will APs be configured while connected to the LAN?

- What settings should be configured as a baseline in all APs?

- Is a particular firmware revision required?

- Will SNMP be enabled on APs during deployment?

Some of these questions may be irrelevant to your chosen WLAN management system, but they should be answered when they apply.

Mounting Solutions

The final aspect of AP selection is choosing the right mounting solution. Bad mounting decisions are frequently seen on Internet blogs ranging from APs duct taped to windows to APs hanging from drop ceilings by their Ethernet connection cables. Most vendors provide mounting options for ceiling, pole, and even desktop options in some cases. Be sure to use the appropriate mounting tools so that the AP will remain fixed. If it moves, such as with the dangling AP hanging from the ceiling, the coverage will change—sometimes significantly. Standard APs should always be fixed to a position so you have one fewer variable in the link.

Configuring Access Points

Configuring APs is a different task for the varying management models. For example, configuring an AP with a WLAN controller can be as simple as connecting it to the Ethernet network, but configuring an autonomous AP is never that simple. This section introduces key points related to AP configuration processes and options for the WLAN designer.

Configuring APs for MCA and SCA

The configuration processes for MCA and SCA are very different. A large part of the decision when configuring an MCA AP is the channel to use. With SCA, this decision is far less weighty as channel selection is related to many APs instead of one AP. With SCA solutions, the channel is defined in the controller and the APs are assigned to a channel, and then they are connected to the network and configured by the controller. The controller decides, not only the channel, but also when each AP may communicate with a target client station.

The configuration processes for MCA architectures depend on the management method: controller-based, cloud-based, autonomous, or mesh APs.

Controller-Based AP Configuration Process

When using lightweight APs, the configuration process is typically as follows:

1. WLAN profiles are created in the controller.

2. APs are assigned configurations or profiles based on MAC addresses.

3. APs are connected to the LAN.

4. APs find the controller using several possible methods.

5. APs receive firmware updates from the controller if required.

6. APs receive configuration parameters from the controller.

7. APs are brought online for operations.

8. APs are monitored by the controller.

Cloud-Based AP Configuration Process

Distributed APs or cloud-based APs have a configuration process that is typically as follows:

1. A cloud service account is created for the customer.

2. APs are provisioned in the cloud account either by the vendor or the customer.

3. APs are connected to the customer's LAN, which is connected to the Internet.

4. APs use the Internet to contact the manager in the cloud.

5. APs receive firmware updates from the cloud if required.

6. APs receive configuration parameters from the cloud.

7. APs are brought online for operations.

8. APs are monitored by the cloud.

Autonomous AP Configuration Process

Autonomous APs are configured either individually or through a WNMS. WNMS solutions are less common today than in the past and post autonomous APs are configured either individually or by loading a configuration set from a TFTP server or through a web-based configuration interface and then simply adjusting parameters, as needed.

Autonomous AP configuration is documented in a step-by-step manner by each vendor. Chapter 6 will provide examples of controller-based, cloud-based, and autonomous AP configurations using various vendor products.

Designing for Client Devices

When designing a WLAN, providing for the needs of clients is a useful design driver. In many cases, designing for the least capable client (typically a mobile phone or barcode scanner) is a best practice. This section introduces common capabilities of various client devices including laptops, tablets, mobile phones, and stationary devices.

Laptops

Laptops were the most common Wi-Fi client just a few years ago. Today, they are still quite popular and on some networks are the most common client. However, tablets and mobile phones have started encroaching on the laptop domination significantly in the past few years.

When considering client devices, you must ask the following questions:

- What PHYs do they support?

- What data rates are supported?

- What channels are allowed?

- What channel widths are supported?

- Do they have DFS support?

- What are the receive sensitivity levels?

Today, most laptops support 802.11n and 802.11ac. However, it is important to know that a laptop supporting 802.11n does not necessarily support the 5 GHz band. Many early laptops supporting 802.11n used chipsets that only operated in the 2.4 GHz band. Additionally, it is important to remember that when a device supports

802.11ac, it can be assumed it is a 5 GHz chipset because 802.11ac operates only in the 5 GHz band.

Just because a laptop supports the 802.11ac (VHT) PHY does not mean that it supports all data rates of that PHY. In fact, in 2015, no device supports all data rates because no devices greater than 4x4:4 exist in the market. Therefore, though the PHY may support very high data rates, your clients will support a limited subset of these data rates depending on implemented features of the PHY. The number of spatial streams, guard interval, and channel width all come together to impact data rates.

Some clients support a limited subset of channels in 5 GHz. For example, it is not uncommon for a 5 GHz client to support only channels 36, 40, 44, 48, 149, 153, 157, and 161. These are the channels that are available in nearly all parts of the world. If you have a large number of clients supporting only these channels, the WLAN design needs to be implemented such that one of these channels is available in all coverage areas. Additional cells can be created using other channels for capacity, but you must provide support for the client base.

Most laptops today support both 20 and 40 MHz channels for 802.11n and most 802.11ac laptops support the 80 MHz channels. Laptops supporting 160 MHz channels will be available in 2016 and beyond, but support for these channels is not likely to be implemented in enterprise WLANs.

DFS channels may or may not be supported. This is the major reason for the middle channels, discussed previously, not being available in many clients.

Finally, it is important to understand receive sensitivity ratings. Laptops tend to use chipsets and antennas that provide for better sensitivity ratings than tablets or mobile phones. For this reason, the WLAN should be designed around the sensitivity of the least capable devices. If the tablet or mobile phone works, the laptop or stationary device likely will, as well. The receive sensitivity rating defines the lowest signal strength at which the receiver can demodulate a given data rate signal. Receive sensitivity is impacted by channel width as well. That is, when using 40 MHz channels, a better signal across the channel is required to get the same MCS as when using a 20 MHz channel.

Tablets

Tablets also support 802.11n and 802.11ac PHYs. However, it is very important to remember that most tablets are only one or two stream clients. Therefore, tablets will not reach the data rates available for laptops that are typically two or three stream clients. Tablets are also likely to have lower receive sensitivity ratings.

Mobile Phones

Like tablets, mobile phones are less likely to support three streams, in fact most support only one stream. Therefore, with mobile phones, it should be assumed that only single stream data rates will be available for the majority of these devices through 2017 or even 2018.

Stationary Devices

Stationary devices fall into two categories: desktop computers and specialty devices. Desktop computers provide exceptional flexibility to the WLAN design as they can be easily upgraded with PCI adapters or USB adapters.

Specialty devices are a different story altogether. These devices, often found in manufacturing and healthcare, may use USB adapters to connect to WLANs, but they are restricted to a specific adapter in many cases. Much of the time, these adapters are still 802.11b/g or 802.11a devices. The reason is simple. These specialty devices often cost many thousands of dollars. They are expected to be used for 5–10 years. Therefore, as they near the end of their life, they still utilize older adapters. Providing for such devices is an essential part of the design process. Figure 4.15 shows a stationary WLAN device used in healthcare. This device monitors blood pressure, pulse rate, etc.

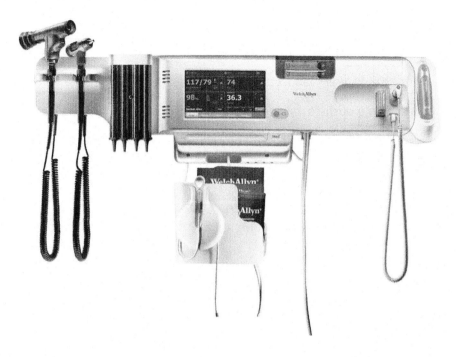

Figure 4.15—Welch Allyn Connex 8500 Series Hospital Wireless Integrated Wall System

Designing for Applications

Designing for applications is actually about designing for application behavior. Application behaviors impact roaming and network requirements like latency, throughput, and availability. This section provides information to assist you in planning for various application requirements and several specific application types.

Roaming Requirements

Stationary devices have no roaming requirements, but all mobile devices have some kind of roaming requirement. For example, a laptop may need to roam from one AP to another, but depending on the application running on the laptop, it may not require continual Layer 3 (IP addressing) connectivity. However, if that same laptop is running softphone software and folds down into a tablet, the user may desire to maintain a call during roaming.

The following devices have demanding roaming requirements:

- Mobile phones acting as VoIP phones

- 802.11 VoIP handsets

- Some push-to-talk devices

The following devices have less demanding requirements, but benefit from roaming:

- Tablets

- Laptops

- Mobile phones not acting as VoIP phones

- Barcode scanners

- Mobile healthcare devices

Roaming design issues are discussed in the later section of this chapter titled, "Planning for Roaming."

Latency Requirements

Latency, as previously defined, is equal to delay. It is a measurement of the time required for bits to be moved from the originating device to the destination device. It is measured in milliseconds. Some applications have stringent requirements on latency and VoIP is the prime example. The general requirement of VoIP is 150 ms latency or less, unidirectionally. This demand indicates that the round-trip time (RTT) could not be more than 300 ms. However, it cannot be assumed that a 300 ms RTT is acceptable. While rare, it is possible that the communication could have a latency value of 120 ms one direction and then 180 ms the other direction. It is still 300 ms in RTT, but the 180 ms direction is unacceptable for normal VoIP communications.

Latency can be impacted in three areas:

- The wireless link

- The wired links

- The processing devices

Interestingly, the processing devices often cause significant latency and are not always considered in the equation. For example, an overloaded router may be delayed in forwarding packets and begin causing extra delay in the network. Additionally, if a VoIP handset uses encryption, the encryption results in extra delay within the handset; however, this is not part of network communications and is typically factored into the voice communications process.

The WLAN designer should test the network for latency, and this should include the full communications path and not just the wireless link. For example, an actual communication through the AP, the switch, the routers, to another switch, and out another AP to a wireless client will give you the full picture of latency for VoIP calls.

> **EXAM MOMENT:** It is important to remember that roaming causes latency in communications. All roaming results in latency, but the WLAN designer should attempt to bring roaming latency to less than 90–100 ms, which will likely prevent it from causing problems for voice calls as long as the non-roaming status of links has a unidirectional delay of 50 ms or less. Such speeds are not uncommon for QoS-based networks with gigabit or faster links interconnecting subnets.

Data-Throughput Demands

In addition to roaming and latency demands, applications have throughput demands. Throughput is the amount of useful data that the network can transfer. It is typically measured in megabits per second (Mbps) or gigabits per second (Gbps).

In some instances, determining throughput demands is easy. For example, you can look up values for specific video or audio codecs to determine their throughput requirements. In other instances, throughput demands can be hard to come by and can often only be acquired through testing. Such tests can be performed by connecting the client and the server for the given application to a gigabit switch and then performing actions in the application and measuring the throughput. This simple test can give you a close estimate of the demands of the application and allow you to better plan for it in scale. For example, if this test resulted in a demand of 120

Kbps, then 20 clients using the application at the same time would need 2.4 Mbps throughput for effective operations.

 Note: **It is always a best practice to either round up to the nearest half Mbps or at least add ten percent to the measured value. For example, 2.4 Mbps would become 2.5 Mbps by rounding up or it would be come 2.64 Mbps by adding ten percent.**

Barcode Scanners

Barcode scanners are used for inventory management in many industries. The devices have gone from being computer-connected devices that depend on the computer to do all of the processing to devices with localized technology for entering locations, quantities, and more. This information is then passed back to a server using 802.11 WLAN connections.

Such barcode scanners often use 802.11b/g technologies, with a few supporting 802.11a. This older technology will constrain your design in areas requiring use of barcode scanners. While they can connect to 802.11n APs (or 802.11ac APs in 5 GHz), they will not benefit from the newer technologies. However, given that their throughput demands are very low, this is not a significant concern.

Healthcare Devices

The primary concern with healthcare devices is availability and durability. The network must be available to the devices as the information they communicate is critical. This means coverage and capacity become important at all new levels. Every location must be covered by at least two APs and the throughput capacity must be sufficient such that critical communication packets are not lost.

Most devices used in healthcare are stationary or nomadic. The nomadic devices are indeed portable, but are not typically used while in motion. Rather they are transported to a room or treatment area and are then utilized in that location. Such equipment includes mobile x-ray units, pulse oximeters, intravenous pumps, and vital sign monitors.

The highly mobile devices that do require connectivity during motion are Wi-Fi phones, supply chain delivery robots, and real-time location tracking devices. The same kinds of demands are placed on these highly mobile devices in healthcare as in other environments; however, in healthcare, like in emergency response, the stakes are higher.

ID Badges

ID badges have traditionally been magnetic strip-based; however, newer badges are using RFID, Bluetooth, and other near-field communications (NFC) technologies. Figure 4.16 shows a Wi-Fi ID badge from Ekahau. This particular badge is an excellent example of what might be used in healthcare settings. The badge is 802.11b/g only. It supports only WEP or WPA2-PSK and cannot use WPA2-Enterprise. It uses 16 mW (12 dBm) of output power. It has a receive sensitivity at the lowest data rate (1 Mbps) of -93 dBm. At 2 Mbps, the expected range is 500 feet or 150 meters. However, it is important to know that such values are typically indicative of free space. Therefore, within a building the range would be much less.

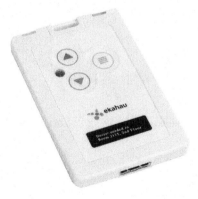

Figure 4.16—Ekahau ID Badge

With these devices in mind, you have probably located a lowest capability device on the network. If this device must have access, you will need to provide 2.4 GHz coverage everywhere, but thankfully it is not a throughput demanding device.

Providing 2.4 GHz APs with sufficient cell overlap for roaming and enough APs for location tracking should meet the needs of this device. The next step would be to ensure that capacity for other 2.4 GHz devices is met, and you will have the proper (or best possible) WLAN for the 2.4 GHz devices.

Location Tracking Systems

The Ekahau device shown in Figure 4.16 is also a real-time location device. In addition to being an ID badge, it can be used to physically locate personnel within the facility. This feature is yet another advantage to healthcare implementations.

The Ekahau A4+ is an example of an asset-tracking tag. It is shown in Figure 4.17 and is also a 2.4 GHz-only device. Running off a USB power source with built-in battery backup, the tag continues to operate even if unplugged temporarily. The range of this device is not specified in the documentation, but it runs at 11.5 dBm output power and should have a range of 50–100 meters in free space.

Figure 4.17—Ekahau A4+ Location Tag with 802.11g

Wireless Cameras

Wireless cameras are IP cameras that rely on 802.11 connections to the network rather than Ethernet connections. They transmit live video streams, or they store video streams on local storage (SD cards, for example) that are accessed and transmitted on demand. Most devices transmit the video streams to a central server that then records the video locally. The throughput demands of the devices will depend on the video codecs and quality implemented. In most cases, the quality can be adjusted and, when lowered, will reduce the throughput demands.

The reality is that many more wireless cameras are not 802.11-compliant, but operate in the same frequency bands. For example, the Lorex Technology wireless security camera system shown in Figure 4.18 uses the 2.4 GHz band with FHSS, but it is not 802.11-compliant. Such devices can cause serious interference for WLANs. The pictured cameras transmit at 16 dBm (40 mW) with omni-directional antennas having a gain of roughly 2 dB. This configuration results in a significant impact on 2.4 GHz devices in a 40–50 meter diameter indoors.

Figure 4.18—Lorex Technology Wireless Security Camera System

Voice/Video

The final application example, having been discussed more fully in the preceding chapter, is voice and video. From a design perspective, latency, and throughput issues must be addressed. For voice communications, latency is the most important factor. For video communications, latency is important and throughput must be accommodated, as well. Voice packets are so small that, if latency is resolved, throughput is rarely an issue.

Table 4.3 shows the requirements at a basic level for voice, video, and data communications. Notice that data communications have no real issues with latency and jitter. These factors are most impacting on real-time applications like voice and video. Additionally, notice that video is not as demanding as voice. This is partly due to the fact that video services may buffer some before playing even for real-time. This is the reason that you may be watching a live stream at the same time as someone else, but their live stream is ahead of or behind yours by a few seconds. Voice systems cannot buffer very much, otherwise too much silence exists on the other end of the connection while the last of the audio is buffered to the listening end.

	Voice	Video	Data
Latency	≤ 150 ms	≤ 200–400 ms	N/A
Jitter	≤ 30 ms	≤ 30–50 ms	N/A
Loss	≤ 1%	≤ .1–1%	N/A but may benefit from less than 2-5% loss for performance reasons
Bandwidth	30–128 Kbps	384–20+ Mbps	Variable

Table 4.3—Voice, Video and Data Compared

Planning for Quality of Service (QoS)

QoS is essential for real-time communications. Voice, video and a few other technologies are time-sensitive and must be delivered rapidly across the network. This section provides information on QoS for the WLAN designer.

QoS Markings and Queues

Traditional QoS, which still impacts wireless links as QoS is an end-to-end solution, which means that it must be implemented throughout the network on the wired and wireless sides to gain the most benefit. Traditional QoS uses queuing methods and frame markings. You should be aware of frames and their basic formats from your CWNA and other networking studies.

Three basic kinds of queuing are commonly used:

- First-In-First-Out (FIFO)—packets leave the device (such as a switch or router) in the order they arrived.

- Fair Queuing—an equal amount of time is given to transmitting for each stream of packets.

- Class-based Queuing—packets belonging to higher-priority classes are transmitted first.

- Reservations—packets may belong to a reservation queue granting them a specific percentage of the throughput available.

802.11 QoS, as originally defined in 802.11e, is effectively a class-based queuing system. Such systems use markings to identify the traffic and place it into classes. Wired networks use Class of Service (CoS), Type of Service (ToS), and Differentiated Services Code Point (DSCP) markings. CoS is a Layer 2 Ethernet marking. ToS and DSCP are Layer 3 IP markings. Today CoS and DSCP are the primary players in wired Ethernet QoS.

EXAM MOMENT: DSCP is Layer 3 QoS on the wired network and CoS is Layer 2 QoS on the wired network and is also referenced as 802.1p. The CoS field is 3-bits wide and has a value from 0 to 7. Table 4.4 lists the CoS values and their accompanying applications.

CoS Value	Application
7	Reserved
6	Reserved
5	Voice
4	Video conferencing
3	Call signaling
2	High-priority data
1	Medium priority data
0	Best effort data

Table 4.4—CoS Values and Applications

DSCP uses a 6-bit value, but the leftmost three bits map the same as the CoS bits. That is, CoS voice is 5 (or 101 in binary) and the DSCP value for voice is 40 (or 101000 in binary). The reality is that some vendors have implemented their own numbers and classes, but the general concept to remember is that a device should map the CoS to a DSCP value for wired network communications and vice versa. With this understanding, you can consider 802.11 QoS.

 Note: **You will hear of 802.1Q user priorities, which are more technically called priority code point (PCP) values. This is still a reference to the 3 bit 802.1p CoS values.**

802.11 QoS

802.11e introduces QoS to the 802.11 family. It implemented a Layer 2 QoS solution for the wireless link. It is the responsibility of the Ethernet-connected devices (APs or controllers) to convert the 802.11e markings to 802.1p and/or DSCP markings for communications on the wired side.

As you learned in your CWNA studies, 802.11 uses the Distributed Coordination Function (DCF) to gain access to the medium and transmit a series of 1s and 0s (a frame). 802.11e introduced the Enhanced Distributed Channel Access (EDCA). The basic enhancement is that 802.11 frames are assigned an access category (AC) in one of four values:

- AC_BK – Background—lowest priority
- AC_BE – Best Effort—lowest priority
- AC_VI – Video—middle priority
- AC_VO – Voice—highest priority

The basic functionality is that higher-priority categories use smaller contention windows. For example, AC_VO begins with a minimum value of 3 and a maximum value of 7, whereas AC_BK and AC_BE begin with a minimum value of 15 and a maximum value of 1023. As you can see, AC_BK and AC_BE frames (standard data) begin their CW at roughly twice the value of the maximum that a voice frame (AC_VO) would have. Therefore, higher-priority traffic tends to gain access to the medium more frequently than lower priority traffic.

Now, the time will come when data traffic has counted down the backoff timer such that it will beat voice traffic to the medium, but the best it could hope for is gaining access to the medium once for every two times that voice does. The real odds are far worse for data traffic, but remember, this is all measured in milliseconds and data traffic will still get through, but latency problems for voice traffic is removed.

The Wi-Fi Alliance created the Wireless Multimedia (WMM) certification to validate that equipment properly implements EDCA as defined in 802.11e. Devices that are WMM certified should be selected for the BoM when QoS is essential.

EXAM MOMENT: Remember that when an AP tunnels to a controller with centralized data forwarding, the WLAN controller converts DSCP values to 802.1Q user priority (UP) tags or 802.1p tags.

Load Balancing

Co-located access points may be used to cover congested areas. STAs associate with an AP that is least loaded with best signal quality, which is effectively called *load balancing*. This increases efficiency of the WLAN. Load balancing mechanisms are proprietary and must be configured on both APs and STAs.

Airtime Fairness

Airtime Fairness is a proprietary feature that seeks to improve the use of airtime. In normal 802.11 operation, contention processes slightly favor devices using more recent physical layer technologies, such as preferring 802.11ac over 802.1b. However, the advantage is very slight and older slower devices still gain access to the medium (air) for significantly large amounts of time (airtime). Further, multiple devices using the same PHY technology, such as 802.11n, may have highly disparate connectivity rates, such as 6.5 Mbps compared with 300 Mbps. As you can imagine, the device with slower data rates takes significantly longer amounts of time to transmit the same amount of data as the higher-rate devices. Airtime Fairness seeks to balance airtime usage instead of balancing the number of frames. This technique improves performance for the entire cell, while minimizing the impact on the lower speed stations.

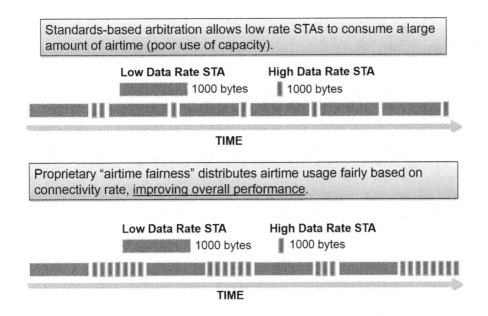

Figure 4.19—Airtime Fairness

Band Steering

Band steering can be an effective tool in all WLANs, but it is particularly beneficial in high-density networks. It works by simply ignoring 2.4 GHz requests and responding to only 5 GHz requests once the 2.4 GHz maximum connection limit is reached. Alternatively, it will always delay a response in the 2.4 GHz band to see if the client attempts to connect on the 5 GHz band. If the client does not connect on the 5 GHz band, the AP may respond to future attempts (probe requests or authentication requests) in the 2.4 GHz band. When wireless clients support dual-band operations, the MAC address is the same for the 2.4 GHz and 5 GHz radios. Therefore, an AP that sees the same MAC address on its 2.4 GHz and 5 GHz radios knows that it is the same client. From there, the AP can push the client to the 5 GHz band where many more channels are available and higher densities can be achieved.

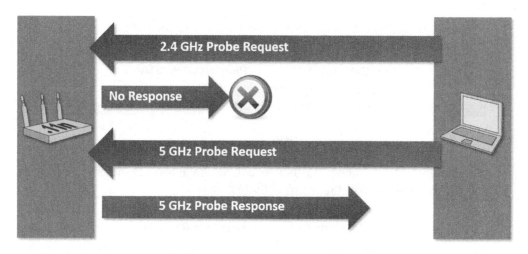

Figure 4.20—Band Steering

Security Solutions

This section provides guidance for designing security solutions including passphrase security, RADIUS server selection, EAP type selection, encryption solutions, and the use of WPS.

Passphrase-Based Implementations

WPA-PSK and WPA2-PSK both use passphrase security. The passphrase is entered into the APs (or WLAN controller or configuration system) and into the clients. If the passphrase is the same on both ends, the connection will be authenticated and encryption keys will be generated.

At first glance, the enterprise WLAN designer may think that passphrase-based implementations have no place in their networks. However, many technologies support only PSK solutions. These include barcode scanners, Wi-Fi phones and other small mobile devices. The complexity of EAP-based authentication (that which is used by a WPA- and WPA2-Enterprise) is simply not implemented on these devices either because it introduces latency problems in many implementations, or it simply has more complexity than the vendor plans to support. The WLAN designer should be able to determine when PSK must be used and when it is not required. This decision should be documented in the WLAN design plans created for the customer.

RADIUS Server Selection

When using the Extensible Authentication Protocol (EAP) for enterprise WLANs, a RADIUS server is required. Selecting the appropriate RADIUS server will be driven by several factors, including:

- The existing infrastructure solutions (Windows, Linux, Cisco, etc.)

- The existing directory services (Active Directory, LDAP, etc.)

- The EAP type required

When selecting a RADIUS server and recommending it in the design, be sure to consider the above three important factors.

EAP Type Selection

Selecting the appropriate EAP type is a factor of desired security and client support. The more secure EAP types require both server and client certificates or at least server certificates, such as EAP-TLS and EAP-TTLS. PEAP is also a commonly used EAP type and as long as it is implemented appropriately, it should provide sufficient security. You can use the table in Figure 4.21 to compare EAP types based on features and requirements.

	EAP-MD5	LEAP	EAP-TLS	EAP-TTLS	PEAP	EAP-Fast
Mutual Authentication	No	Yes	Yes	Yes	Yes	No
Certificates Required	No	No	Client/Server	Server Only	Server Only	No
Dynamic Key Generation	No	Yes	Yes	Yes	Yes	Yes
Costs and Management Overhead	Low	Low	High	Low/Medium	Low/Medium	Low
Industry Support	Low	High	High	High	High	Medium
Credential Security	Weak	Weak	Strong	Strong	Strong	Strong

Figure 4.21—Common EAP Types

The following list shows EAP types that are more commonly used with wireless networks:

- EAP-TLS—client and server certificates required

- TTLS (EAP-MSCHAP-v2)—only server certificates required

- PEAPv0 (EAP-MSCHAP-v2)—only server certificates required

- PEAPv0 (EAP-TLS)—client and server certificates required

- PEAPv1 (EAP-GTC)—used with token card and directory-based authentication systems and only server certificates required

- EAP-SIM—EAP for GSM Subscriber Identity Module—mobile communicators

- EAP-AKA—for use with the UMTS Subscriber Identity Module—mobile communications

Encryption Solutions

802.11 WLANs use only two encryption algorithms internally: RC4 and AES. WEP and TKIP (WPA) use RC4. CCMP (WPA2) uses AES. Many government installations require the use of AES. When it comes to selecting an encryption solution for your WLAN, it is likely to be driven more by the client requirements than anything else (with the obvious exception of governmental and other highly-secure deployments). Clients may only support TKIP (WPA), and therefore you choose to utilize it. In the years from 2015 to 2018 we should see less and less of this backwards compatibility requirement. In fact, to properly implement the newest 802.11 standard as it reads, TKIP cannot be implemented.

WPS

Wi-Fi Protected Setup (WPS) is a push-button security solution that should be used very little, if at all, in enterprise deployments. The basic process is to place the AP/WLAN router into WPS mode and then do the same on the client device or software utility and have the AP/WLAN router and client negotiate a unique set of security information between them. This information is then used in future connections. WPS has proven to have vulnerabilities when not implemented properly and should simply be avoided in enterprise WLANs.

Advanced Security Solutions

Several advanced or enhanced security solutions are available for use with WLANs. These include PPSK, VPNs, endpoint security, WIPS, and BYOD/MDM solutions.

Per-User PSK (PPSK)

Typical implementations of WPA- and WPA2-Personal passphrase-based security use a single common passphrase that is shared by all users for a given SSID. This process can create potential security issues, because all users of the service set will possess the passphrase. The passphrase is used to create a 256-bit pre-shared key that will restrict access to the wireless network and will be used in part to secure individual user data. Manufacturer proprietary mechanisms allow for unique per-user passphrases that will limit the ability for someone to be able to gain knowledge of the passphrase. While the security offered by this solution is not as robust as some implementations of 802.1X/EAP, this option provides many advantages over traditional passphrases that include:

- Allowing granular user-specific control of network privileges, which is not provided by traditional shared passphrases

- Alleviating management burden when a passphrase must be changed due to employees leaving or passwords being compromised

- Providing enhanced accounting functionality

- Enhancing security between users of the same network by preventing decryption of unicast traffic

- Not posing a conflict with 802.11 protocol operations

It is important to understand that PPSK is proprietary and is available from a limited number of WLAN manufacturers. Although it can enhance the way passphrase technology is used, it should not be used as a substitute for enterprise 802.1X/EAP security solutions when they are available as a solution. Figure 4.22 shows the configuration of PPSK in the Aerohive Hive Manager interface.

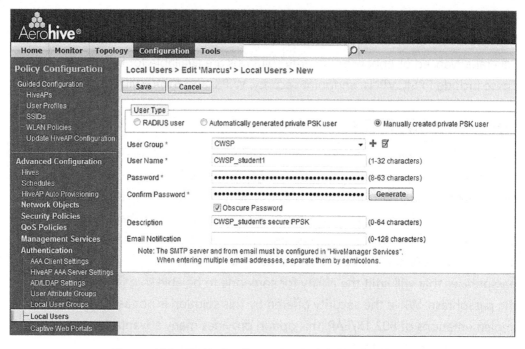

Figure 4.22—PPSK Configuration in Aerohive Solution

VPN Implementation

A common solution for hotspot secure connectivity is the use of a VPN. When connected to most public hotspots, no encryption is provided for the WLAN link. To protect potentially sensitive data that may traverse the link, users are instructed to use secure protocols like HTTPS and SFTP. However, such protocols are not always available and the use of a VPN allows for all communications to be secured. The WLAN designer may choose to recommend a VPN solution that works well with the infrastructure of the organization as part of the security design plan. Many organizations already have devices or servers that can act as VPN endpoints, such as Cisco ISR routers or Windows servers.

Endpoint Security

Endpoint security is used to ensure that the endpoints on the network are secure such that they do no introduce vulnerabilities to the network. Endpoint security can be as simple as running antivirus software or as complex as detecting whether a wireless link is encrypted or not and disallowing it if it is not. For the CWDP exam, be sure to know the basic features of endpoint security software, such as:

- Antivirus
- Configuration checks
- WLAN security enforcement
- Local proxy features
- Content filtering
- Reporting to centralized servers

Wireless Intrusion Prevention Systems (WIPS)

Enterprise-class wireless intrusion prevention system (WIPS) solutions are used to complement an organization's wireless network encryption and authentication platform. The WIPS can be configured to recognize trusted and known wireless devices that inhabit a service area and report changes to the administrator consoles. Additionally, a WIPS is capable of providing collected data to a server regarding the overall security and potential threats that are recognized. When implemented correctly, WIPS solutions can provide a wealth of information as well as protection for your network infrastructure and wireless devices.

WIPS solutions are software-based, hardware-based, and cloud-managed and are capable of monitoring the unbounded wireless medium through the use of a wireless hardware sensor. A WIPS can report captured information to software programs to be recorded in a server database. The WIPS solution will then be able to take the appropriate countermeasures to prevent wireless network intrusions, as needed. These countermeasures are based on identifying the intrusion by comparing the captured information to an intrusion signature database within the WIPS server.

WIPS solutions contain a variety of features from which the WLAN designer can choose, including:

- hardware sensors for monitoring

- 24x7x365 monitoring

- Mitigation features

- Notifications of threats through a variety of mechanisms

- Detecting threats to the wireless infrastructure such as denial of service (DoS) attacks and rogue access points

- Built-in reporting systems

- Integrated RF spectrum analysis to monitor and view the RF spectrum

- Validating compliance with corporate security policy and legislative compliance

- Retaining collected data for further forensic investigation

BYOD/MDM

As Chapter 2 directed, when planning BYOD and MDM, considerations include:

1. Guest access—will you allow non-employees access to the WLAN, and if so, will they access it through the standard network or a separate network?

2. Onboarding—how will guests gain access? Self-service, pre-authorization, etc.?

3. Captive portals—will you require authentication through a captive portal so that you can require acceptance of a use agreement and possibly other impositions?

4. Content filtering—will you limit the websites users can visit to a list, or filter based on content or implement no filtering at all?

5. Network segmentation—how will you separate the guest WLAN from the rest of the enterprise network?

One method of separation is to tunnel guest traffic into the DMZ. This method minimizes the management requirement of filtering the guest traffic on the LAN and working with segmentation methods like IP subnets or VLANs.

Planning for Roaming

Basic roaming works in one of three primary ways:

- Layer 2 roaming across APs within a single controller or without a controller

- Layer 2 roaming across APs connected to separate controllers

- Layer 3 roaming

When Layer 2 roaming occurs, the IP configuration is not lost. With the same IP address and roaming times of typically less than 40 milliseconds, Layer 2 roaming on non-secured WLANs can support streaming technologies like VoIP. Layer 2 roaming across APs within a single controller is called intracontroller roaming. Layer 2 roaming across APs connected to separate controllers is called intercontroller roaming. Vendors handle the actions that take place within or between the controllers according to their proprietary algorithms. The 802.11 standards defines only what should take place as a client STA roams from one AP to another, and they do not specify exactly how the communications must occur within the infrastructure in every detail. This flexibility allows the vendors to provide competitive features in this area and with the demand for VoIP support, this infrastructure solution can indeed be a deal breaker if the vendor's roaming solutions are inefficient. The good news is that the major vendors all have intracontroller and intercontroller Layer 2 roaming solutions that can accomplish the roaming speeds required for wireless VoIP.

Layer 3 roaming occurs when the client STA roams to an AP that cannot provide the same IP configuration, because the AP is located on a different wired network. In such a roaming scenario, the IP address must be reallocated from the DHCP server, and the client STA is placed on a new subnet of the network. The problem with this action is that the client's Layer 3 connections will be lost. If a file was in the process of copying from the client to a server, the file copy process will most likely have to be started again from the beginning. The same is true in the reverse scenario where the file is copying from the server to the client. While this situation is painful for the users, it can't begin to compare with frustrations of dropped calls due to Layer 3 roaming on Wi-Fi phones. To solve this problem, fast secure roaming must be implemented, and the APs across that users would roam must somehow be part of the same wired network or provide a solution to this problem. They may be part of the same wired network through tunneling solutions within the infrastructure. Or they may simply be connected to the same controller, but they must somehow allow the client STA to maintain its IP address.

Implementing Layer 2 roaming without IP configuration loss is not actually very difficult at all in open wireless networks without security. It has been available for many years. The problem is that, previous to 802.11i and 802.11r, there were difficulties in implementing a standards-based secure wireless network that offered very fast roaming. For secure wireless networks to support fast roaming, the 802.1X authentication process has to be accommodated in rapid fashion so that the user can roam without requiring a complete 802.1X authentication exchange to occur. This is typically accomplished using some form of key caching as discussed in the later sections of this chapter.

Finally, in order for roaming to work in a seamless manner, the coverage cells of the APs must overlap. If there is no point of overlap, the client STA will always lose network connectivity for a brief time as the user moves the STA across the non-covered area. Vendors recommend cell overlaps ranging from 15 to 30 percent. The reality is that you can't really measure overlap, but you can determine how many APs can be seen from a given location. Therefore, the goal should be to have at least two visible and usable (meaning sufficient signal strength and SNR) APs at any location where real-time devices may be used.

As a side note, when a user moves his or her laptop around within the coverage area of a single AP, roaming is not required. The user has mobility, but the connection to a single AP is maintained and no roaming occurs.

802.11-2012 includes roaming solutions like Fast Secure Roaming, pre-authentication, and PMK caching. Additionally, PSK implementations can provide standards-based secure roaming as long as a strong PSK is used, and it is altered at some acceptable interval.

Pre-authentication is the first way of removing delay from the roaming process. It is used by a wireless station that hears, during the scanning process, other APs to which it may choose to connect. The full 802.1X/EAP authentication is performed over the Ethernet infrastructure for the purpose of remaining on-channel with its current AP while preparing for connectivity with another AP. Pre-authentication support is optional and therefore not supported by all manufacturers. Figure 4.23 shows the pre-authentication structure for 802.11 WLANs.

The strengths of pre-authentication are:

- It is standardized by the IEEE
- It can be supported on any WLAN architecture
- It is performed prior to roaming and allows for pre-authentication with many different nearby APs

The weaknesses of pre-authentication are:

- It still requires 802.1X/EAP authentication after association
- It is not an efficient solution as it pre-authenticates to APs it may never touch
- It must happen prior to the roam
- It doesn't scale well
- It only trims off from less than 1ms to possibly 3ms of the roam time

Pairwise master key PMK caching is also known as "Fast Roam-Back." In Figure 4.24 you can see the steps required for this type of roaming to occur. The following paragraphs explain the process.

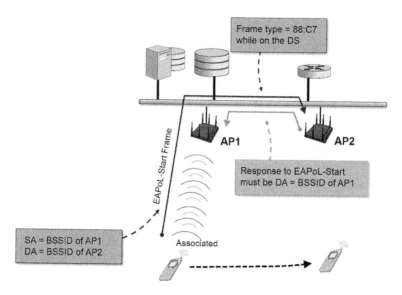

Figure 4.23—Pre-authentication

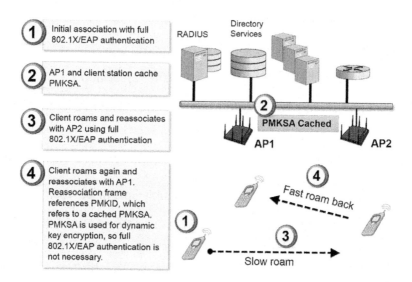

Figure 4.24—PMK Caching

The 802.11 standard allows pairwise master key security associations (PMKSAs) to be cached at the AP (or WLAN controller) and on the wireless station for the purpose of fast roam-back. When a PMKSA is built (through a full 802.1X/EAP authentication) with an AP, the station and AP may continue to use that PMKSA at any point in the future when the station might roam back to the AP in which it was previously associated. The purpose of this feature is to avoid the slow 802.1X/EAP reauthentication process. In order to implement this feature, the client station must include the appropriate pairwise master key identifier (PMKID) in the Reassociation Request frame when it reassociates. Provided the AP still has the PMKSA cached, 802.1X/EAP authentication will be skipped, and the 4-way handshake will immediately ensue.

The strengths of PMK caching are:

- It is standardized by IEEE

- It can be supported by and WLAN architecture

- No traffic overhead is introduced and it has a simple design

The weaknesses of PMK caching are:

- It provides fast roaming only on return to a previously associated AP

- New AP roams still require full 802.1X/EAP authentication

Opportunistic Key Caching (OKC) is a key caching method not defined in the 802.11 standard, though having some commonality with 802.11r (now incorporated into 802.11-2012. OKC) is used both at the supplicant and authenticator for fast roaming. The pairwise master key (PMK) and pairwise master key identifier (PMKID) are retrieved from the initial AP with which the wireless station associates. An identical algorithm is used on the wireless station and WLAN controller/AP, and a unique PMKID is given to the original PMK when it is passed to each AP. The unique PMKID is based on the BSSID of the AP to which the PMK is sent.

OKC remains a proprietary and undocumented solution. It is important to note that for OKC to function it must be supported by the authenticator and the supplicant.

The strengths of OKC are:

- It's a good solution until Voice-Enterprise (802.11r) solutions are available and implemented

- It scales well

- It only requires a single initial 802.1X/EAP authentication

The weaknesses of OKC are:

- It is not standardized

- Not all clients support it

- It is not implemented in a compatible way across all vendors

To understand the impact of 802.11r FT on roaming (now simply part of 802.11-2012), it's helpful to have a reminder of how 802.11i impacted it. To understand how 802.11i impacted roaming, you must first understand the different keys used in 802.11i networks. Remember, the keys are used to secure communications on the wireless link. The following keys are used as you've previously learned:

- **Pairwise Master Key (PMK):** This is the top-level key used in the standard. The PMK is derived from a key generated by EAP or from a pre-shared key (PSK) in smaller implementations.

- **Pairwise Transient Key (PTK):** The key derived from the PMK, Authenticator (AP) address (AA), supplicant (client) address (SPA), Authenticator nonce (number used once) (ANonce), and supplicant nonce (SNonce). A pseudo-random function is used to generate up to five keys. The five keys are the EAPOL-Key confirmation key, the EPOL-Key encryption key, the temporal encryption key, and two temporal message integrity code keys.

- **Group Master Key (GMK):** A supporting key that may be used to generate a group temporal key. The GMK may be regenerated within the AP periodically to reduce the exposure of the group temporal key.

- **Group Temporal Key (GTK):** The key used to protect broadcast or multicast MPDUs on a wireless link.

The term "pairwise" refers to two devices associated with each other. A pairwise master key, for example, is a key used between an AP and a client STA to secure the communications. This is where roaming is an issue because the security was designed to be between a single AP and STA pair. Therefore, some method of quickly acquiring a PTK after a roam was needed.

Once a STA is associated and authenticated to the wireless network, with 802.11i, a PMK secure association (PMKSA) exists between the authentication server and the STA. A PTK secure association (PTKSA) exists between the AP and the STA once the 4-way handshake is completed. The problem, when discussing roaming, is that the accomplishment of such a PMKSA and PTKSA takes time. It can take too much time for real-time applications if some additional mechanism is not in play.

The 802.11i solution to the delay caused by establishing a PMKSA is PMK caching. With PMK caching, as you previously read, the authenticator (the AP) and the STA can cache PMKSAs so that regeneration of the PMKSA is not required at the time of roaming. Instead, the first step in the 4-way handshake is that the authenticator specifies the identifier of the PMK in the first message (Message 1) of the handshake. This functionality means that the process of PMKSA establishment is removed and only the PTKSA must be established. Always remember this rule: if you can remove steps from a process, you will typically reduce the time required to complete the process. By removing the step of PMKSA establishment at roaming time you speed up the process or reassociation with the new AP.

The 802.11r amendment was the first 802.11 attempt to truly define fast secure roaming in any level of detail. It was ratified in 2008 and is now part of the 802.11 standard as amended (802.11-2012). The 802.11r amendment assumes the 802.11i amendment—as would be expected, since 802.11i was ratified in 2004. Remember, when studying IEEE standards, that an amendment ratified today is based upon the original standard and all amendments ratified before today. If you don't keep this in mind, the standard will become very confusing to you very quickly.

Note: **While 802.11r is standardized and has been for a time period quickly approaching a decade, few vendors have existing implementations that use it heavily. As much as the incompatibilities between different vendors are discussed, the vast majority of environments implement only one vendor in a facility or at least per network in that facility. The result is that OKC is still commonly used as the solution in early 2015.**

To begin the explanation of 802.11r, a few key definitions from the standard are in order:

- **Fast basic service set (BSS) transition:** A station (STA) movement that is from one BSS in one extended service set (ESS) to another BSS within the same ESS and that minimizes the amount of time that data connectivity is lost between the STA and the distribution system (DS).

- **Fast basic service set (BSS) transition (FT) 4-Way Handshake:** A pairwise key management protocol used during FT initial mobility domain association. This handshake confirms mutual possession of a pairwise master key, the PMK-R1, by two parties and distributes a group temporal key (GTK).

- **Fast basic service set (BSS) transition (FT) initial mobility domain association:** The first association or first reassociation procedure within a mobility domain, during which a station (STA) indicates its intention to use the FT procedures.

- **Mobility domain:** A set of basic service sets (BSSs), within the same extended service set (ESS), that support fast BSS transitions between themselves and that are identified by the set's mobility domain identifier (MDID).

- **Over-the-air fast basic service set (BSS) transition (FT):** An FT method in which the station (STA) communicates over a direct IEEE 802.11 link to the target AP (AP).

- **Over-the-DS (distribution system) fast basic service set (BSS) transition (FT):** An FT method in which the station (STA) communicates with the target AP (AP) via the current AP.

As painful as it may be, memorizing the preceding list of definitions—at least in your own words—is a key part of preparing for the CWSP exam. Make sure you understand these definitions and what they mean for 802.11 roaming. In addition to these terms, you need to understand that a single PMK is not considered in an 802.11r implementation as a sole entity, such as was introduced in 802.11i. Instead, we must deal with a fast transition key hierarchy. The following definitions will help you understand this hierarchy:

- **PMK-R0:** The first level (or top-level) PMK. The PMK-R0 is derived from the master session key (MSK) when 802.1X/RADIUS is used or from the pre-shared key (PSK) when personal implementations are used.

- **PMK-R1:** The second level PMK. The PMK-R1 keys are derived from the PMK-R0 key.

Remember this hierarchy. The first level is not PMK-R1, but it is PMK-R0.

The core of what 802.11r is all about is allowing a non-AP STA to preauthenticate with an AP to which it may roam at a later time. During the preauthentication process, in a FT implementation, the PTK is derived from the PMK-R1. It's important to remember that the PTK is not derived directly from the PMK-R0, but that it is derived from the PMK-R1.

Preauthentication is optional. If it is to be used, it must be available and enabled on the APs and the client devices. Remember that it is not required of an 802.11-compliant device; however, it will be very useful for wireless networks that must carry voice or other real-time traffic and provide for roaming ability.

As you've seen from the information in Chapter 5 (robust security network (RSN) and authentication and key management (AKM)), the key hierarchy follows a process of derivation. If you understand that key derivation process, this part which pertains to IEEE 802.11r fast transition will not be as painful.

Basically the fast transition (FT) process consists of different levels of the pairwise mater key (PMK). For example, a WLAN controller may hold PMK-R0, while AP1 has PMK-R1 (#1) and AP3 has PMK-R1 (#2). Both PMK-R1 (#1) and PMK-R1 (#2) are derived from PMK-R0. For standard authentication and key management (AKM) processes, there is only one PMK that is created for the authenticated session. In IEEE 802.11 fast transition there are many PMKs at different levels in the device authentication hierarchy.

The strengths of 802.11-2012 FT are:

- Standard based fast roaming
- Voice-Enterprise certification requires them
- It is the most efficient method available today
- Eventually we will see heavy support for it

The weaknesses of 802.11-2012 FT are:

- It has been very slow to market given its 8+ year life
- Wi-Fi Alliance Voice-Enterprise certification only began in 2012
- It introduces many new terms and concepts requiring enhances education

Using Network Planning Tools

Network planning tools include site survey software, network diagramming tools, throughput testing tools, and link calculation software or spreadsheets.

Site survey software typically has the following features to assist in the design process:

- Importing floor plans, including 3D plans
- Placing APs and configuring their settings for simulated propagation views as heat maps
- Defining building materials
- Placing objects on the floorplan that impact propagation
- Generating plan reports

Figure 4.25 shows the Ekahau Site Survey software used to define wall materials in a WLAN design.

Network diagramming tools are very important to describe the interconnectivity and service requirements on the network. They contain network diagrams showing the relationship between controllers and APs, controllers/APs and services (DNS, DHCP, TFTP, NTP, etc.), and other supporting roles (RADIUS servers, Certificate Authorities, etc.).

Throughput testing tools are useful to gather screenshots or raw data that defines the throughput discovered during the site survey. This information will be used to support the design and the fact that it meets the business requirements.

Finally, link calculation software or spreadsheets should be used when designing bridge links. They assist in the process, but also ensure that everything has been performed that should be, such as antenna alignment, output power adjustments, and other settings.

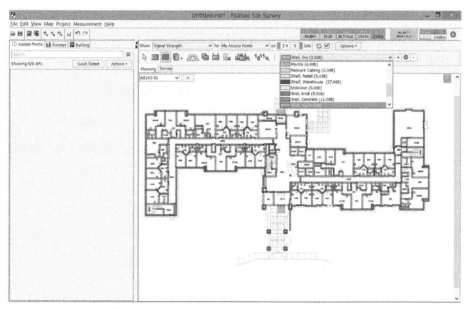

Figure 4.25—Wall Materials Specification

Chapter Review

In this chapter, you learned about the process of designing a WLAN. You considered the various components that must be planned and selected to have a full enterprise WLAN solution. In the next chapter, you will explore some WLAN design issues for specific scenarios beyond those referenced in this chapter.

Facts to Remember

Be sure to remember the following facts as you prepare for the CWDP certification, and be sure that you can explain the details related to them:

- When selecting WLAN architectures, the basic choices are among controller-based, cloud-based, and autonomous architectures.

- Centralized data forwarding requires that all data be sent to the controller and then to the final destinations from there.

- Distributed data forwarding allows data to be sent from the APs directly to the final destinations.

- RRM can be used for dynamic channel assignment for APs.

- A primary goal in channel planning is the reduction of CCI and ACI.

- 802.11ac does not operate in 2.4 GHz, though dual-band 802.11ac devices are sold as they use 802.11n in the 2.4 GHz band.

Chapter 5:

Advanced WLAN Design

In this chapter:

- Designing Branch Office Solutions

- Designing Mesh Networks

- Designing Bridge Links

- Specific Use Cases and Vertical Markets

Objectives:

3.8 Design branch and remote office WLAN deployments, including authentication services, WAN connections, Virtual Private Networks (VPNs), split tunnel forwarding, and AP selection and configuration.

3.9 Design mesh networks, including mesh access networks, mesh backhaul solutions, channel planning, band selection, and redundancy.

3.10 Design bridge links, including determination of appropriate line of sight (visual and Radio Frequency (RF), band selection, channel selection, output power levels required, data rate requirements, antenna selection, link budgets, and Point-to-Point (PtP) and Point-to-Multi-Point (PtMP) links.

3.17 Design WLANs for specific use cases and vertical markets, including high-density design, large public venues (LPV), healthcare, education, retail, hospitality, outdoors, public hotspots, and government deployments.

n the preceding chapter, information was provided for standard enterprise WLAN deployments, including bridge links. This chapter addresses specific scenarios, such as branch office solutions, mesh networks in more detail, bridge links in more detail, and specific use case scenarios and vertical markets.

Designing Branch Office Solutions

Branch offices are remote locations of an organization. While the organization may, and typically does, have a primary headquarters location that may employ hundreds or thousands of employees, branch offices typically employee less than a few hundred or even less than fifty. However, the branch office may still require a WLAN solution. Most vendors offer branch office solutions. To implement such a solution, issues, such as WAN connections, VPNs, authentication services, and AP selection must be considered.

WAN Connections

To implement a branch office, some connection is needed to the primary location. Depending on the distance from the headquarters, three options may exist; leased lines, Internet-based connections, or wireless bridges.

When using leased lines, a monthly fee will be required, and the costs can be rather high for faster data rates. However, the line will be dedicated to passing business traffic between the branch office and headquarters. At the same time, in some implementations, no local Internet is provided, and all user Internet activity must pass through the leased line.

Leased lines come in many forms and speeds. They can be implemented as full or partial lines, meaning that the full potential data throughput of the line is made available or only part of it. They can support speeds of more than 100 Mbps but are very pricey at such speeds.

Internet-based connections are very popular. They typically use VPNs for data security and can also support speeds of more than 100 Mbps. The cost of such connections is typically less than a leased line per Mbps. The next section on VPNs addresses important considerations related to Internet-based connections between offices.

Finally, wireless bridges can be used to connect branch offices. This option is most useful in metropolitan organizations. Such organizations may exist in one large metropolitan area, and wireless links may be implemented between the various locations in a hub-and-spoke or ring model or a hybrid.

VPNs

VPNs have been used to create WAN-type connections for over a decade. They are a low-cost solution to remote office connections. In many cases, for less than $200 within the United States, you can implement a VPN with 5–10 Mbps potential for WAN-type traffic.

It is important to remember, when planning remote WLANs, that a VPN solution using an Internet connection may not have the throughput you first expect. Some business lines have equal uplink and download speeds. Many have uplink speeds of approximately ten percent of the downlink speed. Therefore, a 50 Mbps Internet connection will only provide a roughly 5 Mbps WAN link, as both ends will be constrained by the uplink speeds.

However, if the headquarters location has an uplink speed of 50 Mbps and the remote office has a downlink speed of the same, the traffic from the headquarters to the remote office will support faster speeds, but the traffic from the remote office to the headquarters will be slower.

When considering a connection such as the one just described, the traffic flow must be planned. If more traffic will flow from headquarters to the branch office, which is the likely case, a mismatched link may work well. If equal traffic will flow in both directions, or if more traffic will flow from the branch office to the headquarters, such a link will likely be insufficient.

Note: **In many cases, remote offices download far more data than they upload. This behavior is because the organization's servers are often located at the headquarters. Therefore, small request packets are sent to the headquarters, large data packets are sent to the remote office, and small acknowledgement packets are sent to the headquarters. Such traffic flow is common, but each scenario must be analyzed individually.**

When implementing a VPN, the decision between tunneled forwarding and split tunnel forwarding must be made. In nearly all scenarios, split tunnel forwarding is best. Figure 5.1 shows the split tunnel concept in use. The benefit of split tunnel is simply that all Internet traffic can pass directly out to the Internet. The negative aspect of split tunnel is that any Internet filtering that is required must be duplicated at each branch office. If the VPN link provides sufficient throughput, some organizations will choose to perform tunneled forwarding so that all Internet filtering, monitoring, and reporting can be configured and managed at the headquarters location. Others will implement policy-based Internet content filtering so that the rules can be created at headquarters and then replicated to remote or branch offices without much effort.

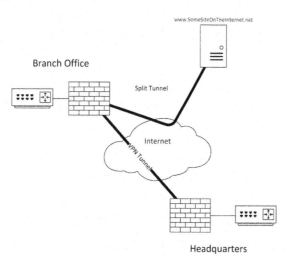

Figure 5.1—Split Tunnel Mode

AP Selection and Configuration

AP selection and configuration is also important for branch offices. Many vendors provide remote APs or remote wireless routers. Remote APs, technically, should be standard APs, but they come configured to use a remote controller or work with a cloud-managed solution. Some vendors call wireless routers remote APs. If the device has local switch ports and a WAN/Internet port and performs routing, it is a wireless router and not an AP regardless, which the vendor chooses to call it.

Configuring a remote AP is much the same as a local AP, with the possible exception of the use of a tunneling management solution, like HREAP. When using HREAP or similar protocols, client traffic is switched at the branch, and management and control data is passed to headquarters across the WAN link. Additionally, client authentication can be performed locally if the controller is not available. When the controller is available (for instance, the WAN link is up), even data can be tunneled across the WAN if desired.

 Note: **Prior to Release 7.2, FlexConnect was called Hybrid REAP (HREAP). It is now always referred as FlexConnect. While the name has changed, the features and functions are mostly the same**

Per Cisco documentation, with respect to client authentication (open, shared, EAP, Web authentication, and NAC) and data packets, the WLAN can be in any one of the following states, depending on the configuration and state of controller connectivity, as follows:

- **Central authentication, central switching**—In this state, the controller handles client authentication, and all client data is tunneled back to the controller. This state is valid only in connected mode.

- **Central authentication, local switching**—In this state, the controller handles client authentication, and the FlexConnect access point switches data packets locally. After the client authenticates successfully, the controller sends a configuration command with a new payload to instruct the FlexConnect access point to start switching data packets locally. This message is sent per client. This state is applicable only in connected mode.

- **Local authentication, local switching**—In this state, the FlexConnect access point handles client authentication and switches client data packets locally. This state is valid in standalone mode and connected mode.

- **Authentication down, switch down**—In this state, the WLAN disassociates existing clients and stops sending beacon and probe requests. This state is valid in both standalone mode and connected mode.

- **Authentication down, local switching**—In this state, the WLAN rejects any new clients trying to authenticate, but it continues sending beacon and probe responses to keep existing clients alive. This state is valid only in standalone mode.

In connected mode, the access point provides minimal information about the locally authenticated client to the controller. The following information is not available to the controller:

- Policy type
- Access VLAN
- VLAN name
- Supported rates
- Encryption cipher

When implementing branch office solutions, it becomes very important to consider the control, management, and data planes. These terms are used to reference categories of traffic. Control traffic is that which determines network activity and available resources. It is the set of communications that control the cooperation and interaction between wireless devices in a network. Examples include load balancing, RRM, and roaming features. Management traffic is that which configures network devices and resources. Examples include network configuration, updating firmware, reporting, and monitoring. Data traffic is standard user data. The WLAN solution you are implementing will, in some way, deal with each of these traffic categories, and how it does will impact the availability and performance of the WLAN.

Authentication Services

The final planning element for the branch office is authentication services. Given that EAP and RADIUS servers are used in large deployments that are likely to have branch offices, the method by which RADIUS servers are deployed must be considered. The common RADIUS server options include:

- Local RADIUS—Install a RADIUS server at each branch location for local wireless station authentication.

- RADIUS proxy—Install a RADIUS proxy at the branch location and rely on a remote RADIUS server for authentication.

- Remote RADIUS—Use the WAN link to authenticate with a remote RADIUS server.

The most important thing to remember, related to Wi-Fi roaming, is that a remote RADIUS server, whether accessed directly or through a local proxy, will cause greater latency in authentication communications. The result of this can be problematic VoIP connections when users roam from AP to AP. This can be resolved by either installing a local RADIUS server or by using WPA2-PSK or WPA-PSK for roaming VoIP SSIDs at the branch location.

Designing Mesh Networks

Mesh networks comprise multiple APs that are interconnected providing multi-hop links back to the wired network or to a 4G or otherwise wireless backhaul. To plan for mesh networks, you have to understand their basic characteristics, plan for backhaul solutions, use the proper band for your needs, implement an effective channel plan, and provide for redundancy. This section provides coverage of these important issues.

Mesh Access Networks

Mesh access networks are implemented in order to provide client access. Their purpose is not simply to provide redundant links as a backhaul, which is discussed next. Instead, they are implemented so that clients at many locations, where wired access may not exist, can reach the target network through some number of hops across the mesh network.

In a mesh access network, the APs interconnect directly with each other, with one or more APs connecting to a wired network or a separate wireless network, such as a 4G LTE link to a service provider. When implementing mesh access networks, consider the following important guidelines:

- Each wireless link adds extra latency in the link as the AP receiving must be listening and, after receiving, will transmit to the next AP, and so on, in the line.

- Due to the nature of WLANs, it is expected that some wireless frames will be lost and not arrive at the next mesh AP. The result is retransmissions, which incur delays not typically seen in modern wired links.

- When a single radio exists in each AP, it must switch between service clients and connecting to the other mesh APs; therefore, dual-band APs are typically used for mesh AP links.

Mesh Backhaul Solutions

Planning mesh backhaul solutions is quite similar to planning bridge links. In fact, devices sold as mesh APs and configured as backhaul solutions are often implemented exactly like a PtP or PtMP bridge link configuration. The link budget must be determined based on the desired data rate and the link distance. For example, the vendor may document that a 300 Mbps two stream mesh link requires an SNR of 30 dB. This means that, at each end of the link, the distance between the signal and the noise floor must be 30 dB or greater. Such a demand is challenging to achieve as two antennas must be used and gaining 30 dB SNR over a significant distance is difficult.

Band Selection

A major decision in mesh implementations is the choice of band. In the past, many mesh networks were built on the assumption that 2.4 GHz clients would connect to the network, and 5 GHz links would be used to build the mesh. This is no longer the only option. Today, it is quite common to have 5 GHz clients, and they must be supported as well. In some cases, a mixture of 2.4 GHz mesh link radios with 5 GHz client access radios, and others with 5 GHz mesh link radios and 2.4 GHz client access radios, can work well, effectively forming a dual-overlay network, but the channel planning for the 2.4 GHz side is very challenging. Therefore, it is more common to implement 5 GHz mesh links (using channels that may not be supported by the clients) and 5 GHz client access as well as 2.4 GHz client access.

Channel Planning

Channel planning in mesh networks is important. It is more challenging for a 2.4 GHz mesh, just as it is for standard 2.4 GHz WLANs. This is still the result of the limit of three channels in the band. However, with careful planning, it is possible to create a limited-scale mesh network using 2.4 GHz radios.

When you must implement a large-scale mesh network, you are practically required to use 5 GHz radios. It is for this reason, that some mesh APs are only capable of implementing mesh links with 5 GHz. Using 5 GHz channels provides support, in many areas of the world, for DFS channel usage, which may not be available for client access. These DFS channels, when available, can be used to provide mesh links and then the non-DFS channels can be used to provide client access radios; however, it is important to remember that when two radios are so close together (in the same AP enclosure), ACI can occur even across two channels of separation. Therefore, it would be best to implement lower DFS channels with higher non-DFS channels and higher DFS channels with lower non-DFS channels.

Redundancy

The finally element in planning mesh links is redundancy. Redundancy should be provided such that if a single mesh AP fails, alternate links back to the wired or wireless connected network are still available. For example, Figure 5.2 shows a non-redundant mesh network and Figure 5.3 shows a redundant mesh network.

Figure 5.2—Non-Redundant Mesh Links

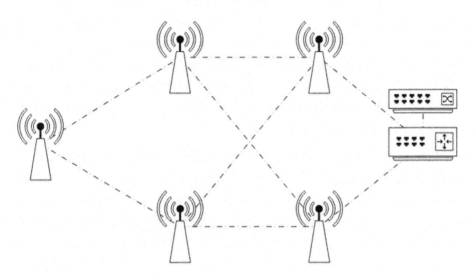

Figure 5.3—Redundant Mesh Links

Designing Bridge Links

Like mesh links, bridge links require planning related to SNR, but they also require planning related to line of sight, output power, antenna selection, and more. This section provides more details than previously presented on implementing effective bridge links.

PtP and PtMP Links

Bridge links fall into two categories: PtP and PtMP. You learned the basics of these link types in your CWNA studies. PtP links use two bridges, and only two bridges. The two bridges form an 802.11 link between them (authentication and association and secure authentication) and bridge traffic across the link. PtMP links use either omni-directional or semi-directional antennas at one location and high-gain antennas at other locations. The central location forms multiple bridge links to the other locations. The problem with true PtMP links over distance is that the two remote bridges cannot hear each other and can cause collisions at the central bridge. Some vendors may implement proprietary timing protocols to address this, but even such solutions result in less throughput than two separate PtP links compared to three bridges involved in a PtMP link.

Figure 5.4 shows the use of two PtP links on separate channels. Notice one link is using channel 48 and the other channel 149. This prevents CCI and ACI at the central location where two bridges are operating. The ability to use high-gain antennas means that greater distances can be achieved as well. Finally, because the two links are separate, the full data rate and throughput of the link will be available for each bridge link.

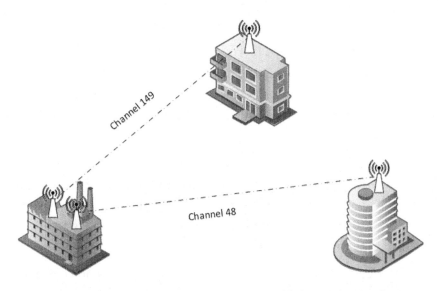

Figure 5.4—Efficient Bridge Links Using Multiple PtP Connections

This brief overview of PtP and PtMP introduces bridging. The remainder of this section covers the details of implementing such bridge links, including ensuring line of site, meeting data-rate requirements, selecting the appropriate band and channels, calculating link budgets, managing output power levels, and antenna selection and alignment.

Line of Sight (Visual and RF)

If you stand on top of a tall building, you can see for a very great distance. You may even be able to see for many miles on a very clear day. If you can physically see something, it is said to be in your *visual line of sight (visual LoS)* or just your *line of sight (LoS)* for simplicity. This visual LoS is actually the transmission path of the light waves from the object you are viewing (transmitter) to your eyes (receiver). Visual LoS is an apparently straight line from your perspective, but light waves are subject to similar behavior as RF waves like refraction and reflection, and, therefore, the line may not actually be straight. Consider an object you are viewing in a mirror. The object is not directly in front of you, and yet it appears to be showing that visual LoS is not necessarily a straight line between two objects.

Since RF is part of the same electromagnetic phenomenon as visible light, behaviors similar to visual LoS exist. However, RF LoS is more sensitive than visual LoS to interference near the path between the transmitter and the receiver. You might say that more space is needed for the RF waves to be seen by each end of the connection. This extra space can actually be calculated and has a name: the *Fresnel Zone* (pronounced *frah-nell*).

 Note: Start with the visual LoS and then determine whether you have RF LoS. For long-distance outdoor links, you will never have RF LoS if you do not have visual LoS; however, you may not be able to see as far as the link reaches so you may have to rely on topography maps of the area.

The Fresnel Zones, named after the French physicist Augustin-Jean Fresnel, are a theoretically infinite number of ellipsoidal areas around the LoS in an RF link. Many WLAN administrators refer to the Fresnel Zone when it is more proper to refer to the First Fresnel Zone according to the science of Physics. While it may be the intention of most WLAN administrators to reference the First Fresnel Zone when they speak of only the Fresnel Zone, it is important that you understand the difference. The First Fresnel Zone is the zone with the greatest impact on a WLAN link in most scenarios. The Fresnel Zones have been referenced as an ellipsoid-shaped area, an American football-shaped area, and even a Zeppelin-shaped area. Figure 5.5 shows the intention of these analogies.

Fresnel Zone

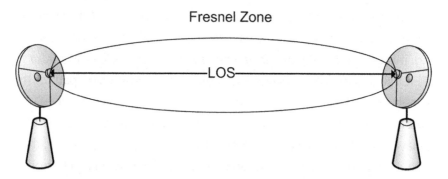

Figure 5.5—The Fresnel Zone

In this text, the First Fresnel Zone or Fresnel Zone 1 will be called *1FZ* from this point forward, for simplification. Since 1FZ is an area surrounding the LoS, and this area cannot be largely blocked and still provide a functional link, it is important that you know how to calculate the size of 1FZ for your links. You will also need to consider the impact of earth bulge on the link and 1FZ.

 Note: **You will not need to memorize the formulas provided here for the CWDP examination; however, they will prove a useful reference for you when you need to create PtP or PtMP links in the future.**

To calculate the radius of the 1FZ, use the following formula:

$$radius = \sqrt{\ 72.2 \times (D/(4 \times F))}$$

Where *D* is the distance of the link in miles, *F* is the frequency used for transmission in GHz, and *radius* is reported in feet. For example, if you are creating a link that will span 1.5 miles, and you are using 2.4 GHz radios, the formula would be used as follows:

$$72.2 \times \sqrt{(1.5/(4 \times 2.4))} = 28.54 \text{ feet}$$

This formula provides you with the radius of the 1FZ, and, of course, doubling the result would give you the diameter, if you needed it to be calculated. However, it is important to realize that a blockage of the 1FZ of more than 40% can cause the link to become non-functional. To calculate the 60% radius, so that you can ensure it remains clear, use the following formula:

$$clearance\ radius = 43.3 \times \sqrt{(D/(4 \times F))}$$

Where *D* is the distance of the link in miles, *F* is the frequency used for transmission in GHz, and *radius* is reported in feet. Using the same example we used to calculate the radius of the entire 1FZ, you will now see that the 60% clearance radius is only 17.12 feet. However, this leaves no room for error or change. For example, trees often grow into the 1FZ and cause greater blockage than they did at the time of link creation. For this reason, some WIRELESS LAN engineers choose to use a 20% blockage or 80% clearance guideline, and this is the recommended minimum clearance of the CWNP program as well. So how would you calculate this? Use the following formula:

$$recommended\ radius = 57.8 \times \sqrt{(D/(4 \times F))}$$

Once you have processed this formula, you will see that the recommended minimum of 80% clearance (recommended maximum of 20% blockage) results in a 1FZ radius of 22.8 feet.

 Note: **Since it is always better to be safe, rather than sorry, when creating WLAN links, you will probably want to make it a habit to round your Fresnel zone calculations upward. For example, you would round the *recommended radius* to 23 feet in this example.**

You might be wondering why you calculate the radius instead of the diameter. The reason is simple: you can determine where the visual LoS resides and then measure outward in all directions around that point to determine where the 1FZ actually resides. Remember, the 1FZ does not reside in a downward direction only. It might seem that way since you are usually dealing with trees and other objects protruding up from the ground as interference and blockage objects. However, it is entirely possible that something could be hanging down from a very-high position—such as a bridge—and encroach on the 1FZ from above the visual LoS. Additionally, buildings and other objects can cause blockages from the sides. For example, if you are attempting to create a PtP link that has visual LoS between two buildings on either side of the link in a downtown area, the two buildings may encroach on the 1FZ, resulting in insufficient signal strength for a consistent connection.

In the real world, many links are created without calculating and measuring the Fresnel Zone. Instead, the links are established as a combination of visual LoS and signal strength received (SNR). That is, if visual LoS exists and sufficient signal strength is received, it follows that the 1FZ is at least currently, sufficiently clear.

Another factor that should be considered in 1FZ blockage, is the Earth itself. As you know, the Earth—it turns out—is round. When you and another person are farther apart (or any two objects for that matter) there will be a greater likelihood that the Earth is between you. This is demonstrated in Figure 5.6.

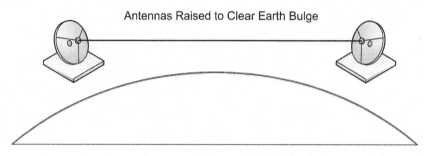

Figure 5.6—Earth bulge simply illustrated

If you are creating wireless links over distances greater than 7 miles using WLAN technologies, you will need to account for earth bulge in your antenna positioning formulas. Again, you will not need to memorize this formula for the CWDP examination, but you will need to know that earth bulge is a potential problem in outdoor wireless links over greater distances. The formula for calculating the extra height your antennas will need to compensate for earth bulge, is:

$$Height = D^2/8$$

Where *height* is the height of earth bulge in feet and *D* is the distance between antennas in miles. Therefore, if you are creating an 8 mile link, you would process the following formula:

$$11^2/8 = 15.12 \text{ feet}$$

Using the guideline of rounding up, you would raise the antenna height by 15.5 to 16 feet to accommodate for earth bulge.

To bring all the discussion of Fresnel Zones together, it is important you learn to deal with 1FZ obstructions. If the obstructions are coming up from the ground into the

1FZ and there are no obstructions anywhere above it, you can often solve the problem by simply raising the antennas involved in the communication link. For example, if there is a forest with maximum tree height of 23 feet that is between the two antennas and there is a distance of 11 miles that must be spanned, you can calculate the needed height for the antennas, including earth bulge, with the following formula:

$$minimum\ antenna\ height = (57.8 \times \sqrt{(11/(4 \times 2.4))}) + (11^2/8)$$

This might seem complex at first, but it is a simple combination of the recommended 1FZ clearance formula and the earth bulge formula. The result is 77 feet. This means you will need to install very-high towers, and you will also need to monitor the forest, though it is unlikely that the trees would grow that much more into the 1FZ in a few years. Additionally, you will likely be required to acquire permits for the towers in most regulatory domains or you may be able to mount antennas on the top of taller buildings.

If the obstructions are coming into the 1FZ from the sides, such as buildings intruding into the pathways, you will have to either calculate the 1FZ for a different frequency to see if you can get the clearance or you will have to raise the antennas above the buildings. You may also be able to create a multi-hop link to "shoot" around the buildings if you can gain access rights to a third location that can be seen (RF LoS –, including 1FZ) by both of your locations.

Notice that it was an option to calculate the 1FZ with a different frequency. Because the Fresnel zones are a factor of wavelengths (hence frequencies) and not a factor of antenna gain or beamwidth, which is very important to differentiate, you can often successfully implement a PtP link using different frequencies. For example, the 77-foot antenna height to allow us to communicate over the top of the forest across 11 miles can be lowered to only 55 feet if you are using 802.11 devices in the 5 GHz range. However, the trade-off is in distance. The 2.4 GHz signals are detected more easily than 5 GHz signals at a distance due to the receiving area of the antenna element and the length of the signal wave, but 5 GHz signals have a narrower 1FZ.

An example of this is a link that travels only about a city block (.1 miles). In the 2.4 GHz spectrum, the 1FZ radius would be approximately 6 feet. In the 5 GHz spectrum, the 1FZ would only be about 4 feet. Remember, this means 6 feet or 4 feet out from the center point in all directions. Therefore, a 5 GHz link traveling between two buildings for two tenths of a mile would require a space between the buildings of about 8 to 9 feet, while the 2.4 GHz link would need a space between the buildings of about 12–13 feet. These factors are important considerations.

Data-Rate Requirements

Data-rate requirements are defined for a bridge link. For example, if you desire 30 Mbps throughput, you will require a 65 Mbps link. The vendor documentation for the bridge should inform you of the signal-to-noise ratio (SNR) required to achieve a particular data rate.

Background RF noise, which can be caused by all the various systems and natural phenomenon that generate energy in the electromagnetic spectrum, is known as the *noise floor*. The power level of the RF signal relative to the power level of the noise floor is known as the *signal-to-noise ratio* or SNR.

Think of it like this. Imagine you are in a large conference room. Further, imagine that hundreds of people are having conversations at normal conversation sound levels. Now, imagine that you want to say something so that everyone will hear you; therefore, you cup your hands around your mouth and yell. You could say that the conversations of everyone else in the conference room is a noise floor and that your yelling is the important signal or information. Furthermore, you could say that the loudness of your yelling relative to the loudness of all other discussions is the SNR for your communication.

In WLAN networks, the SNR becomes a very important measurement. If the noise floor power levels are too close to the received signal strength, the signal may be corrupted or it may not even be detected. It is almost as if the received signal strength is weaker than it actually is when there is more electromagnetic noise in the environment. You may have noticed that when you yell in a room full of people yelling, your volume does not seem so great; however, if you yell in a room full of people whispering, your volume seems to be magnified. In fact, your volume is not greater, but the noise floor is less. RF signals are impacted in a similar way.

247

Technically, SNR is defined as the difference between the noise floor and the signal in dB. The formula for calculating SNR is simple:

SNR = noise floor value in dBm - signal strength value in dBm

If the noise floor is rated at -95 dBm and the signal is detected at -70 dBm, the SNR is 25.

> **EXAM MOMENT:** Know how to calculate SNR. If given a noise floor rating value and a signal strength value, be prepared to calculate the SNR. Remember the simple formula of *noise floor value - signal strength value = SNR*. Know that the signal strength may be provided in mW and will need to be converted to dBm, but the mW value will usually be a basic value, such as -0.1 or -0.01.

Data rates, therefore, are achieved by getting the appropriate signal strength to the remote bridge, which is a factor of output power and antenna gain. However, the band and channel you select will also impact the bridge link. You should choose the band that will provide the greatest likelihood of a successful link. Generally speaking, 2.4 GHz links work better over longer distances, but 5 GHz links are typically simpler to implement, because they are exposed to less interference. As to channel selection, always select a channel that provides the least CCI and ACI at each bridge location. Remember that both bridges will operate on the same channel so the chosen channel must be clean at both ends of the link (the RF activity between the ends of the bridge link is not as important as the activity near the ends).

The *Received Signal Strength Indicator (RSSI)* is an arbitrary measurement of received signal strength defined in the 802.11 standards. No absolute rule exists as to how this signal strength rating must be implemented in order to comply with the IEEE standard other than the fact that it is optional, it should report the rating to the device driver, and it should use 1 byte for the rating providing a potential range of 0 to 255.

In reality, no vendors have chosen to use the entire range. For example, Cisco uses a range of 0 to 100 (101 total values) in their devices, and most Atheros-based chipsets use a range of 0–60 (61 total values). The IEEE does specify that an RSSI_MAX parameter should exist, which would be 100 for Cisco and 60 for Atheros. The RSSI_MAX parameter allows software applications to determine the range implemented by the vendors and then convert the rating value into a percentage. It would not be very beneficial if the client software reported the actual rating to the user. Because of the different ranges used by the different vendors, using the actual rating would result in unusual matches. By this I mean that an RSSI rating of 75 in a Cisco client is the same relative rating as an RSSI rating of 45 in an Atheros chipset (assuming they are using similar linear stepping algorithms internally). Therefore, most applications use percentages.

If an Atheros-based client card reported an RSSI of 47, the software application could process the following formula to determine the signal strength in percentage:

$$47/60 * 100 = 78.3\% \; \textit{signal strength}$$

How does the software know to use the maximum value of 60? From the RSSI_MAX parameter that is required by the IEEE standard. Symbol, for example, used an RSSI_MAX of 31. This means there is a total of 32 potential values with 31 of the values actually representing the some level of usable signal strength. Most vendors have chosen to use an RSSI of 0 to represent a signal strength less than the receive sensitivity of the device and, therefore, a signal strength that is not usable. In the end, an RSSI of 16, with a Symbol client would be 50% signal strength. An RSSI of 50 with a Cisco client would be 50% signal strength, and an RSSI of 30 with an Atheros client would be 50% signal strength. This variance is why most client software packages report the signal strength in percentage instead of RSSI. The formula to calculate percentages from RSSI values is:

$$\textit{Signal Strength Percentage} = RSSI/RSSI\_MAX$$

Where RSSI is the rating specified for the specific vendor chipset and RSSI_MAC is the highest RSSI rating possible. The result is the signal strength percentage value you see in so many wireless LAN client software packages.

Now, let's make this even more complex—just for fun. Earlier it was stated that a Cisco rating of 75 is the same as an Atheros rating of 45, assuming the use of the same linear stepping algorithm. By linear stepping algorithm, it is meant the connection between dBm and RSSI rating. For example, one might assume that a dBm of -12 gets an RSSI rating of 100 for Cisco and that a dBm of -12 gets an RSSI rating of 60 for Atheros. It would make sense to assume that the RSSI_MAX parameter is equal to the same actual dBm signal strength with all vendors; however, since the IEEE leaves it up to the vendors to determine the details of RSSI implementation (mostly because it is an optional parameter anyway), the different vendors often use different dBm signal strengths for their RSSI_MAX parameter. What is the result of this complexity? You may show a 100% signal strength for one client device and show a lesser signal strength for another client device from the exact same location. Your assumption may be that the client device with the lesser signal strength is actually providing inferior performance when, in fact, they are identical.

How can this be? Consider a situation where two vendors use an RSSI_MAX value of 100. However, one vendor (vendor A) equates the RSSI rating of 100 to -12 dBm, and the other vendor (vendor B) equates the RSSI rating of 100 to -15 dBm. Now assume that both vendors use a linear stepping scale for their ratings, where a decrease in dBm of .7 causes the RSSI rating to drop by 1. This means that, at -15 dBm, vendor B will report 100% signal strength, but vendor A will have dropped the RSSI rating four times to a value of 96 and report a 96% signal strength. You can see how one might assume that vendor B's client is performing better because it has a higher-percentage signal strength when, in fact, the two clients simply use a different implementation of the RSSI feature.

Due to these incompatibility issues, RSSI values should only be compared with the values from other computers using the same vendor's devices. RSSI values should never be conceptualized as universal or in any way determinant of the value in one vendor's adapter over another vendor's value. Apples must be compared with apples—or to avoid confusion—Ciscos with Ciscos and D-Links with D-Links.

The RSSI rating is also arbitrarily used to determine when to reassociate (roam) and when to transmit. Vendors will decide what the lowest RSSI rating should be before attempting to reassociate to a BSS with a stronger beacon signal. Additionally, vendors must determine when to transmit. To do this, they must determine a clear channel threshold. This is an RSSI value at which it can be assumed that there is no arriving signal and, therefore, the device may transmit.

> **EXAM MOMENT:** Remember that RSSI is the signal strength rating that is vendor-specific, even though it is based on limited IEEE standard specifications. Also, remember that the RSSI_MAX value determines the upper value of the RSSI rating.

Output Power Levels

Output power levels impact the SNR at the receiver. Both bridges should be configured with the same output power levels. This is true even if one bridge is using an omnidirectional antenna. Using antennas to provide gain in the link will result in a stable and matched link. Using very-high-output power on one end can result in a mismatched link. For example, if the end with an omnidirectional antenna has high-output power (say 100 mW) to get signals to the other bridges, and the other bridges have output power of only 10 mW but with higher gain antennas, there may be a mismatch where the omnidirectional antenna cannot pick up significant signal to process frames.

Antenna Selection

Antenna selection is based on link distance, data-rate requirements, and regulatory constraints. Because regulatory constraints cannot be effectively defined on a global basis, they are not tested on the CWDP exam. This section addresses only link distance and data-rate requirements related to antenna selection.

The previous section on data-rate requirements emphasized the point that particular data rates require specific or better SNR levels at the receiver. Such SNR levels are achieved based on output power of the bridges but are also impacted by the antenna gain.

Antenna gain is referenced in dBi, and the direction of the antenna is defined in antenna charts known as Azimuth (horizontal—the view from the top down on an omni antenna) and Elevation (vertical—the view from the side on an omni antenna).

These charts provide insight into the gain of the antenna through a measurement called *beamwidth*.

Different antennas have different beamwidths, and this beamwidth is the measurement of how broad or narrow the focus of the RF energy is as it propagates from the antenna along the *main lobe*. The main lobe is the primary RF energy coming from the antenna. Beamwidth is measured both vertically and horizontally, so do not let the term *width* confuse you into thinking it is a one-dimensional measurement. Specifically, the beamwidth is a measurement taken from the center of the RF signal to the points on the vertical and horizontal axis where the signal decreases by 3 dB or half power. In the end, there is a vertical and horizontal beamwidth measurement that is stated in degrees. Figure 5.7 shows both the concept of the beamwidth and how it is measured, and Table 5-1 provides a table of common beamwidths for various antenna types (these antenna types are each covered in detail later in this chapter).

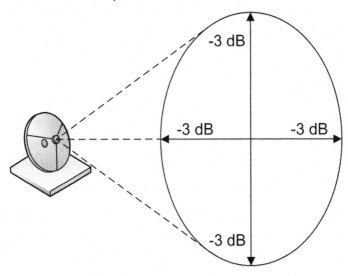

Figure 5.7—Beamwidth Illustrated

EXAM MOMENT: Remember that the beamwidth is calculated where the signal reaches half power or -3 dB or half power.

While beamwidth measurements give us an idea of the propagation pattern of an antenna, they are less than perfect in illustrating the actual areas that are covered by the antenna. For more useful visual representations, you will want to reference Azimuth and Elevation charts.

Antenna Type	Horizontal Beamwidth	Vertical Beamwidth
Omni-directional	360 degrees	7 to 80 degrees
Patch/panel	30 to 180 degrees	6 to 90 degrees
Yagi	30 to 78 degrees	14 to 64 degrees
Sector	60 to 180 degrees	7 to 17 degrees
Parabolic dish	4 to 25 degrees	4 to 21 degrees

Table 5.1—Various beamwidths for antenna types

Where the beamwidth calculations provide a measurement of an antenna's directional power, Azimuth and Elevation charts, which are typically presented together, provide a visualization of the antenna's propagation patterns. Figure 5.8 shows an example of an Azimuth chart, and Figure 5.9 shows an example of an Elevation chart.

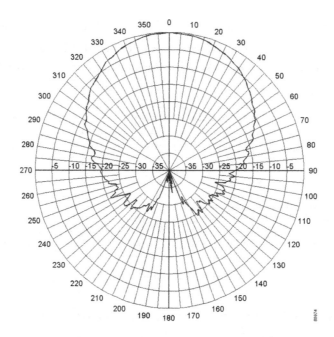

Figure 5.8—Azimuth chart

The difference between an Azimuth and Elevation chart is simple: the Azimuth chart shows a top-down view of the propagation path (to the left, in front, to the right, and behind the antenna), and the Elevation chart shows a side view of the propagation path (above, in front, below, and behind the antenna). Think of these charts in terms of a dipole antenna that is positioned vertically upright. If you are standing directly above it and looking down on it, you are seeing the perspective of an Azimuth chart. If you are beside it and looking at it from a horizontally level position, you are seeing the perspective of an Elevation chart.

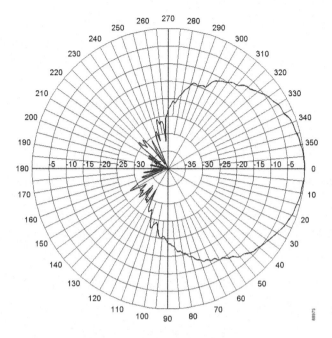

Figure 5.9—Elevation chart

The Azimuth chart in Figure 5.8 is a chart of the Cisco 9.5 dBi sector antenna referenced. As with most Azimuth charts, the direction of propagation is represented in the upward direction; however, the actual direction will depend on how you position the antenna. The chart is reporting the different signal strength you can expect at different degrees from the antenna. For example, at 90 and 270 degrees (to the immediate left and right of the antenna's intended propagation direction) you will see a loss of approximately 20 dB. Directly behind the antenna, at 180 degrees, you will see a loss of approximately 35 to 50 dB. This is a sector antenna and is intended to propagate its energy in one direction but in a fairly wide path.

The Elevation chart in Figure 5.9 is for the same Cisco antenna. You will notice that the pattern of propagation is very similar to the Azimuth pattern. Like most Elevation charts, it is shown with the primary radiation direction to the right. Remember, this is intended to represent what you see looking at the antenna's propagation pattern from the side view. You can see that this antenna as very similar levels of loss along the same degree levels as the Azimuth chart.

EXAM MOMENT: Azimuth charts show the propagation pattern from a top-down perspective. Elevation charts show the propagation pattern from a side perspective.

When it comes to antenna alignment, multiple methods are available:

- **Laser sighting**—good for long distance links to establish the initial connection.

- **RSSI alignment**—good for aligning short distance links and fine tuning all links.

- **Level alignment**—good for aligning fairly close antennas at the same or similar elevations.

- **Sight alignment**—uses rifle-like sights and is good for short to medium-range alignments.

Some vendors will suggest that bridge links using omni-directional antennas require no alignment; however, even such links can benefit from elevation alignment, when possible. That is, if the omni-directional antenna can be placed at the same elevation as the remote omni-directional, semi-directional, or highly-directional antennas, improved SNR can be achieved.

Link Budgets

Ultimately, all of the information presented in this section leads to the need for a link budget to implement a quality bridge connection. The term budget can be defined as a plan for controlling a resource. In a wireless network, the resource is RF energy, and you must ensure that you have enough of it to meet your communication needs. This is done by calculating a *link budget* that results in a *system operating margin (SOM)*. Link budget is an accounting of all components of power, gain, loss, receiver sensitivity, and fade margin. This includes the cables and connectors leading up the antenna, and the antennas themselves. It also includes the factor of free space path loss. You will take the knowledge you have gained of RF propagation and free space path loss and the information related to RF math, and use that to perform link budget calculations that result in a SOM.

When creating a financial budget, money management coaches often suggest to their clients that they should monitor how they are currently spending their money. Then they suggest that these individuals create a budget that documents this spending of money. The alternative would be to go ahead, and create a financial budget without any consideration for what are actually your expenses . You can see that the latter simply will not work. First, you have to know how much money you need to live and then you design your budget around that knowledge.

 Note: **Link budgets in wireless connections are a lot like financial budgets. You have to meet your needs regardless of what you want. Make sure you have the signal strength needed for the data rate desired.**

Similarly, in wireless LAN links, you will need to first determine the signal strength that is required at the receiving device and then figure out how you will accomplish this with your link budget. The first calculation you should perform in your link budget is to determine the minimum signal strength needed at the receiver. This is called the *receive sensitivity*. The receive sensitivity is not a single dBm rating, but it is a series of dBm ratings required to communicate at varying data rates.

For example, Table 5-2 shows the receive sensitivity scale for a particular device.

dBm Power Level	Data Rate
-94 dBm	1 Mbps
-93 dBm	2 Mbps
-92 dBm	5.5 Mbps
-86 dBm	6 Mbps
-86 dBm	9 Mbps
-90 dBm	11 Mbps
-86 dBm	12 Mbps
-86 dBm	18 Mbps
-84 dBm	24 Mbps
-80 dBm	36 Mbps
-75 dBm	48 Mbps
-71 dBm	54 Mbps

Table 5.2—Receive Sensitivity Table for a Device

There are actually two ways to think of the receive sensitivity; the absolute weakest signal the wireless radio can reliably receive, and the weakest signal the wireless radio can reliably receive at a specific data rate. The lowest number in dBm, which is -94 dBm in Table 5-2, is the weakest signal the radio can tolerate. This number is sometimes referenced as the receive sensitivity or the *absolute receive sensitivity*. In more accurate terminology, the receive sensitivity of a card is the complete series or system of sensitivity levels supported by the card.

The receive sensitivity ratings are determined by the vendors. They will place the radio in a specially constructed sheilded room and transmit RF signals of decreasing strength. As the RF signal strength is decreasing, the bit-error rate in the receiving radio is increasing. Once this bit-error rate reaches a vendor-defined rate, the power level in dBm is noted, and the radio is configured to switch down to the next standard data rate. This process continues until the lowest standard data rate for that 802.11-based device (1 or 6 Mbps) can no longer be achieved, and this dBm becomes the lowest receive sensitivity rating. In the end, a lower receive sensitivity rating is better, because it indicates that the client device can process a weaker signal.

The reason you need to know the receive sensitivity rating is that it is the first of your link budget calculations. The SOM is the amount of received signal strength relative to the client device's receive sensitivity. If you have a client device with a receive sensitivity of -94 dBm and the card is picking up the wireless signal at -65 dBm, the SOM is the difference between -94 dBm and -65 dBm. Therefore, you would use the following formula to calculate the link budget:

$$SOM = RS - S$$

Where S is the signal strength (the second link budget calculation used to determine the SOM) at the wireless client device and RS is the receive sensitivity of the client device. Plugging in our numbers looks like this:

$$SOM = (-94) - (-65)$$

The resulting SOM is 29 dBm. This means that the signal strength can weaken by 29 dBm, in theory, and the link can be maintained. There are many factors at play when RF signals are being transmitted, and this number, 29 dBm, will act as a good estimate. You may be able to maintain the link with a loss of 32 dBm, and you may lose the link with a loss of 25 dBm. The link budget is a good estimate and should not be taken as a guarantee for connectivity.

 TIP: **Think of the receive sensitivity rating of a wireless LAN adapter as its "emotional intelligence." The receive sensitivity determines how sensitive it is to the signals passing by it, much like a human's emotional intelligence level determines how sensitive he is of the signals put off by other humans (facial expressions, sighs, etc.).**

It is rare to calculate the link budget or SOM for indoor connections. This is because most indoor connections are not direct line-of-sight type connections, but instead they reflect and scatter all throughout the indoor environment. In fact, someone can move a filing cabinet and cause your signal strength to change. It can really be that fickle.

Outdoor links are the most common type of links where you will need to create a link budget and determine the SOM. A detailed link budget can be much more complex than that which has been discussed here. For example, it may include consideration for earth bulge, the type of terrain, and the local weather patterns. For this reason, some vendors provide link budget calculation utilities.

Consider an actual example of a link budget calculation. Figure 5.10 shows a site-to-site link being created across a distance of 200 meters with IEEE 802.11 bridges.

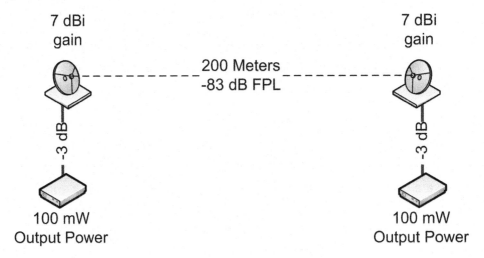

Figure 5.10—Sample Link Budget

Based on the output power of the bridge, the attenuation of the cables, the gain of the antennas, and the free space path loss, you can calculate the link budget since the receive sensitivity of both bridges is -94 dBm. The calculations are as follows:

Link Budget calculation #1: 100 mW = 20 dBm

Link Budget calculation #2: 20 dBm - 3 dB + 7 dBi - 83 dB = -59 dBm

Link Budget calculation #3: (-94 dBm) - (-59 dBm) = 35 dBm

SOM = 35 dBm

When you create outdoor bridge links, a fade margin is a practical requirement. Careful link budget calculations should be made to determine the SOM and then you should pad that budget. Not drastically, but pad the budget. The fade margin will give you two things; a more consistent link and a longer lasting link. Without the fade margin, you may notice that the link drops periodically in certain seasons of the year, or the link simply fails to work after several months or years (due to changes in foliage or other environmental factors). Padding the budget with a fade margin helps in creating a more durable link.

Because of the variableness of wireless links, it is not uncommon to "pad the budget" much like a project manager may do for "risk factors" in a project. The padding of the budget is needed because the weather does change, trees grow, and buildings are built. These factors, and others, can cause the signal to degrade over time. By including a few extra dB of strength in the required link budget, you can provide a link that will endure longer. The extra signal strength actually has a name, and it is *fade margin*.

Specific Use Cases and Vertical Markets

When implementing WLANs, it is important to consider specific use cases and the variances within vertical markets. A vertical market is a particular kind of industry or organization, such as healthcare, hospitality, or government deployments. This section provides quick guidance on some areas of importance for focus in specific use cases and vertical markets.

High-Density Design and Large Public Venues (LPV)

High density, very high density, and large public venue installations (like stadiums) require careful planning. Characteristics of high-density networks include:

- Many more APs with lower output power settings

- Implementation of solutions like band steering and load balancing to improve capacity

- Use of directional antennas in strategic locations to accommodate more APs

Healthcare

Healthcare deployments have the following characteristics:

- Requirements for stringent security to protect patient information

- Many mobile devices, including pagers, push-to-talk phones, VoIP handsets, and health devices

- Unusual building materials, such as lead lined walls

- More and more hospitals are providing guest wireless access

Education

Education deployments have the following characteristics:

- Government regulations related to content filtering

- Sometimes in old buildings with all walls of block or poured concrete

- Allowance of personal student devices on the network, in some instances

- Provision for iPads and laptops for student use

Retail

Retail deployments have the following characteristics:

- Barcode scanners used for inventory

- Shelving, creating unusual propagation patterns

- In some cases, guest access is desired

- Remote management and connectivity may be required

Hospitality

Hospitality deployments have the following characteristics:

- Require guest access, may be free or paid access

- May have sound proofing materials between rooms impeding propagation, in some instances

- Heavier capacity requirements than the past with modern savvy Wi-Fi users bringing laptops, tablets, and mobile phones

Outdoors

Outdoor deployments have the following characteristics:

- Less benefit from MIMO technologies in wide open areas

- Harder to restrain signals to smaller cell sizes

- Use of sector or directional antennas may accommodate outdoor networks better

- Ruggedized APs should be used

Public Hotspots

Public hotspots have the following characteristics:

- Guest users accessing the network

- May require a captive portal for pay processing

- Should disable client-to-client communications, when possible

- Should include a disclaimer of responsibility/liability

Government Deployments

Government deployments have the following characteristics:

- Must comply with government orders and regulations

- Often have strict security requirements

- May constrain upgrades for several months or years, while awaiting new orders that comply with new hardware and software

- May have long approval time windows

Chapter Review

In this chapter, you learned about advanced WLAN design scenarios and explored bridging, remote offices, and specific use case scenarios.

Facts to Remember

Be sure to remember the following facts as you prepare for the CWDP certification, and be sure you can explain the details related to them:

- When implementing WAN connections, consider the control, management, and data plan functions of the WLAN solution.

- VPNs may be used with split tunnel configurations so that local Internet connections pass directly to the Internet.

- Authentication service decisions often include local RADIUS, RADIUS proxy, or remote RADIUS.

- Mesh access networks are implemented to provide client access to the network or Internet.

- Mesh backhaul solutions are used to provide a connection from one network to another.

- When designing bridge links, alignment is essential and must be considered both horizontally and vertically.

- To accomplish the desired data rate, you must determine the receive sensitivity of the bridge.

- With the receive sensitivity data, a link budget can be calculated.

- It is essential to consider unique or applicable characteristics and issues in vertical markets and specific use case scenarios.

Chapter 6:

WLAN Deployment

In this chapter:

- Device Staging

- Implementing Channel Plans

- Configuring the Infrastructure

- Installing Different WLAN Architectures

Objectives:

4.1 Perform device staging according to organizational policies and design recommendations and installation devices according to vendor specifications and the WLAN design.

4.2 Implement channel plans according to the design recommendations including manual channel assignments through controllers, cloud solutions, and autonomous configurations. Configure automated channel management features according to common operational method provided by major vendors.

4.3 Configure infrastructure devices where necessary to support the WLAN including routers, DHCP servers, DNS services, and switches.

4.4 Understand the basic installation procedures used for different WLAN architectures including controller-based, cloud-managed, distributed, autonomous, and virtual controller.

WLAN deployment is not specifically a part of the design process; however, the WLAN designer may be called upon to perform the actual installation designed. For this reason, the designer should be aware of more than the capabilities of a system, but of the actual methods used for installation. Key issues include device staging, implementing channel plans according to the design, configuring the infrastructure when needed, and installing different WLAN architectures, such as controller-based and cloud-managed solutions.

Device Staging

Device staging is the process used to prepare devices for deployment. It is the collection of preliminary tasks performed before placing a device in production. Device staging is not unique to WLANs. It is used for desktop and laptop computers, tablets and mobile phones, servers and network appliances, and any other device placed onto the network. This section will focus on device staging for APs and WLAN controllers, which are the two primary devices deployed in WLANs other than the WLAN clients themselves.

Staging Policies and Design Recommendations

Staging policies can be considered from two perspectives: pre-staging for remote deployment and staging for local deployment. Pre-staging for remote deployment occurs when you configure a controller or AP for use at a different location. In a staging lab you can simulate the remote IP network so that everything can be configured, appropriately. Then, the device is shipped to the remote location for plug-and-play operation. This policy for deployment can be useful when few technical employees work at the remote locations. It is commonly used in retail as well as other distributed organizations.

Staging for local deployment involves the same basic process, except a device may be configured with all required settings except IP addresses for the target subnet and other subnet-specific settings as the device will likely be installed by a skilled technician who can configure those settings, as needed.

Staging policies should define the categories of configuration items that must be configured or modified before a device is connected to the active network. These categories can include:

- Default usernames and passwords
- Default IP addresses
- Default security settings
- Default operational services

The design recommendations play a significant role in staging. The design recommendation will define security settings and operational services. For example, it may specify that WPA2-PSK be used for some mobile device requiring it. Therefore, an SSID for this configuration must be created. It may also specify that WPA2-Enterprise be used for standard access. Another SSID will be created for this configuration. The point is that the design recommendation will drive the configuration options chosen during device staging.

An additional consideration for staging is that of cloud-managed solutions. With autonomous APs, staging occurs with each AP. With controller-based APs, staging occurs in the controller, and then APs are connected to the network and configured from the controller. With cloud-managed solutions, staging occurs in the cloud management interface.

A typical cloud-managed solution will provide containers or policies used to configure networks and devices. The devices can be assigned to containers or policies before they are ever connected to the LAN. When connected to the LAN, the device gains an IP configuration set from the DHCP server and then connects to the cloud across the Internet. Once connected to the cloud, the AP is configured according to the container or policy in which it is placed. As you can see, cloud-managed solutions are similar to controllers in this respect in that the staging occurs outside the AP but directly and automatically configures the AP as soon as it is connected.

Installing Devices per Vendor Specifications

Vendors often provide installation guidance that can be useful in the staging process. The documentation will remind you of items that should be changed in order to comply with your internal security or performance settings. Figure 6.1 shows the configuration guide for a Cisco 3600 series AP.

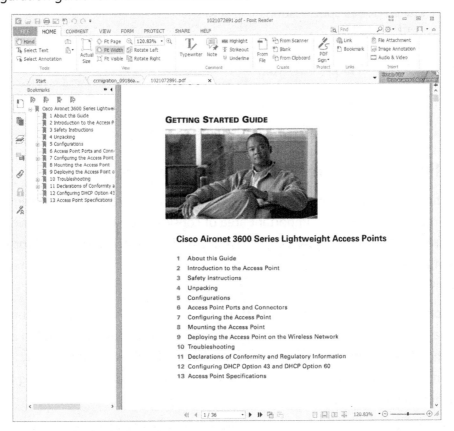

Figure 6.1—Configuration Guide for Cisco AP

Key areas of importance are the safety instructions, unpacking, and configuration. Guides such as this should be read carefully, particularly in large-scale deployments to be certain that no key configuration requirements have been missed.

Additional areas of importance in vendor specifications or installation guides include:

- Mounting instructions

- Troubleshooting guidance

- Infrastructure configuration requirements

- Detailed device specifications

    o Output power

    o Frequencies used

    o Antenna characteristics

    o AC or PoE power requirements

Installing Devices per Design Recommendation

In addition to vendor recommendations, devices should be installed according to the design recommendation. An important area of consideration here is the physical mounting location and orientation of the APs. An AP installed in a different location or orientation than that required by the design recommendation will result in a very different RF propagation pattern.

It is important to remember that, even though most indoor APs rely only on internal antennas, those antennas still have a propagation pattern. They may function best when the AP is mounted on the ceiling or the wall, but they will certainly only function in the method intended by the design if they are mounted according to the design recommendation.

APs should also be configured with the appropriate power settings based on the design recommendation. The design may call for the use of Radio Resource Management (RRM) with constraints on maximum power levels, but even if that is the case it is important to configure the APs (or controllers) to accommodate that design specification. The next section will address configuring channel plans, which is performed by configuring channels on APs, including power settings, or configuring RRM on controllers, including maximum and possibly minimum power settings.

Implementing Channel Plans

During the design process, APs are placed either physically or virtually in the environment and channels for 2.4 GHz and 5 GHz are selected with output power settings chosen to provide the coverage desired. The WLAN installer must configure the APs according to this channel plan so that the implementation complies with the design. This section provides an overview of the processes used to assign channels in the three primary architectures: controller-based, cloud-managed, and autonomous.

Manual Channel Assignments

When managing APs through the controller, two primary options exist: automatic channel management or manual channel configuration. Figure 6.2 shows manual channel configuration for HP APs through the HP controller.

 Note: **In Figure 6.2, the Channel setting is currently set to Automatic. By clicking the drop-down box, the WLAN implementer can choose the desired channel based on restrictions in the regulatory domain**

Figure 6.2 shows a dual-band AP with a 2.4 GHz and a 5 GHz radio. In most systems, you can use manual channel assignments on one band and automatic on the other, if you desire. Some prefer to use an automatic channel assignment in only one band. For example, you may manually assign channels in 5 GHz, but allow for automatic channel and power settings in 2.4 GHz where more interference is likely to occur.

Figure 6.3 shows the configuration of AP channels in the Aerohive Hive Manager cloud solutions interface. As you can see, the configuration interface is much the same as a controller. The difference is that a controller may update the AP immediately, but many cloud-managed systems only update the AP when you push the configuration to the AP.

 Note: **It is important to remember that the 5 GHz band is quickly becoming utilized in ways not seen in the past. For example, HD video devices often operate there as well as other non-802.11 devices.**

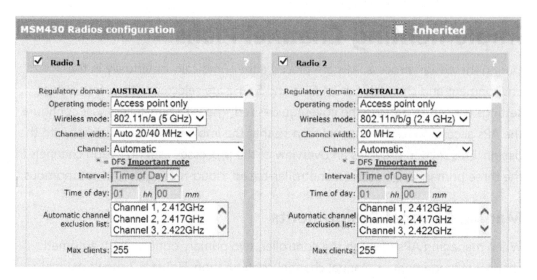

Figure 6.2—Manual Channel Configuration—Controller

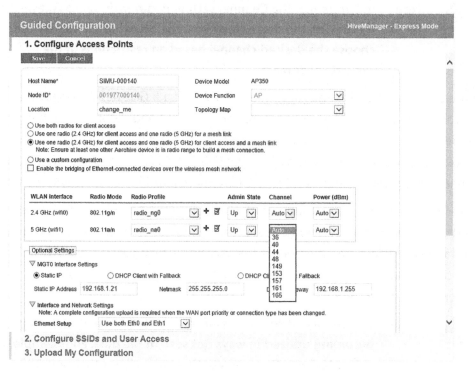

Figure 6.3—Manual Channel Configuration—Cloud Solutions

When using autonomous configuration, the AP is directly configured. Configuration may be performed via a command-line interface (CLI), a Web-based GUI, or a management utility.

Figure 6.4 shows the configuration of a Cisco WAP371 AP using the Web-based management interface.

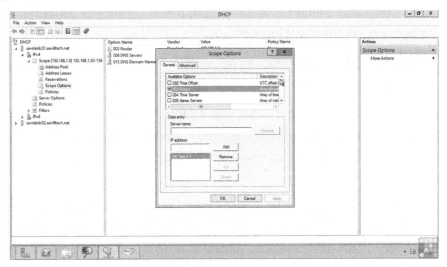

Figure 6.4—Managing DHCP Scopes on Windows Server 2012

EXAM MOMENT: Many APs support protocol capture. In some instances, you must configure the AP to the channel and channel-width that you wish to capture. Only then can you begin capturing 802.11 frames using the AP.

Manual channel assignment is time consuming, but it provides the WLAN designer and administrator with the greatest control over channel usage. Automatic channel assignment is addressed next.

Automated Channel Management

Automated channel management, also called Radio Resource Management (RRM), automatically configures the channels and output power settings of APs based on feedback provided to the WLAN controller. The general process is that APs provide scanning feedback of what they hear at their locations to the controller. The controller takes this information and makes decisions about how to best configure each AP. Additional features may be available due to the use of RRM, such as:

- **Coverage hole mitigation**—if a client is remaining connected at a very low data rate, the controller may determine that the client is in an area with a weak signal and, therefore, adjust output power settings of surrounding APs to better cover the client location.

- **Down AP mitigation**—when an AP is offline, the controller can increase the output power of nearby APs to make up for the loss of the down AP.

The primary benefit of RRM is in the fact that it can adjust for changes in the environment. For example, if someone installed a row of metal filing cabinets, it will drastically change propagation patterns in the environment. This may result in eventual adjustments of RRM.

In most RRM or automated channel management implementations, you can define when analysis should occur. For example, you can configure it to occur hourly, daily, or weekly. In very stable environments, weekly analysis is sufficient. In highly dynamic environments, like warehousing and shipping and receiving, more frequent analysis may be required.

The information gathered by RRM solutions varies by vendor, but commonly includes:

- Channel utilization (sometimes called traffic load or throughput)
- Noise
- Interference (typically includes both Wi-Fi ACI and non-Wi-Fi energy detect)
- Coverage (measured by RSSI received from clients)
- APs detected in the area

With this gathered information, the controller or cloud-management solution can dynamically configure the environment to work with or around detected issues. For example, it can move an AP to a channel where fewer APs are seen or where channel utilization is much lower.

Actions that can be taken by an RRM solution include:

- Adjusting transmit power

- Changing channels

- Monitoring radio resources

EXAM MOMENT: In many RRM implementations, APs go off channel for a period of time, typically less than 100 ms, to monitor other channels for noise and interference.

Configuring the Infrastructure

A WLAN will not work without the proper supporting infrastructure. Most wired networks will already provide the infrastructure services needed by a WLAN. In new installations of wired and wireless networks together, the infrastructure should be implemented to support both. This section describes common configuration actions required on routers, switches, DHCP servers, and DNS servers to support WLANs.

Configuring Routers

Wired routers are used to interconnect network segments. Small networks may have only a single router between the network and the Internet. Large networks may have hundreds of routers distributed across dozens of locations. These routers include logic for directing IP traffic to the intended destinations, but they often contain logic that prevents specific traffic or only allows specific traffic through. This logic is often implemented as access control lists (ACLs). An important part of configuring routers for WLANs is ensuring the passage of WLAN-related protocols such as LWAPP, CAPWAP, RADIUS, and LDAP.

LWAPP and CAPWAP are tunneling protocols used between the APs and controllers. The 802.11 frames are sent through the tunnel to the controller for processing unless distributed forwarding is available. When distributed forwarding is used, 802.11 data frames are processed and forwarded at the APs and management and control information is processed at the controllers through the tunnels. To ensure LWAPP and CAPWAP support in the routers, be sure to enable UDP ports 12222 and 12223 (LWAPP) and 5246 and 5247 (CAPWAP).

RADIUS is likely to be implemented in any large enterprise network in which a new WLAN or upgraded WLAN is being installed. In such scenarios, configuring the routers for RADIUS operations is not likely to be required. If RADIUS has not been used previously, the ports used for RADIUS authentication and accounting should be enabled in the routers. UDP 1812 is used for authentication, and 1813 is used for accounting in modern RADIUS servers. Older RADIUS servers may use 1645 and 1646 for authentication and accounting respectively.

LDAP is a directory access protocol implemented in Microsoft, Novell, and Linux systems. The well-known TCP and UDP ports for LDAP are 389.

 Note: **While the well-known ports have been listed for common protocols used in WLAN installations, it is important to remember that ports can sometimes be modified by administrators. Always verify that the configuration is using a standard port for the protocol, particularly if communications are not working.**

Configuring Switches

Two important configuration options should be made on switches to which APs connect: VLANs and PoE settings. When the SSID gets its VLAN from the switch port, the port must be configured to participate in that VLAN. Most APs configure VLANs internally, but it is not uncommon to see the AP/SSID receiving its VLAN from the switch port configuration.

PoE settings must also be appropriately configured. Some switches allow you to choose between 802.3af and 802.3at on a port. They also allow you to enable or disable PoE for the port. Ensure that the switches are configured with the appropriate switch port settings where APs are connected.

Configuring DHCP

DHCP configuration is important. First, the DHCP server should be configured to provide IP addresses sufficiently for the WLAN. A very common problem with WLANs is DHCP pool exhaustion. In such cases, the user sees a connection but is often told that the Internet is not available or that the connection is not working properly. Of course, the blame is always placed on the WLAN, even though the actual problem is with the DHCP server. Figure 6.4 shows the management of DHCP scopes on the popular Windows Server platform.

Additionally, DHCP servers may be configured to specify Option 43 to point to controllers. This DHCP configuration setting allows APs to find the controllers for configuration and firmware. While APs may use other methods, this is one of the most efficient.

Configuring DNS

DNS is used to resolve hostnames to IP addresses. In WLANs, this is a method of determining the controller IP address for APs. They can resolve a specific hostname, that comes preconfigured in the APs and use that IP address to reach the controller. This is an alternative to DHCP option 43. Figure 6.5 shows the management of DNS on Windows Server 2012.

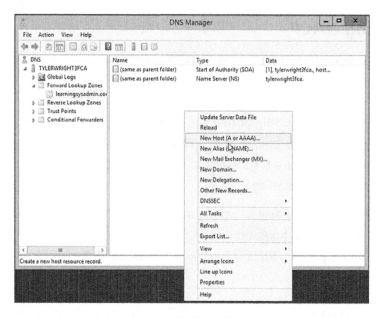

Figure 6.5—Managing DNS on Windows Server 2012

Installing Different WLAN Architectures

The CWDP should know how to install different WLAN architectures. The actual installation is not part of the design process; however, the CWDP may be called upon to assist in or even perform the installation of the designed network. In this section, you will review the installation processes for controller-based, cloud-managed, distributed, virtual controller, and autonomous architectures.

Controller-Based Installation Process

When using a WLAN controller, the first step of the installation process is to make one or more controllers active on the network. The controller can be mounted in a rack-mount system with switches and routers and typically is mounted in this way in enterprise deployments. Additionally, controllers can be desktop mounted, but this is more common in smaller WLAN deployments for branch offices or small businesses using controllers that support only 3–10 APs.

The next step is to power on the controller and either run a wizard for initial configuration or manually configure all settings. Wizards typically include settings like the following:

- Name for the controller
- Administrative account information
- IP address used for management
- VLAN settings for management
- Mobility, roaming, RF, or AP group names
- Network names (SSIDs)
- RADIUS server settings
- Radio settings (for 2.4 GHz and 5 GHz)
- RRM settings
- NTP server settings

After configuring minimum settings, per the baseline configuration specified in the WLAN design, APs may be connected to the network to discover the controller. The APs will be configured to support the SSIDs and radio settings configure in the controller profiles.

Cloud-Managed Installation Process

Installing a cloud-managed network is similar to a controller-based network, with the primary exception being that the configuration of the networks and APs takes place in an off-premise system—the cloud. As an example, the Meraki WLAN solution is cloud based. The steps to install a Meraki network include:

1. Configure the network in the cloud dashboard.

2. Prepare firmware upgrades for selected APs.

3. Ensure the firewall settings are appropriate for the APs to locate the cloud.

4. Provide for AP IP addresses (either with DHCP or static addresses).

5. Mount, Ethernet connect, and power the APs.

6. Verify the power LED is solid green (no clients connected) or blue (clients connected). When flashing blue, the firmware is updating

7. Connect to the WLAN and verify network functionality.

Distributed Architecture Installation Process

Distributed architecture networks are often cloud managed. Therefore, the installation process is the same as a cloud-managed network. The difference is in operations. If the cloud connection fails, no local network functions will be impacted during normal operations. In most cloud-managed networks, this ability to continue operations is also true today.

Virtual Controller Installation Process

Virtual controller networks use one of the APs as a WLAN controller. Such solutions are available from Aruba Networks as a leading example. Cisco offers a virtual controller as a VM solution running in VMware and a FlexConnect Mobility Express in-AP controller that is similar in features to the VM solution. This section will focus on the in-AP solution, like that available from Aruba Networks and the Cisco Mobility Express solution.

Many virtual controller solutions provide an all-in-one configuration. For example, they may include RADIUS servers and captive portals internal to the virtual controller so that such features can still be utilized in the, typically, smaller networks that deploy in-AP virtual controllers.

The basic installation steps for a virtual controller installation include:

1. Stage the first AP.

2. Mount, Ethernet connect and power the AP.

3. Run the configuration wizard.

4. Configure the controller settings much like a hardware controller.

5. Configure the networks.

6. Configure additional settings you desire.

7. Stage, mount Ethernet, connect and power on additional APs.

EXAM MOMENT: Some vendors will not allow a virtual controller on the same network as a hardware controller. When a hardware controller is used, it would conflict with virtual controllers.

Autonomous Installation Process

The autonomous installation process is performed on each AP individually, unless a centralized management solution is used to push configurations down to the APs. In the latter case, the APs are still considered autonomous and do perform all WLAN functions locally, including authentication and data processing.

As an example of the autonomous installation process, the next several pages document the initial setup and configuration of a Cisco WAP371 AP, which is a good 802.11ac 3x3:3 AP for lab use.

Like most APs, the Cisco WAP371 can be configured in a Web interface accessed by Internet Explorer 7.0 or later, Chrome 5.0 or later, Firefox 3.0 or later, or Safari 3.0 or later. Additionally, the AP uses PoE for power, though a wall outlet power source may be purchased.

Once connected to power, the guide in Figure 6.6 can be used to troubleshoot using the LEDs.

Label	Activity	Description
Power	Off	The WAP371 is out of power.
	Solid (Green)	The Cisco WAP371 is powered on, booting, or in normal operation with PoE.
	Solid (Amber)	The Cisco WAP371 is powered on, booting, or in normal operation with External Power Adapter
	Flashing (Green or Amber)	The Cisco WAP371 is upgrading the firmware, or is acquiring an IPv4 or IPv6 address.
	Solid (Red)	The Cisco WAP371 fails to boot with both firmware images.
WLAN	Off	Wireless is disabled, for both 2.4 GHz and 5 GHz.
	Solid	Wireless is enabled.
	Green	Concurrent mode enabled.
	Amber	5 GHz is in use.
	Blue	2.4 GHz is in use.
	Flashing	The WAP371 is transmitting or receiving data.
LAN	Off	No Ethernet link.
	Solid Green	GE Ethernet link is active.
	Solid Amber	FE Ethernet link is active.
	Flashing	The WAP 371 is transmitting or receiving data.

Figure 6.6—Cisco WAP371 LED Guide

If configured in a staging environment without a DHCP server, after 60 seconds the WAP371 will fall back to a stating address of 192.168.1.245. When DHCP is available, you must determine the assigned IP address either using a network scanner or by viewing the DHCP leases, if you have access to the DHCP server.

When the IP address is known, connect to that address using a supported Web browser. The Web logon screen will be displayed, and the default username and password is cisco and cisco as shown in Figure 6.7.

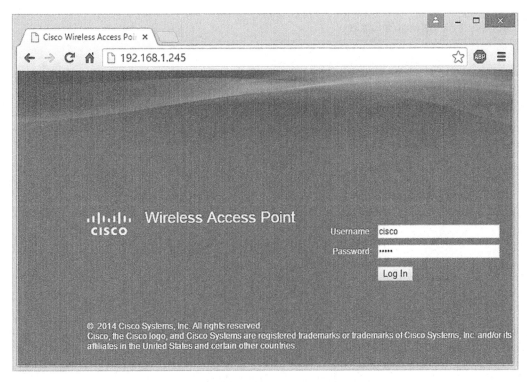

Figure 6.7—Logging onto the Cisco WAP371 AP

The WAP371, like many autonomous APs today, launches an AP setup wizard, by default, shown in Figure 6.8.

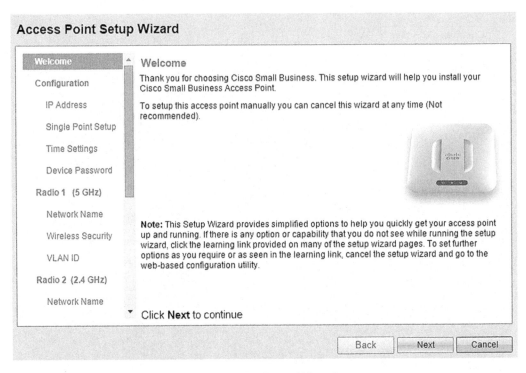

Access Point Setup Wizard

Welcome	**Welcome**
Configuration	Thank you for choosing Cisco Small Business. This setup wizard will help you install your Cisco Small Business Access Point.
IP Address	To setup this access point manually you can cancel this wizard at any time (Not recommended).
Single Point Setup	
Time Settings	
Device Password	
Radio 1 (5 GHz)	
Network Name	**Note:** This Setup Wizard provides simplified options to help you quickly get your access point up and running. If there is any option or capability that you do not see while running the setup wizard, click the learning link provided on many of the setup wizard pages. To set further options as you require or as seen in the learning link, cancel the setup wizard and go to the web-based configuration utility.
Wireless Security	
VLAN ID	
Radio 2 (2.4 GHz)	
Network Name	Click **Next** to continue

Back   Next   Cancel

Figure 6.8—Setup Wizard

Figure 6.8 shows the options that could be configured through the wizard interface. These options include:

- AP IP address
- Use of single point setup (which allows multiple WAP371 APs to be configured based on the configuration of a single AP)
- Time settings
- Logon password
- 5 GHz radio settings
- 2.4 GHZ radio settings
- Captive portal settings

The WAP371 is sold as a small business AP, and it provides configuration options accordingly, which include features like captive portals.

If the wizard is cancelled, the AP presents a change password screen, as it is a best practice to modify the password. After the password is changed, you must log on again using the new password. If you decide you want to run the AP setup wizard again later, you can click the link that reads Run Setup Wizard.

The four major configuration options of any autonomous AP are the radio, the wireless networks, the LAN connection, and security. To configure the radios on the WAP371 AP, click the Wireless link on the left side. In most cases, the 5 GHz and 2.4 GHz radios are configured separately. When configuring the radio, an important setting is output power. In many cases, the design specification will call for a specific mW or dBm value, but the configuration interface may use different terminology. For example, in Figure 6.9 the interface allows for Full (100%), High (50%), Medium (25%), or Low (12%). There is no information in the interface or in the built-in help that tells you the actual mW or dBm values of these settings. The reason for this is often simply that the actual output power will vary depending on the PHY used. In 2.4 GHz for example, the WAP371 may use the HT, ERP, or HR/DSSS PHYs. When this AP uses the HR/DSSS or ERP PHY, it will have a maximum output power of 17 dBm +/- 1.5 dBm. When it uses the HT PHY, it will have a maximum output power of 17 dBm if a 20 MHz channel is used, but a maximum output power of 14 dBm if a 40 MHz channel is used. Therefore, when a 40 MHz channel is used, the Low setting would be a different output power level than when a 20 MHz channel is used.

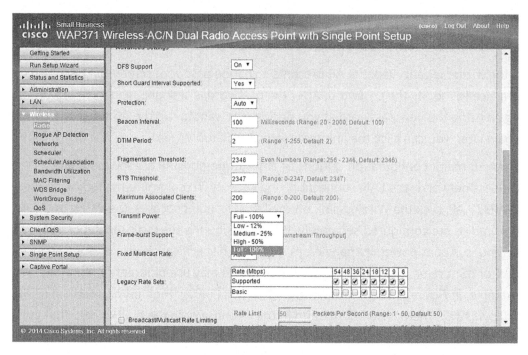

Figure 6.9—WAP371 Power Settings

To meet the design specifications, you must know these details about the chosen AP.
Figure 6.10 shows the output power specifications for the WAP371 AP.

Transmitted output power	2.4 GHz
	• 802.11b: 17.0 +/- 1.5 dBm @ CH6, all rates
	• 802.11g: 17.0 +/- 1.5 dBm @ CH6, 6 Mbps
	• 802.11g: 15.0 +/- 1.5 dBm @ CH6, 54 Mbps
	• 802.11n(HT20): 17.0 +/- 1.5 dBm @ CH6, MCS0
	• 802.11n(HT20): 14.0 +/- 1.5 dBm @ CH6, MCS15
	• 802.11n(HT40): 12.0 +/- 1.5 dBm @ CH6, all rates
	5 GHz UNII-1 (5150 to 5250 MHz)
	• 802.11a: 10 +/- 1.5 dBm @ all rates
	• 802.11ac(HT20): 10 +/- 1.5 dBm @ all rates
	• 802.11ac(HT40): 11 +/- 1.5 dBm @ all rates
	• 802.11ac(HT80): 11 +/- 1.5 dBm @ all rates
	5 GHz UNII-2 (5250 to 5350 MHz)/UNII-2 Extended (5470 to 5725 MHz)
	• 802.11a: 16.0 +/- 1.5 dBm @ 6 Mbps
	• 802.11a: 15.0 +/- 1.5 dBm @ 54 Mbps
	• 802.11ac(HT20): 16.0 +/- 1.5 dBm @ MCS0
	• 802.11ac(HT20): 13.0 +/- 1.5 dBm @ MCS9
	• 802.11ac(HT40): 18.0 +/- 1.5 dBm @ MCS0
	• 802.11ac(HT40): 13.0 +/- 1.5 dBm @ MCS9
	802.11ac(HT80): 13.0 +/- 1.5 dBm @ all rates
	5 GHz UNII-3 (5725 to 5850 MHz)
	• 802.11a: 18.0 +/- 1.5 dBm @ 6 Mbps
	• 802.11a: 15.0 +/- 1.5 dBm @ 54 Mbps
	• 802.11ac(HT20): 18.0 +/- 1.5 dBm @ MCS0
	• 802.11ac(HT20): 13.0 +/- 1.5 dBm @ MCS9
	• 802.11ac(HT40): 18.0 +/- 1.5 dBm @ MCS0
	• 802.11ac(HT40): 13.0 +/- 1.5 dBm @ MCS9
	• 802.11ac(HT80): 18.0 +/- 1.5 dBm @ MCS0
	• 802.11ac(HT80): 13.0 +/- 1.5 dBm @ MCS9

Figure 6.10—Output Power Specifications for the WAP371 AP

Additional settings that should be configured based on the design specifications include the wireless networks. Figure 6.11 shows the networks configuration area in the WAP371 interface.

Several settings should be considered for the wireless networks. These include the SSID and security settings that should be configured based on the sepcification. Vendor-specific settings should also be considered, such as channel isolation and band steering, as seen in Figure 6.11. Channel isolation, when enabled, disallows client STAs to communicate with each other through the AP. They can only communicate with the network infrastructure. This setting should nearly always be enabled for guest and public networks.

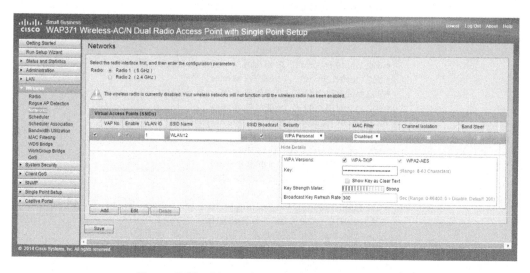

Figure 6.11—Networks—Configuration Screen

Band steer is used to drive traffic to the 5 GHz band. It must be enabled for both radios in the WAP371, but once it is enabled it will steer dual-band clients to the 5 GHz band, which is typically far less congested than the 2.4 GHz band.

APs from different vendors will have very different interfaces, but the same basic settings can be configured and should be defined in the design specification. These settings include SSIDs, output power settings, channel settings, security settings, and vendor-specific features.

Chapter Review

In this chapter, you learned about the basic processes used in WLAN installation. These steps were covered in your CWNA studies as well and have been reviewed here as a step between WLAN design and WLAN validation.

Facts to Remember

Be sure to remember the following facts as you prepare for the CWDP certification, and be sure that you can explain the details related to them:

- Device staging should be performed according to organizational policies.

- Design recommendations or specifications may define usernames and passwords, IP addresses, security settings, and operational services among other items.

- Vendor specifications will include guidance on mounting, troubleshooting, and configuration in general.

- Implementing channel plans involves mounting the APs in the right locations and configuring both channels and power settings appropriately.

- Automatic channel management (also referred to as RRM) can provide coverage hole and down AP mitigations.

- APs often go off channel in RRM implementations to scan other channels for reporting.

- Routers should be configured to allow LWAPP, CAPWAP, RADIUS, and LDAP communications through.

- Switches should be configured for PoE and VLAN assignments.

- DHCP services should be provided and configured to avoid scope exhaustion.

- DNS servers are often configured to resolve hostnames for the location of WLAN controllers by APs.

Chapter 7:

Design Validation

In this chapter:

- Post-Installation Site Surveys

- Design Failure Remediation

- Validation Tools

- Troubleshooting Procedures

Objectives:

5.1   Identify the purpose and methods of post-installation site surveys, including application validation, coverage assurance, capacity requirements, and load handling.

5.2   Describe remediation processes used when validation fails, including channel adjustments, output power adjustments, installing additional hardware, removing hardware, and changing additional configuration options.

5.3   Understand and use the appropriate tools in the validation process, including spectrum analyzers, protocol analyzers, throughput testers, and documentation.

5.4   Understand and implement methods for troubleshooting coverage problems, capacity problems, security configuration issues, roaming delays, low-data-rate clients, QoS failure, and client connectivity issues.

The design validation process involves many tools used during the pre-design site survey. Tools include site survey software, protocol analyzers, spectrum analyzers, and throughput testers. The key skills of a WLAN designer, in the design validation phase, include post-installation site surveys, design failure remediation, use of validation tools, and general troubleshooting procedures. This chapter provides information for all four areas.

Post-Installation Site Surveys

The post-installation site survey, also called a validation survey, is performed to ensure that the implemented WLAN meets the design specifications, and more important, the business and user requirements established during requirements analysis. Several areas are tested during a validation survey, including:

- Coverage assurance
- Application validation
- Capacity requirements
- Load handling

Coverage Assurance

Coverage assurance is more than simply verifying that the WLAN signal can be seen from everywhere that the WLAN needs to be available for use. It becomes more complex because the coverage must be proper coverage and not simply the presence of signal.

Proper coverage is measured in signal strength (dB or RSSI). For example, your design requirements may have specified that all clients can connect with -65 dB signal at all required locations and that all required locations have at least two visible APs at all times. With such a design specification, the validation survey should be used to verify the signal strength and AP presence coverage requirements.

Site survey software can be used for this process. To enable channel scanning (you need only scan the known used channels, for example 1, 6, and 11, if you are only interested in validating your APs), and then slowly move through the building while indicating your location on the floor plan. When you are finished with this process, you can generate appropriate heat maps that show coverage with signal strengths and available APs at various locations. Figure 7.1 shows such a heat map in AirMagnet Survey Pro.

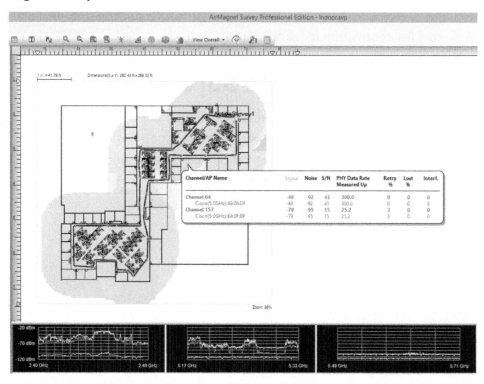

Figure 7.1—AirMagnet Survey Pro with Signal Strength and Available APs

Application Validation

In addition to coverage assurance, application validation should be performed. This requires an active site survey or the simple use of the application. With an active site survey, data can be transmitted using protocols that are utilized by the application (UDP or TCP) and by simulating application specifications (packet sizes, number of packets per second, etc.). Figure 7.2 shows AirMagnet Survey Pro with iPerf statistics that are helpful in application validation.

Another method of application validation is the actual use of the application. For example, if VoIP is to be used and the handsets are available, the validator can place a call using the handset and then roam throughout the area to ensure proper VoIP operations and roaming support. If call quality suffers on a consistent basis, a QoS or interference problem is likely occurring. If calls are dropped, an interference or roaming problem may be occurring.

The applications are the driver behind the WLAN. If the applications are not working, the WLAN is not working—this is the perspective of the users. For this reason, application validation is one of the most important steps in the validation survey process.

EXAM MOMENT: Application validation can be performed using site survey software, throughput testers, and the actual applications themselves.

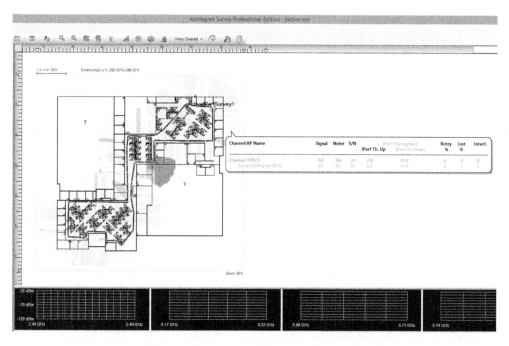

Figure 7.2—AirMagnet Survey Pro with iPerf Statistics

Capacity Requirements

Capacity requirements can be validated theoretically and actually. To validate capacity requirements theoretically, you can simply verify the WLAN design in implementation has minimal CCI and ACI, sufficient APs in each location, and proper signal strength to provide the required data rates. To validate capacity requirements actually, you can perform simulated throughput tests that load the network as if the expected number of users were connecting and using the applications for which the design was targeted.

Issues that prevent proper capacity include:

- Improper channel configuration

- Improper output power settings

- Insufficient hardware

- Too many APs using a given channel near each other

- Disabled features, such as frame aggregation and band steering

Load Handling

Load handling is closely related to capacity. Capacity is often thought of as the number of users that can connect to the network, but it is actually the number of users that can connect to the network and perform their needed functions. Therefore, load handling is a subset of capacity.

Load handling can be tested with throughput testers, but this does not always reveal the truth about the load capabilities of the WLAN. For example, when using a throughput tester with one client connected to an AP, you are proving the throughput that AP can handle when it does not have to perform processing related to any other clients. As soon as additional clients are introduced (and many APs are marketed stating they can handle 400 or more connections per AP), the throughput will be impacted. This is, in part, due to management overhead of the WLAN, but it is also, in part, due to the extra processing the AP must perform in order to handle all of the clients that are connected.

The ideal load handling test is performed using multiple clients. For example, if you test the throughput of a WLAN (given a single AP with multiple stations) with 2 connected clients and it provides 143 Mbps TCP throughput in aggregate, but this drops to 139 Mbps TCP throughput in aggregate with 5 connected clients and then to 137 Mbps TCP throughput with 10 connected clients, you can assume that the throughput will continue to drop as clients are connected. From this analysis, you can determine the maximum number of clients you can have connected to an AP and still achieve the desired capacity.

 Note: **Applications, such as PureLoad, can be used to simulate real world applications. They are best at testing the ability of a server to handle multiple clients, but if the client is run from a wireless station, it can provide valuable feedback on the WLAN's capabilities as well.**

Design Failure Remediation

The result of the validation survey will often be the discovery of problems in the WLAN. Design failure remediation is used to resolve these problems. Problems often occur in relation to coverage, capacity, and functionality. This section provides descriptions of the common remediation actions used to resolve such problems. The later section, Troubleshooting Procedures, will identify how to determine which of these actions are required to resolve the problem.

Channel Adjustments

When capacity or load handling suffers, channel adjustments, output power adjustments, and the installation of additional hardware may be required. Channel adjustments include both configuring the appropriate channels and setting the proper channel widths.

The main driving force behind a validation survey is to verify that the network was implemented according to the plan and that the plan actually results in the desired operational state. If the wrong channel is used on an AP, it can cause unneeded CCI or ACI. The channel plan in the design specification should be followed, but due to propagation behaviors, problems may occur even when the design specification is followed.

The wrong channel widths can also be problematic. For example, if the channel plan called for the use of 20 MHz channels throughout and a few APs were accidentally configured to use 40 MHz channels, these APs are very likely to cause interference (CCI and/or ACI) with other cells. Channel widths can be discovered using site survey software or protocol analyzers.

Output Power Adjustments

Just as the proper channel and channel width must be used, the proper output power settings must be used. When output power settings are too high, excessive CCI and ACI are the result. When output power settings are too low, coverage holes are created. As stated in Chapter 6, to set output power settings appropriately, you must know how the vendor represents the power settings in the configuration interfaces. At times, the interface shows a percentage of output power and you must know the maximum power setting to configure it appropriately. At other times, the interface may simply show levels of power, such as 1, 2, 3, 4, and so on. These power levels are not actual mW or dBm values. You must know what these levels represent in the specific vendor APs implemented.

> **EXAM MOMENT:** It is important to map the configuration interface settings to actual power levels if you are to configure an AP appropriately. Otherwise, your configuration actions are nothing more than guesswork.

Installing Additional Hardware

It is possible that the validation survey will reveal that too few APs have been installed. This can be determined when insufficient capacity is provided or when coverage holes exist. When one of these exists, the complex process of adding an AP must be performed. You must consider the following questions when adding an AP to the design:

- On what channel will the AP operate?

- What channel width should be used?

- What output power settings should be used?

- Must any other APs be reconfigured to allow for the new AP?

- Is Ethernet connectivity available at the location?

- How will the AP be powered?

Removing Hardware

In other scenarios, it is actually required to remove APs. In some cases, an over-engineered WLAN will result in excessive CCI and/or ACI, and performance can be improved by removing some APs. When an AP is removed, it must be verified that coverage holes have not been created.

Additional Configuration Options

Several additional configuration options may be required and determined from the validation survey. These include the following:

- Correcting infrastructure service misconfigurations like DHCP options, DNS resolution and router settings.

- Enabling or disabling features like band steering and load balancing.

- Enabling enhanced features of modern PHYs, like frame fragmentation, frame aggregation, and short guard intervals (SGIs).

- Swapping out antennas to better provide coverage.

- Enabling or disabling RRM features.

Validation Tools

The primary tools used in validation are site survey tools, (covered in detail in preceding chapters) and spectrum and protocol analyzers. This section covers spectrum and protocol analyzers as used in the validation process, as well as throughput testers.

Spectrum Analyzers

Spectrum analyzers are useful in validation surveys for the location of new interference sources and to measure duty cycle on a channel. High-duty cycles can be a predictor of future load handling problems, or they may indicate a current load handling issue on the RF side. Figure 7.3 shows the AirMagnet Spectrum XT report viewing duty cycle.

AirMagnet Spectrum XT

WiFi Spectrum Environment Overview

2.4 GHz

This report provides information on channels 1, 2, 3, 4, 5, 6, 7, 8, 9, 10, 11, 12, 13, 14 operating in the frequency range 2.402 GHz to 2.842 GHz. The Maximum and the Average Power represents the maximum and average power levels across all channels in the 2.4GHz Band. This table also provides the number of APs, stations and phones found on the respective channels. Duty Cycle is defined as the percentage of time that a signal power above that of the noise floor is detected by the application.

Channel	Average Power (dBm)	Maximum Power (dBm)	Average Duty Cycle (%)	Number Of APs	Number Of Stations	Number Of Phones
1	-100	-41	26.86	22	1	0
2	-100	-29	22.15	1	0	0
3	-100	-10	12.93	0	0	0
4	-100	-10	10.82	0	0	0
5	-97	-10	17.57	1	0	0
6	-97	-10	8.26	15	1	0
7	-97	-11	9.09	7	0	0
8	-97	-12	5.83	0	0	0
9	-103	-12	6.37	0	0	0
10	-103	-14	12.27	0	0	0
11	-103	-17	11.17	29	4	0
12	-103	-36	14.82	0	0	0
13	-103	-36	8.84	0	0	0
14	-108	-36	0	0	0	0

Spectrum Density Snapshot

The Spectrum Density graph shows the "popularity" of a particular frequency /power reading over time . The X-axis shows the frequency or channel for the 2.4GHz radio band; the Y-axis shows the minimum and maximum power readings in dBm .

Figure 7.3—AirMagnet Spectrum XT Showing Duty Cycle

Spectrum analyzers have common views, though they may use different names. Real time FFT views show the RF energy for each frequency at the moment. Spectrum density or waterfall views typically show the most saturated areas in the viewed frequency band. Channel duty cycle, if available, shows the percentage of time the RF channel is busy with signal processing or RF modulations being transmitted. Figure 7.4 shows examples of these views in AirMagnet Spectrum XT.

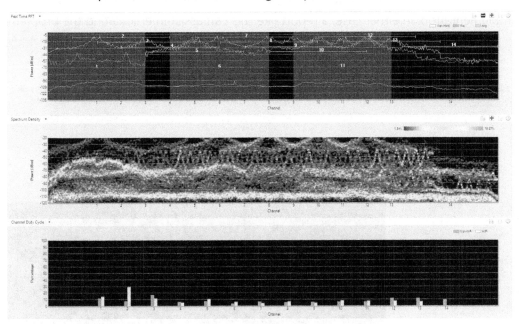

Figure 7.4—Viewing the Spectrum in AirMagnet Spectrum XT

Protocol Analyzers

Protocol analyzers can be used to measure Wi-Fi performance and to identify applications running on the network. Even with in-depth requirements analysis, it is not uncommon to miss some applications used on the network and sometimes to miss important applications. For example, when you see specific protocols, you know a particular application type is in use.

Protocols like SKINNY, SIP, MGCP, and H.323 indicate that VoIP is in use. Protocols like HTTP, HTTPS, and others may indicate Web applications. Protocols like SNMP,

SSH, and SFTP can indicate management processes. A protocol analyzer can report on such network actions and help you tune the WLAN for unforeseen applications.

Modern WLAN-specific protocol analyzers can also generate useful reports and monitoring screens that will help in the post-validation survey process. For example, Figure 7.5 shows the list of interfering APs detected in an area. Note that channel 10 is in use. This may be a configuration error, or it may be an example of a bad RRM implementation. In either case, a report like this can assist in eradicating the problem.

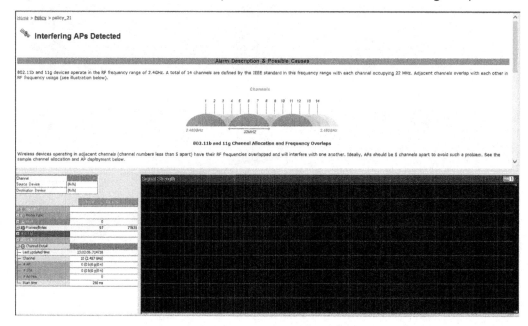

Figure 7.5—Viewing Interfering APs in AirMagnet Wi-Fi Analyzer Pro

Throughput Testers

Throughput testers may be included in other applications (site survey software and protocol analyzers) or they may be dedicated applications. Throughput tests can be useful in confirming the WLAN is working as intended, but they are also useful in documenting the same. Using screenshots and reports, you can prove the network is functioning as it should.

Figure 7.6 shows the throughput test view in AirMagnet Wi-Fi Analyzer Pro. It shows both uplink and downlink throughput results and the detailed information about the SSID connection. You can also view packets/second, signal strength vs. noise, CRC errors per second, and retries per second. For example, in Figure 7.6, the retries per second are shown as 10 with a 1% rate, which is acceptable for VoIP communications. The CRC errors are less than 10%, which is likely acceptable as well.

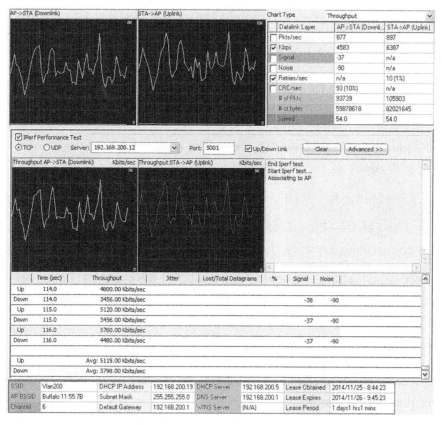

Figure 7.6—AirMagnet Wi-Fi Analyzer Pro Throughput Tester

The AirMagnet Wi-Fi Analyzer Pro throughput test engine depends on an IPerf server and can use TCP or UDP for communications. The IPerf server can be a standard computer on the other side of the WLAN link, or it may be embedded in hardware or an appliance.

Documentation

Documentation should be created to prove the validation survey was completed and to provide guidance to the organization. Validation survey documentation should describe the following:

- Summary—What was tested and why?

- Test Members—Who was involved in the testing process?

- Requirements Overview—What were the requirements of the design specification?

- Testing Methods—What tests were performed and what tools were used?

- Testing Results—Provide tables and/or graphs listing important results, such as connectivity, capacity, throughput rates, data rates, signal strength, etc.

- Recommendation—What would you suggest the organization do based on the validation survey results?

Troubleshooting Procedures

Troubleshooting procedures must be understood in order to resolve common problems that are discovered in the validation survey process. This section introduces troubleshooting methodologies and then provides guidance for common issues discovered when validating installed WLANs.

Troubleshooting Methodologies

A methodology can be defined as a standard way to do something; therefore, a troubleshooting methodology is a standard way to troubleshoot. The benefit of methodologies is multifaceted. First, they help to ensure that you do all the things you need to do to complete a task or set of tasks. Second, they provide you with collective knowledge when developed over time. Collective knowledge is that knowledge that you do not possess yourself and yet you benefit from it. For example, most people have never researched the statistics to know if wearing a seat belt is safer than not wearing a seat belt when driving; however, the research done by others is trusted and, therefore, seat belts are worn (It also helps to motivate people when the law requires it.). A good troubleshooting methodology will cause you to take steps for which you may not fully understand the purpose, but you will still get the benefit.

Three different methodologies are covered in this section, as well as one concept (systems thinking) that will help you in the troubleshooting process. The three methodologies are:

- OSI Model

- Hardware/Software Model

- Symptom, Diagnosis, and Solution

 Note: **You will not be tested on the troubleshooting methodologies documented in this section, "Troubleshooting Methodologies." They are provided for your reference and to help you become a better troubleshooter.**

OSI Model
The OSI model can be used for troubleshooting purposes. The concept here is to walk up or down the OSI model analyzing the system at each layer. This allows you to break the problem into logical sections and then verify that the system is operating properly in each of these sections (OSI layers). You may choose only to analyze Layers 1 through, 3 or you may choose to evaluate all seven layers (or even eight layers if you are considering the user layer, which is sometimes called Layer 8).

Layer 1 is the physical layer, and this would mean evaluation of the WLAN client devices or infrastructure devices to ensure that they are working properly at the hardware level. For example, is the radio still functioning appropriately or not? With client devices, this can be tested quickly by removing the WLAN client device (assuming it is a USB, CardBus, or another kind of removable device) and installing it on another computer that is using the exact same model device and is working. If the new computer stops working too, the WLAN device is most likely at fault at the hardware level or the software level (firmware). If it is an AP and you have a spare, you could load the identical configuration on the spare and place it in the same exact location to see if the problem persists. If it does not, again, the radio – or some other hardware/firmware point—may be failing.

An additional key is to evaluate the hardware used by Layer 1 (sometimes called Layer 0). Once you get to the wired network, you may also evaluate patch panels, connectors, and cabling at this point. Another area where failure may occur in relation to Layer 1 is the Ethernet connection between the AP and the wired LAN. If your clients are authenticating and associating with the AP, but they cannot obtain an IP address from your DHCP server (assuming you are using one), the Ethernet connection may not be working. Go to a wired client, and try to connect to the AP via the Ethernet connection. Can you? If not, verify that the Ethernet cable is good, that the port on the switch is working, and that the Ethernet port in the AP is still functioning (by connecting directly to the AP and trying to connect).

The second layer you will usually evaluate is Layer 2. This is where the bridges and switches live. Make sure the switch ports are still working properly, that VLANs are configured appropriately, and that port security settings are set accurately on your switches. Check the configuration in your bridge or bridges to ensure that they are configured correctly. Be sure the wireless link on all wireless bridges is still working and that the signal strength is still acceptable for operations. Because bridges evaluate incoming frames and forward based on information in the frame, be sure that bridging rules or filters are setup appropriately. Of course, with both bridges and switches, the problem can be at the cable and connector level, but you will have checked that already at Layer 1.

If you have evaluated the radios, cabling, and connectors at Layer 1 and you have checked the bridges and switches at Layer 2 and you have still not found a solution, you might have to move on to Layer 3. Here you will need to check the routing tables to ensure proper configuration. Make sure any filters applied are accurate. Using common desktop operating system tools like ipconfig, ping, and ARP, you can ensure that you can route data from one location on the network to another.

Finally, if you have tested the first three layers and cannot find a problem there, the network infrastructure is probably working fine. It is time to move to the upper layers. Look at the configuration settings in your applications and client software for WLAN utilization. Be sure that the authentication mechanisms are correctly installed and configured. Try using different tools and software that provide the same basic functionality. Do they work? If so, there may be a compatibility problem with the specific application you are using and the hardware on which it is operating. Many WLAN administration tools (protocol analyzers, for example) work with only a limited number of devices.

As you can see, the OSI model of troubleshooting can help you both focus and move through a sequence of testing procedures until you find the true source of the problem. The concept has only been lightly considered here, but you can take it farther by learning more about what happens at each Layer and the tools that can be used to test at that layer. For example, you can use a spectrum analyzer to test and troubleshoot the physical layer and a protocol analyzer to inspect the data-link layer of WLANs.

Hardware/Software Model

The Hardware/Software model is a troubleshooting methodology that is used in an attempt to narrow the problem to either hardware or software. There are certain problems that are commonly hardware problems, and there are others that tend to be software problems. Many administrators will attempt to troubleshoot software first and then hardware. Others will do the opposite. In most cases, the situation will help you to determine which should be your first point of attack. If everything is working in a system except one application, that is often a good sign that the software is the problem. If multiple applications that use the same hardware are experiencing the same problem, that is often a good sign that the hardware is the problem. These are not absolute rules, but they are good general guidelines.

Symptom, Diagnosis, and Solution

In WLANs, there are hardware problems that present certain symptoms. The Symptom, Diagnosis, and Solution methodology may be used in such cases.

While we cannot provide you with an exact list of symptoms mapped to problems, the lists in Table 7-1 and 7-2 are good places to start.

Problem	Symptoms
Client adapter failed	Device driver will not load, client cannot connect, OS reports errors loading the device
Firmware outdated	No support for newer security features, poor performance, reduced stability
Improper antenna installed or antenna disconnected	RF coverage in the wrong place, signal too weak at a distance
Bad cables	Could cause improper power for PoE devices or low SNR for antennas

Table 7.1—Hardware Problems and Symptoms

Table 7.2 lists common software problems and their symptoms.

Problem	Symptoms
Client software misconfigured	Client cannot connect, cannot receive an IP address, unable to browser the network
Improper passphrase entered	Client associated with the AP but cannot logon to the network
DHCP server down	Client associates with the AP but cannot acquire an IP address
RADIUS server down	Client associates with the AP but cannot logon to the network

Table 7.2—Software Problems and Symptoms

Because certain symptoms usually surface with specific problems, many issues can be resolved in a way similar to human health issues. Look at the symptom, identify the most likely cause (diagnosis) and then treat it (solution). Repeat this process until the problem is resolved.

Defining the symptoms means gathering information about the problem. What is happening? Where is it happening? What technology is involved? Which users, if any, are involved? Has it always been this way? Answering questions like these will help you determine the various details about the problem. Good questions are at the core of effective problem definition.

Based on the information gathered from your symptoms analysis, what is the most likely cause, or what are the most likely causes? You can treat one or all, but you will most likely learn more by treating one cause at a time. In others, try one solution based on your diagnosis first and evaluate the results. This gives you expert knowledge over time or what some call "intuition."

The solution is the potential fix for the problem. You may try replacing a USB PC adapter, because you determine that based on the symptoms the most likely cause is a failed adapter. After replacing the adapter, you note that you are experiencing the exact same problem. Next, you may decide to try both adapters in another machine that is currently using the same adapter model and is working. When you do this, both adapters work in the other computer. Next, you may attempt to reload the drivers in the malfunctioning computer, but this does not help either. In the end, you discover that the USB port is experiencing intermittent failures in the malfunctioning laptop. You send it to the vendor for repairs.

Systems thinking is the process of analyzing all interdependent components that comprise a system. In other words, it is the opposite of being narrow-minded in the troubleshooting process. Some administrators blame everything from network connectivity to application errors on an operating system or a particular brand of PC instead of looking for the actual problem. While some operating systems and some PC brands may seem more prone to problems than others, the reality is that there are probably thousands of individuals out there who have had the opposite experience as you. In other words, if you like the computers from company A because they are very stable, and you don't not like the computers from company B because of your experience with them, there is likely someone (or thousands) out there who feels exactly the opposite because of his or her experience.

The point is simple—rather than focusing on a vendor that you do not like, you must focus on the actual problem and seek a solution. When you do this you are less likely to just reinstall every time a problem occurs.

You want to ask questions like:

- What are the systems or devices between this device and the network or what is the device with which it is attempting to communicate?

- What other devices are attempting to communicate with the same system at this time?

- What has changed in the environment within which the system operates?

- Has the system been physically moved recently?

Asking these kinds of questions causes you to evaluate factors that are more related to the actual system you have in place and less related to the vendors that have provided the components. Indeed, if a vendor has provided you with bad components over a period of time, you will likely discontinue partnering with that vendor; however, blaming the problem on a single vendor every time does not help solve the problems you are facing right now. For that, you need systems thinking and a good methodology.

Whether you adopt one or more of these methodologies, pursue another methodology or create one of your own, you should consider how you troubleshoot problems and then be sure it is an efficient and effective process.

Coverage Problems

Coverage problems are indicated by several symptoms:

- Display of weak WLAN signals in client software

- Inability to connect to the WLAN

- Low data rates in use

- Inability to maintain connectivity during roaming

Coverage problems are resolved in several ways:

- Adding more APs

- Increasing AP output power

- Replacing antennas with higher gain antennas

Capacity Problems

Capacity problems are indicated by several symptoms:

- Inability to connect to the WLAN

- Low throughput rates

- High-latency issues

Capacity problems are resolved in several ways:

- Adding more APs

- Implementing band steering

- Implementing load balancing

- Disabling lower data rates

Security Configuration Issues

Security configuration issues are manifest by several symptoms:

- Clients cannot authenticate

- WLANs are shown with no security

- Server certificates are not validated

Security configuration issues are resolved in several ways:

- With PSK, verifying the passphrase is correct

- Ensuring that all SSIDs have appropriate security implemented

- Ensuring that clients are validating server certificates

Additional security configuration errors certainly occur. In nearly all cases, it is a simple process to resolve them. If authentication is failing, be sure to validate all of the components in the authentication chain: client (supplicant), AP, controller, RADIUS server (authentication server), passphrases, certificates, etc.

Roaming Delays

Roaming delays are manifest by several symptoms:

- Dropped VoIP calls

- Corrupted video in live streams

- File transfer interruptions

Roaming delays are resolved in several ways:

- Implementing PSK

- Implementing OKC

- Implementing 802.11 FSR

- Implementing pre-authentication

- Implementing PMK caching

Low-Data-Rate Clients

Low-data-rate clients exist because low-data rates are allowed (basic rates) and because they do not have sufficient signal strength to connect at higher data rates. To resolve low-data-rate clients:

- Install more APs or increase AP output power to provide strong signals in all areas

- Disable lower data rates in the basic rate lists (for example, disable 1, 2 and 5.5 in 2.4 GHz, and disable 6 and 9 in 5 GHz)

QoS Failure

QoS failure is manifest by several symptoms:

- Dropped VoIP calls

- Poor quality VoIP calls

- High-latency (delay) rates

- High-jitter rates

QoS failure is resolved in several ways:

- Verify QoS configuration settings on the AP, controller, routers, and any devices in the communication flow

- Ensure that WLAN QoS settings are appropriately configured so that high-requirement applications get more air time

Client Connectivity Issues

Client connectivity issues are generally either coverage issues or security issues. They can be resolved using the techniques referenced in the appropriate earlier sections. Additionally, interference should be suspected and resolved if located using a spectrum analyzer.

Chapter Review

In this chapter, you learned about validation surveys and their importance in ensuring a well performing WLAN. You learned about the basic processes performed, the remediation procedures, the tools used, and the troubleshooting processes for various and common problems.

Facts to Remember

Be sure to remember the following facts as you prepare for the CWDP certification, and be sure that you can explain the details related to them:

- Proper coverage is measured in signal strength, such as dB or RSSI.

- The number of available APs per location is also an important coverage factor.

- Application validation can be performed using simulators or the actual applications.

- Capacity requirements can be impeded because of improper channel configuration, improper output power settings, insufficient hardware, and disabled features.

- Load handling should be performed to ensure that the WLAN can handle the applications and clients under load, and not just when a single client is used.

- When APs are configured to the wrong channel according to the design specification, they are very likely to create CCI or ACI.

- Improper output power settings may also create CCI or ACI.

- Spectrum analyzers can show undetermined interference sources and duty cycles.

- Protocol analyzers can reveal applications running on the network.

- When low-data-rate clients exist, it is likely a signal strength problem and it can often be resolved by installing more APs and disabling lower data rates.

Appendix A:

Seven Rules for Accurate Site Surveys

This article is used by permission. It was originally written by Keith Parsons in 2009; however, the content still applies to many site surveys, though modern site-survey tools help significantly with many of the recommendations. More information about Keith is in the Introduction to this book.

The process of gathering appropriate and accurate data during a Site Survey is as simple as following a few easy rules.

Break the rules, however, and you could end up with totally useless—but colorful—Heat Maps that have no value to your organization.

These rules have been gleaned through hundreds of site surveys and through teaching over hundreds networking professionals how to use AirMagnet Survey products.

Rule 1—Calibrate Your Drawing Properly

Setting the underlying 'grid' is critical. If you don't accurately calibrate the drawing to reflect the reality of the actual building, with the drawing on your screen—all your data will be virtually worthless. This is #1 because it is the most important step, and you should always do it right as soon as you open a new project.

Do NOT use a doorway as your 'baseline' to calibrate from. Use a longer dimension, as long as you can measure. I use a Laser measuring device that works out to 50m or so. Measuring wheels, long tape measures, laser, or sonar all work. Just try to find the longest edge. You only need to have one dimension to accurately calibrate a drawing that comes to you with the correct aspect ratio.

Better yet, have the CAD folks drop a Dimension Line underneath the actual building on the drawing to give you an even more accurate line to calibrate against.

 Note: **While we're on the subject of the drawing, try to get your drawings as simple as possible and just pure black and white. 'Flatten' the drawing down to just the simple floor plan, no need for furniture, plants, where the jacks are located. Just simple black on white walls in your drawing is best.**

Rule 2—Set the Channel Scan to the Correct Frequencies

Scan ONLY the channels you want, and don't scan the channels you don't want. This sounds simple... but making a mistake here can cost you greatly in the accuracy of the post survey data. If you 'accidentally' set it to scan ALL channels (over 200 are available to scan)—even at only 250ms each (1/4 second) the system will nearly a minute of time to return back to the starting channel (and you can walk quite a long way in a minute!)

I recommend setting the scan channels to the 11 (or 13) base 2.4GHz channels and the 5GHz channels for your regulatory domain (in the US this can be the 4 Indoor Only, plus the 4 Indoor or outdoor channels) and do a passive survey of the outside perimeter of your building first.

This will give you a nice capture of your neighbors, as well as your 'leaking' RF. But better yet—it will give you a nice set of channels to concentrate on when moving indoors to do the real Site Surveys.

Perhaps even do two survey walks, one for 2.4GHz and one for 5GHz channels. That, or watch the bottom left corner of your survey screen and don't move to the next data capture point until the channel scan marker returns back to '1'.

Scan what you want, and don't scan what you don't want!

Rule 3—Set Your Guess Range Properly

This goes by the more professional term 'Signal Propagation Assessment'—but it basically means how far do you want AirMagnet Survey to 'guess' (Interpolate) in between your captured data points.

A **really** accurate survey would set this down to one meter. But the problem there would be that you'd have to go and click on every single meter of space in your building. Accurate yes, but practical, no.

Or the opposite, go to the center of your building and take a single data snapshot... then set the Guess Range to 50 meters... This one is easy and quick, but not accurate at all.

Reality is somewhere in between. AirMagnet Survey has a couple of pre-defined options for you. You do not have to use these pre-defined Signal Propagation Assessment (SPA) numbers. Use what you think appropriate for your site. The smaller the better. It will force you to take more data points and thus get more accuracy.

Most indoor buildings I like about 5m SPA.

Rule 4—Set Appropriate 'Snap Rate' For Your Situation

The automatic snap rate is based on a time. You set the number of seconds when AirMagnet Survey will take an extra 'snapshot' of your RF information. Too fast and you'll get 'blue lines' with too much information and slow down your processing. Too few and your snaps will be too spread out. (Think of Goldilocks... just right...)

If you are doing a Manual (red dot only) survey—be sure to take a snapshot no further than what your SPA is set to. So if you set your 'Guess Range' or SPA at 5m, you must take a snapshot (click) at least every 5m.

Rule 5—Capture on Both Sides of What You Care About

No *'One Way Guesses'*. This happens when you don't capture on both sides of what you care about. If you take one data capture point on the inside perimeter of your building, and don't also take one on the outside, then AirMagnet Survey doesn't know anything about the 'thickness' (in RF Attenuation) of the exterior wall. It 'learns' this by having data captures on both sides of the wall.

If you don't care about the RF leaking outside, then this is fine. But if you do care about some area, whether it be inside or outside, you must do data captures on both sides.

Thus another corollary to this rule—**Capture Outside In, Not Inside Out**. Capture on the perimeters of the rooms you want to prove coverage—not one single shot from the center of each room.

One additional part to this rule; If you have 'special' places you need to be real sure about—then take extra data captures at those locations, (*i.e.*, CEO's desk, Board Room, etc.

Rule 6—Click Accurately

You don't actually walk through walls, walk on water, or fly when you are doing a Site Survey—don't have your data look like you did or your credibility will be shot.

Prepare your walking paths in advance. You might even put little numbers on your drawing before you import it with the locations where you want to click (capture data)—and then you'll just have to play 'connect the dots' with your feet later during the survey.

The old adage, Fail to Plan means Plan to Fail... holds true in this respect. I've seen many people who get lost, or get stuck down the end of a hallway and don't seem to know what to do with the survey, or where to go next. Preparation is key on this point.

If you can't easily find yourself on the floor plan—it is a skill that can be practiced you know—then work on it until you are comfortable moving around in three dimensional space.

When you are doing a 'manual' survey, with red dots only. The dots are connected with dashed lines. These dashed lines without blue dots can go through walls, walk on water, and fly... it's the autosnap blue dots we worry about.

 Note: One trick to use while doing a survey. While standing still at the end of one data capture point, place your mouse cursor at the next place you plan on stopping, then start walking. When you arrive at the designated point, you only need to 'click' and the data point is collected right under where the cursor was waiting.

Anytime you can see a specific marking on a blueprint or floor plan, add a click for accuracy. Yes, you could walk the entire hall and AirMagnet Survey would place all the data points as soon as you finished the length of the hall. But accuracy improves as you have intermediate accurate click points.

If you don't go to all the locations and click accurately, you'll be tempted to increase your SPA to 'fill in' the missing data points (no one likes to see white spots on their heat maps.

Rule 7—Always, Always Do a Passive Survey

You might have a reason to also do an Active Survey (see article on Passive vs Active Surveys)—but you ALWAYS must do a Passive Survey on the entire building you care about. I'd also recommend doing a Passive Survey on the exterior of the building as well.

A Passive Survey can give you information on your neighbors, others, and all of your own devices. This is especially important for determining Frequency Interference. If you don't have your neighbor information in your Active Survey you can easily miss the interference on specific frequencies. Additionally, this can show you where your 'collision domains' are.

In addition to these rules that pertain to Passive Surveys, Active Surveys have some rules of their own.

Additional Rules for Active Surveys

Capture Data from ALL Access Points

It is quite easy to do an active survey and only get data on a subset of your Access Points. You can merge this with a Passive Survey data set and end up with what looks like an accurate survey, but it is NOT. You need to have ALL Access Points included in your Active Survey for accurate representation of your RF WLAN environment.

Capture to the Edge

When capturing Active Survey data from an Access Point, it is easy to not go to the edge of the coverage area... it's so far to walk—so we might stop as soon as we can see the coverage meets some design goal, like -65dBm. But this is where the failure lies. The easiest requirement to design for a WLAN is RF Coverage, but it is only the first of many requirements (see False God of dB article). The hard thing to deal with is the interference, and you'll only learn about this if you capture data to the edge of each Access Point's coverage area. (*Yes, I know this is hard and expensive to do!*)

Do NOT Set Roaming Too Aggressive

I understand you have the great power to over-ride the WLAN NIC's roaming decision process with AirMagnet Survey's Roaming Options. This makes surveying much faster and easier. Don't succumb to the temptation! If you set the Roaming Option to only connect at 54, 48, and 36 data rates, then your data will only show 54, 48, and 36 data rates. Since you didn't capture the other data rate information, we can't show it to you.

In reality, your client cards will roam according to their own algorithms and will downgrade to whatever data rates are supported in the Access Points.

And another adage that should always be remembered with respect to wireless LANs—**just because you can, doesn't mean that you should**.

De-Skew Data in Sticky Situations

Sometimes when taking an Active Survey the data gets a bit 'skewed' in the direction of travel. Away from the Access Points. If this is the case you'll need to do two Active Surveys for each Access Point, one clock-wise and one anti-clockwise and then merge those together to 'de-skew' the stickiness.

Merge All Actives before Merging With Passive

Just like it says.

If You Don't Do Active Surveys Right—Don't Do Active Surveys At All

If you do Active Surveys wrong, you'll end up with a less accurate and 'worse' data set than not doing any Actives at all.

Conclusions

Obey these rules or else... Or else your data you capture will be suspect at best, and totally useless at worst.

Also—don't let your sub-contractors break the rules or 'cheat' on you either. Check out the *How to 'Cheat' Using Survey—Don't be a Victim* article.

Keith Parsons, CWNE #3

The WLAN Iconoclast

March 9th, 2009

Orem, UT, USA

Appendix B:

Wi-Fi Site-Surveying 101

This article is used by permission. It was originally written by Andrew von Nagy as a blog post in 2013. It appears here in a slightly edited version. More information about Andrew is in the Introduction to this book.

What is Wi-Fi Site Surveying?

Wi-Fi site surveying is a critical component of deploying a successful modern WLAN that meets user expectations and the needs of the organization. The site survey process allows you to understand the unique RF propagation characteristics of the facility and environment into which you are deploying the WLAN. You can validate previously gathered design parameters obtained through predictive modeling using live network measurements to ensure that the deployed WLAN will meet the established coverage, capacity, and performance goals. This section introduces various types of Wi-Fi site surveys and provides guidelines on site surveying to meet the demanding needs placed on a modern WLAN.

Remember that a modern Wi-Fi network must not only provide adequate coverage throughout the environment but must also provide sufficient capacity to meet aggregate demand while simultaneously achieving a high level of application performance and a satisfactory user experience. This is accomplished by maintaining high-signal strength and a high SNR for client connections. These two factors allow clients to transmit at maximum data rates, achieve higher application throughput, and reduce individual client airtime utilization. Your Wi-Fi network design should also minimize medium contention by avoiding co-channel interference among both APs and clients and distributing clients and traffic load across the available spectrum. The goal of a site survey is to design and validate that these criteria are being met throughout the entire service area.

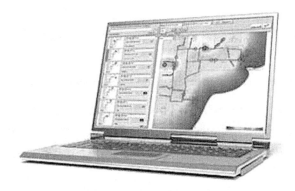

Figure B-1—Site Survey Software

Three types of site surveys exist:

1. Predictive modeling

2. Pre-deployment (often called "AP-on-a-stick") surveys

3. Post-deployment surveys

I recommend that you perform all three types of site surveys for modern WLANs. However, post-deployment site surveys should **always** be performed (never eliminate this step)! If peak client density and capacity significantly differ between coverage areas, you might need to gather service requirements for those areas and design individualized Wi-Fi plans for them accordingly. I covered predictive modeling in a previous blog post, Tips for Accurate Predictive Site Surveys [included in Appendix C]. Now, let's discuss pre-deployment and post-deployment site surveys, which have different objectives. I will also discuss Active and Passive surveying techniques that can be used for both pre- and post-deployment surveys.

Pre-Deployment Site Surveys

A pre-deployment site survey is performed before a WLAN network deployment. This type of survey determines the RF signal propagation characteristics of the environment. Measuring and recording the RF behavior in a facility results in a better WLAN design—one uniquely tailored to the physical properties of the environment. You can also use it to verify and adjust a preliminary Wi-Fi network design and to minimize changes to purchase orders once you have procured and installed your WLAN equipment. Spectrum analysis is an integral part of a pre-deployment site survey. Use it to identify and remediate sources of RF interference that could cause WLAN performance issues.

The following are the goals of a pre-deployment site survey:

- Determine the optimal locations for access point placement.

- Verify coverage in all required areas at the desired minimum signal strength and SNR.

- Ensure that adequate coverage overlap exists for client roaming.

- Establish a baseline of the RF noise floor in each area (using spectrum analysis).

- Identify sources of RF interference that will impact WLAN performance and require remediation or incorporation into the WLAN design.

- Validate actual client performance (when an active site survey is performed).

Notice that a pre-deployment site survey includes design criteria prior to deployment of the WLAN infrastructure, such as AP placement. This is one of the major benefits of performing a pre-deployment site survey because moves/adds/changes are more expensive and time-consuming when identified using a post-deployment site survey.

Post-Deployment Site Surveys

A post-deployment site survey is performed after the WLAN equipment has been installed and configured. This type of site survey reflects the RF-signal propagation characteristics of the deployed WLAN. At this point, you have already installed the network equipment, and the focus of the survey is to validate that the installation matches the final network design.

The goals of a post-deployment site survey are

- Verification of sufficient RF-signal strength and SNR throughout the coverage area (this includes spectrum analysis, which is described in the Tips section later in this post. [The referenced section is not included in this document.])

- Verification of adequate coverage overlap between adjacent Wi-Fi access points for fast roaming.

- Measurement and reduction of co-channel interference (CCI) among access points operating on the same channels.

- Validation of actual client performance (when an active site survey is performed).

The post-deployment site survey provides an opportunity for you to make adjustments before putting the network into production. Perform a passive site survey after deployment to measure RF-signal levels from multiple installed WLAN access points as a cohesive system. By doing so, you can validate that the network installation matches the final network design.

Active and Passive Site Survey Techniques

An active site survey is performed when the survey device (a client device) associates to a wireless access point to measure signal strength, noise, bidirectional performance characteristics, and other connection parameters. Measurements are recorded for only a single access point at a time, but they reflect the actual performance characteristics that client devices will experience once the network goes into production. Active site surveys are required to reflect the coverage and performance characteristics for each client device type. For access points that include transmit beamforming or smart antenna systems, an active survey should always be performed. However, active surveys do not record information on neighboring Wi-Fi installations that might cause interference. Therefore, active site surveys are best performed prior to WLAN installation, during a pre-deployment site survey to design the internal Wi-Fi network for proper coverage, signal quality, and capacity.

 Note: **For access points that include beamforming or smart antenna systems, an active survey should always be performed, and signal strength should be recorded from both the client and AP, since signal gain due to beamforming only occurs in the downlink direction. A passive survey should also be performed to establish the effective cell size for AP discovery and association by clients since broadcast management traffic does not use beamforming.**

A passive site survey is performed when the survey device passively scans the RF environment. This type of survey detects all Wi-Fi access points operating within range and measures their received signal strength, noise, and other signal characteristics (depending on the survey application). The survey device typically performs channel scanning across multiple channels in succession to detect access points that are either part of the internal network or belong to neighboring Wi-Fi installations. This method provides detailed information about the interaction among multiple APs regarding channel assignment, coverage overlap, and ACI/CCI (adjacent-channel interference/co-channel interference). It also provides information about multiple virtual SSIDs and SSID availability in various locations. However, passive site surveys do not measure WLAN performance characteristics and can only provide signal strength assessment based on broadcast management traffic like beacons. This approach can also provide an accurate Wi-Fi coverage assessment and cell sizing for access points that use beamforming or smart antenna systems, because those APs do not use beamforming to direct management traffic to a single client— they broadcast it. This allows you to perform passive surveys successfully by monitoring management traffic, regardless of whether or not the APs use beamforming for data traffic.

 Note: **Passive surveys measure broadcast management frame signal strength, whereas active surveys measure data frame signal strength.**

Clients discover and assess access point signal strength for initial association and roaming using either passive scanning of broadcast beacon frames, for which beamforming cannot occur, or through active scanning (probing), which often does not provide a sufficient amount of data to allow beamforming to take effect. Passive site surveys still provide an accurate assessment of Wi-Fi cell sizing for client association and roaming, but not for client performance once connected. Passive site surveys are best performed after WLAN installation, during a post-deployment site survey, to validate Wi-Fi network coverage, channel planning, and ACI/CCI levels.

Active and passive site surveys may be performed either pre or post WLAN network installation. Performing both pre-deployment and post-deployment site surveys is critical to success for a high-density WLAN due to the complex RF design that is required to provide high performance for a large, dense client population.

Site Surveying Best Practices

Follow these guidelines for successful site surveying (in addition to the guidelines for predictive site surveys):

Define Coverage Requirements

Before performing the survey, establish the minimum signal strength, minimum SNR, and desired AP coverage overlap requirements the network design must meet in all locations. Recommended values are a minimum -67 dBm RSSI, minimum 25 dB SNR, and 10–20 feet of overlap at these signal levels between APs. These values can be carried over from a predictive site survey, if performed.

Survey Both Frequency Bands

Perform the survey primarily on the 5 GHz frequency band to determine optimal AP placement, cell overlap, and co-channel separation. Use the 5 GHz band because at shorter distances between APs, which is typical in high-density environments, the coverage is nearly identical to the 2.4 GHz band. However, 5 GHz signals typically suffer greater attenuation through most RF obstructions and require adequate measurements to ensure sufficient coverage and capacity (no coverage holes!).

The survey must also include signal measurements on the 2.4 GHz frequency band. You can accomplish this while measuring the 5 GHz band if your channel scanning includes both frequency bands for a passive site survey or if you use two Wi-Fi adapters at once during an active site survey. If you cannot survey both bands at the same time then make a second pass through the environment.

Channel Scanning

When performing a passive site survey, configure the survey software to scan only the channels that the production WLAN will be using. The number of channels scanned can affect the accuracy of the sampled data. If you select too many channels, it can take a significant amount of time for the survey software to scan all of them. If you spend an insufficient amount of time at every physical location then the sampled data will not accurately reflect the location where you recorded it. Monitor the survey software to ensure that you scan all the channels at every sampling location. If performing auto-sampling, also ensure that your walking pace allows sufficient time to scan all channels between each sampling location.

Signal Propagation Assessment

Configure the client survey software with the correct signal propagation assessment, which controls how far away from collected data points the software will estimate RF-signal quality. The distance should mirror your walking pace if using automatic data sampling or should reflect the distance between manual data sampling locations. In general, shorter signal propagation assessments provide more accurate data but

require more data collection points. Use a distance between 10–20 feet
(3–6 meters); the smaller the better.

Collect Sufficient Data Points

Related to the signal propagation assessment value, be sure to collect enough data
points throughout the coverage area during the site survey. Collect them at distances
that match the signal propagation assessment value, typically every 10–20 feet (3–6
meters). If you do not collect sufficient data points, the survey will display areas
where no measurements were taken within the signal propagation assessment
distance. These areas might appear to be without RF coverage and will prevent an
adequate assessment of signal strength and coverage for network design validation.
To prevent this from occurring, make sure to collect sufficient survey data points; do
not increase the signal propagation assessment value!

Survey Both Sides of RF Obstructions

For site survey measurements to reflect the signal attenuation characteristics of an RF
obstruction accurately, it is necessary to survey on both sides of the object. If you do
not, the survey software will attempt to predict the signal loss through an object
based only on a pre-defined object type (drywall, for example), which is essentially a
guess and might not be accurate. Sampling data on both sides of the obstruction
provides accurate RF signal attenuation and signal strength measurements, which are
critical to network design, as it relates to providing adequate coverage and
minimizing co-channel interference. For example, how much coverage and
interference will an AP mounted outside an auditorium provide inside the
auditorium?

Access Point Hardware

Use the exact access point models, antennas, and accessories that will be installed in
the production WLAN to ensure accurate measurements of signal propagation and
performance characteristics. Access points should be placed in the correct locations

and at the appropriate height and orientation at which they will be used in production.

Access Point Configuration

Disable dynamic radio management on the survey APs during the site survey to avoid channel and power changes that could result in incorrect measurements. Configure APs with the transmit power levels that will be used in production or the levels estimated in the preliminary design.

Active Site Survey Techniques

When performing an active site survey, use either a production client device operating in site survey mode or configure the survey client radio to mimic a production client device, including power output, power-save, and 802.11n spatial stream settings. Align survey client settings with the least-capable client device considered critical on the production WLAN. This ensures that network performance is adequate for all client devices. If possible, it is advantageous to use multiple client device types that will be used on the production network as part of the site survey process and to test clients in all orientations in which they will be used (for example, landscape versus portrait). Perform the active site survey with only one access point at a time to ensure your client is associated with the correct AP to gather measurements. Configure your survey client to associate exclusively with the BSSID of the survey AP to prevent roaming. Using only one AP at a time is time consuming; some engineers may opt to use more APs at once to minimize the time required to complete the survey but also risk not gathering sufficient data for every AP location. The choice is yours!

Ensure that the site survey client captures data at the edge of the contention range for each AP (for example, -85 dBm). This ensures that you collect sufficient data to accurately estimate co-channel interference among multiple APs.

 Note: **Sometimes active survey data is skewed based on the walking path, typically the path away from the access point. If the data appears to be skewed, perform two active surveys in opposite**

walking directions and then merge them to obtain more accurate data.

Design Validation

Perform 20% of a pre-deployment site survey and then stop to validate the network design against the predictive site survey. If you find significant differences between the measured RF-signal propagation characteristics and the predictive model then adjust the network design to incorporate the newly collected data. This process allows you to identify design changes that could affect AP placements early in the pre-deployment site survey process and can prevent surveying incorrect locations.

Spectrum Analysis

Include spectrum analysis in both pre-deployment and post-deployment site surveys to provide a baseline of the RF noise floor in the environment and identify potential sources of RF interference that could negatively affect the WLAN. Use a dedicated spectrum analyzer hardware adapter to provide more accurate data than a Wi-Fi adapter, which typically only guesses RF noise levels based on received 802.11 data frames. Spectrum analysis solutions are available that integrate directly into the same software program used to perform the site survey, simplifying data collection and recording. If you use a separate software program to collect spectrum data, ensure the data is recorded and that it can be accurately mapped back to the original physical locations for future playback and analysis.

Documentation

Document the exact installation locations, mounting methods, and non-wireless requirements, such as available switch port capacity and cabling runs from switch closets to AP locations.

Do you have additional tips on site surveying? Please leave your comment below and let's discuss!

Cheers,

Andrew

Appendix C:

Tips for Accurate Wi-Fi Predictive Site Surveys

This article is used by permission. It was originally written by Andrew von Nagy as a blog post in 2013. It appears here in a slightly edited version. More information about Andrew is in the Introduction to this book.

What Are Predictive Site Surveys

Predictive site surveys use computer-based software programs to model the facility and RF environment. These programs allow you to outline the required coverage areas using facility blueprints, define facility structures to estimate RF signal attenuation, establish thresholds for minimum signal strength and application throughput that clients must achieve, predict the quantity, location, and type of access points that should be installed, and provide channel and power settings that maximize spectral capacity while minimizing co-channel and adjacent-channel interference (CCI/ACI).

The goal of a predictive site survey is to establish design criteria, such as AP quantity and placement with relative confidence. Doing so will then reduce the amount of effort required to perform the typically labor-intensive pre-deployment site survey ("AP-on-a-stick"). One of the major benefits of predictive modeling is the ability to quickly simulate various deployment scenarios and to narrow design alternatives. A predictive site survey will never be 100% accurate, and though it might not replace pre-deployment or post-deployment site surveys, it can help expedite them. When you perform adequate requirements gathering and planning, predictive site surveys can result in a Wi-Fi network design that meets requirements with a high level of confidence. It also provides validation of the forecasted AP capacity from the requirements gathering process and allows you to make adjustments by taking unique facility characteristics into consideration.

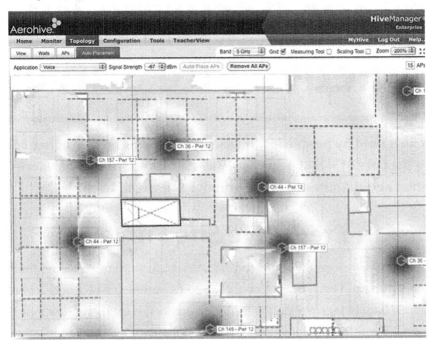

Figure C-1— Predictive Site Survey Software

There are numerous software-based and Web-based predictive site survey applications to choose from:

- AirMagnet Planner (software)

- Ekahau Site Survey (software)

- TamoSoft TamoGraph Site Survey (software)

- Aerohive Planner (Web-based)

- Aruba AirWave NMS (server-based NMS)

- Cisco WCS/NCS/Prime NMS (server-based NMS)

- Motorola LANPlanner (software)

- Xirrus Wi-Fi Designer Cloud (web-based)

Predictive site surveys should follow proper requirements gathering and capacity forecasting to meet all design goals for coverage and capacity.

Tips for Accurate Predictive Site Surveys

Use the guidelines in this section to facilitate successful predictive site surveys.

Blueprint Calibration

Use blueprints that are accurately scaled representations of the facilities or coverage areas in which the WLAN will be installed. Calibrate (or "scale") blueprints in the modeling software so they represent the correct physical dimensions of the coverage area. If necessary, use a known distance between two reference points that are fairly far apart from each other to scale the blueprint as accurately as possible. A small error when defining a short distance between two points on the map results in a more serious error in scale when applied to the entire map than would a small error when defining a large distance. For example, scale the blueprint using the width of the building rather than the width of a cubicle, door, or ceiling tile.

When importing electronic or scanned blueprints into predictive modeling site survey software, be sure to enter the drawing dimensions accurately. These programs often ask for the dimensions of the entire drawing; not the building or floor plan. The drawing's dimensions must take into account any extra whitespace or outdoor areas surrounding a building.

Access Point Equipment Selection

Select the appropriate access point models, antennas, and accessories to use in various areas based on facility characteristics and desired coverage patterns.

Document the access point models, mounting, and external antenna orientation (if applicable) that have been selected to provide the proper coverage patterns and to minimize co-channel interference.

Transmit Power Levels

Determine appropriate access point power levels based on client device capabilities, which you learned during the requirements gathering process. Configure the access point power output similar to that of the client devices to provide successful bidirectional communication with minimal co-channel interference. Also consider differences in receive sensitivity between APs and client devices, if known, which might allow APs to transmit at slightly higher power than clients.

Access Point Capacity

Estimate the peak client device density in each coverage area to ensure that the planned AP capacity is sufficient to process the client and application throughput load on the WLAN. Use the forecasted AP capacity from the requirements-gathering process as a starting point for the number of access points required in the environment or in individual coverage areas if requirements significantly differ between areas.

Start with a foundation of dual-radio access points to provide a base layer of coverage and capacity for each area. If you need additional capacity, use the techniques described in the Facility Characteristics section of my high-density guide to supplement the base WLAN deployment. These techniques include deploying APs with directional antennas, deploying additional APs on 5 GHz, or installing additional APs in locations where RF obstructions will limit signal propagation to augment capacity in specific areas.

Access Point Placement

Determine the proper placement of access points to provide sufficient RF signal strength and coverage overlap between APs. The coverage overlap enables client devices to maintain high-data rates throughout the environment and roam effectively. Base the minimum signal strength on client manufacturer recommendations or device specifications for receive sensitivity (minimum RSSI and SNR) needed to achieve the maximum supported data rate. If client receive sensitivity specifications are not published and cannot be acquired from the manufacturer, use a minimum RSSI of -67 dBm and SNR of 25 dB in all locations for planning purposes.

 Note: **Given the diversity of client devices in most networks, network designers typically use a minimum RSSI of -67 dBm for multimedia-grade network design as a baseline.**

You can best determine coverage overlap by ensuring that multiple APs provide coverage at the required minimum signal strength at the edge of each AP coverage area, to facilitate client roaming. If clients will be moving at a higher speed than the typical pace of someone walking (about 5 MPH/8 KPH), then you might need to increase the amount of coverage overlap to provide sufficient time for AP discovery and fast roaming before the client connection with the initial AP becomes degraded.

Channel Plan

Validate that the dynamic or static channel plan assigns 2.4 GHz and 5 GHz channels optimally to minimize co-channel interference. Co-channel interference is minimized when AP placement provides adequate RF signal attenuation between different access points operating on the same channel. In high-density environments, co-channel interference is often the most significant limiting factor of performance and capacity. If you cannot eliminate co-channel interference, which is likely in the 2.4 GHz band, consider adjusting AP placement. It might be necessary to revise the number of dual-radio APs in the base coverage layer and supplement capacity with additional APs on 5 GHz. Finally, ensure that neighboring Wi-Fi APs are operating on nonadjacent 5 GHz channels to prevent adjacent-channel interference.

The ratio of 5 GHz to 2.4 GHz access point radios in the network design will determine the appropriate band steering ratio for client devices.

3-D Planning

The predictive site survey software should be capable of estimating signal propagation in 3-dimensions, that is, across multiple floors of a multi-story building. This will ensure that co-channel interference is minimized across floors through proper access point placement that is typically not directly above or below one another on adjacent floors and through proper channel planning so that APs that are near one another on adjacent floors are not assigned the same channels.

Compile Your Results

The result of a predictive site survey should include an initial Bill of Materials (BOM), which includes the following items:

- All access point hardware and accessories, such as antennas, power injectors, and mounting hardware

- Detailed equipment installation locations and instructions, including proper angling of external antennas

- Configuration parameters, such as channel assignments and power levels

- Graphical heat maps of anticipated coverage levels

Appendix D:

Wi-Fi Design for Capacity

This article is used by permission. It was originally written by Andrew von Nagy as series of blogs in the Aruba Networks community. It appears here in a slightly edited version. More information about Andrew is in the Introduction to this book. More info about Aruba Networks can be found at ArubaNetworks.com.

Great Wi-Fi Starts with Proper Design

I'm sure that we have all experienced poorly designed Wi-Fi networks. When a technology is so ubiquitous, so easily accessible, and is increasingly the most relied upon method of Internet access for mobile devices and cloud computing, then there are bound to be some issues. Unfortunately, the prevalence of underperforming Wi-Fi networks is still much too common for my liking.

Great Wi-Fi starts with proper design. There are various approaches to WLAN design that have evolved over time, ranging from providing basic coverage to maximum capacity and situations in-between.

At one end of the spectrum, we have a basic coverage-oriented design. This was the historical way of designing a WLAN that simply involved ensuring adequate signal strength from access points was present in desired locations. At the other end of the spectrum is a design focusing on maximum capacity. This involves careful RF planning in order to integrate the most Wi-Fi cells as possible into a physical area.

Figure D-1—Coverage and Capacity

The problem with both of these approaches is that they are the extremes and aren't applicable for many wireless networks. Basic coverage designs may still work for warehouses and some retailers and maximum capacity designs are great for stadiums and large conferences, but both have serious drawbacks for everyone else. Coverage designs can't meet modern capacity demands with the proliferation of laptops and mobile devices, while maximum capacity designs would result in over-built networks that IT departments can't afford.

The majority of WLANs need to be designed to balance coverage and capacity requirements against cost of deployment, complexity, stability, and supportability. A balanced design is appropriate for most modern WLANs, which face increasing device density and business reliance on the WLAN. There is undoubtedly a much heavier dependence on capacity requirements than ever before, but a lack of adequate methodology and tools leaves many guessing, 'how many APs do I really need?' Common methodologies that are used involve sticking a finger in the air and guessing based on some random number of desired clients per AP or coverage size per cell. But these fall well short of providing a solid foundation on which an entire WLAN design will be built.

There has to be a better way. We need a methodology that:

- Provides an accurate analysis of capacity requirements in order to determine the appropriate number of APs to meet current and future demand, while not overbuilding the network.

- Integrates frequency re-use as a critical design element during RF planning in order to ensure that the AP density required can be implemented successfully without causing significant co-channel interference (CCI).

- Includes accompanying resources that simplify some of the complexity in the Wi-Fi eco-system and makes successful Wi-Fi design more attainable for everyone, novice and expert alike.

I am releasing the Revolution Wi-Fi™ Capacity Planner completely free to the community with these goals in mind. It is accompanied with a user guide that outlines the methodology and explains the concepts used in the tool. This follows previous resources that I have published on WLAN capacity planning, including presentations (PDF slides) and worksheets.

The Revolution Wi-Fi™ Capacity Planner is available at:
www.revolutionwifi.net/capacity-planner

The Revolution Wi-Fi™ Capacity Planner is a vendor analysis tool based on Microsoft Excel (sorry, lots of math was involved, and I'm not a great software developer) that provides predictive capacity analysis and fills a critical gap in the WLAN design process. The intended use of the tool is in an iterative design approach with RF planning in order to balance capacity, coverage, and frequency re-use requirements into a holistic WLAN design.

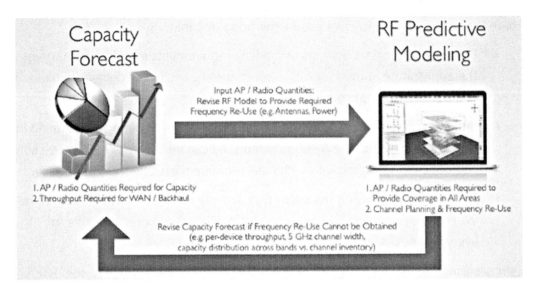

Figure D-2—Capcity Forecast/RF Predictive Modeling

Use cases for the tool include:

- Predictive WLAN design

- Quick and efficient 'what-if' scenario analysis

- Wi-Fi training and education

- Analyze how mixed client populations affect performance

- RFP responses for initial project pricing

- Bill-of-Material (BOM) creation

- Reference documentation for projects or customer deliverables

Aruba Networks understands the need for proper capacity planning and WLAN design. I'd like to thank the Aruba team for their support of this project and for adding their voice to mine in advocating for improved Wi-Fi planning and design.

Contention Delay Killed the WLAN Star

The Wi-Fi industry seems dominated by discussions on the ever-increasing bandwidth capabilities and peak speeds brought with the latest product offerings based on 802.11ac. But while industry marketing touts Gigabit capable peak speeds, the underlying factors affecting WLAN performance have changed little.

802.11ac does bring modest gains in speed through higher-order modulation with 256-QAM, but the practical limitations of its use greatly reduce its benefit. The bulk of recent improvements in peak speeds are not due to some magical advancement in RF capabilities that grant us new bandwidth or capacity, but stem from the more mundane explanation that we are simply using the spectral resources we have in a different, re-arranged, fashion through wider channel widths. With wider channel widths we are effectively "robbing Peter to pay Paul." That is, we are stealing spectrum from neighboring APs in order to increase potential peak speeds any single AP.

This new arrangement can work well in consumer, home, and rural applications where AP density is low enough that wider channels allow us to utilize dormant spectrum that we weren't using prior. However, in enterprise environments where all available unlicensed spectrum is already being utilized we have no such luxury as dormant spectrum. Using wider channel widths may or may not make sense based on a number of factors, ultimately boiling down to the resulting effect on medium contention.

Medium contention is the true driver in the success or failure of a WLAN, and we must effectively understand its effect on WLAN performance in order to design and optimize our networks.

A Framework for Network Performance

Let's begin by providing a frame of reference for network telecommunications performance in general. The two largest factors in network performance are bandwidth and latency (also referred to as delay). These two are inextricably tied together. We increase bandwidth through improvements that allow higher speeds (through lower packet serialization delay) and more data in transit at once (for example leveraging lower end-to-end delay with larger TCP window sizes). We reduce latency by minimizing geographic delay, serialization delay, and contention delay (as Martin Geddes has expertly explained: www.martingeddes.com/think-tank/third-epoch-telecoms/). Stated another way, we increase bandwidth by reducing the amount of time it takes to send bits from one point to another.

We are at a point where we've squeezed the most geographic delay we can out of the system since communications are transmitted near the speed of light. We have also reduced serialization delay (and improved bandwidth speeds) by enormous amounts to the point at which there is little gain left to be realized. We can see an example of this with 802.11ac; the use of 256-QAM over a highly variable and lossy wireless link is extraordinary, but the practical use of this higher packet serialization rate (what Wi-Fi engineers refer to as modulation rate) is limited to a range of a few meters from the access point. Truly little additional gains can be realized in this area.

So what is left to improve network performance is the reduction of variable contention delay.

Factors Affecting WLAN Contention

In order to optimize WLAN performance we need a thorough understanding of the factors affecting medium contention. This requires Wi-Fi engineers to focus on evaluating airtime demand by clients, optimizing cell density (clients per radio), using all available spectrum, and carefully designing frequency re-use.

Factors of Wi-Fi contention include:

1. **Airtime Demand**—the amount of time that each client or AP requires in order to transmit the data required by one or more applications. This is largely a function of AP and client capabilities, application throughput and packetization characteristics, and resulting spectral efficiency.

2. **Cell Density**—the number of transmitters within a Wi-Fi contention domain (frequency or channel) and their airtime demand (probability of transmission) affects the frame error and retransmission rate. The goal is

to optimize cell density to efficiently utilize AP and channel resources without overloading a Wi-Fi cell and causing significant contention-induced performance degradation.

3. **Spectrum Inventory**—the number and width of Wi-Fi channels available that will be used to segment users into different contention domains to avoid sharing airtime and capacity. This one is pretty simple to understand: the more spectrum we have, the more we can segment users, co-locate APs if necessary, and increase aggregate WLAN capacity. A more nuanced examination includes analysis of tradeoffs between the number of channels and channel width to optimize WLAN performance and capacity.

4. **Frequency Re-Use**—the ability to effectively re-use Wi-Fi channels to avoid co-channel interference (CCI), which is another form of contention-induced performance degradation.

We use capacity planning to model airtime demand, provide the appropriate quantity of access points that optimizes cell density (clients per radio) to prevent contention induced performance degradation, and perform what-if scenario analysis related to spectral efficiency (such as channel width permutations). This is the foundation of the Revolution Wi-Fi Capacity Planner tool.

We use RF planning to leverage our spectrum inventory into a design that provides optimal RF frequency re-use, which allows APs to co-exist without causing co-channel interference (CCI), which is another form of contention-induced performance degradation. This includes channel and transmit power planning, AP placement, and appropriate antenna selection to focus signal propagation.

Finally, we must integrate capacity and RF planning together in an iterative design approach to achieve a final WLAN design that provides sufficient coverage and capacity to meet the needs for each unique network environment.

Understanding 802.11 Medium Contention

Contention delay is the biggest factor affecting WLAN performance that WLAN administrators have direct control over to optimize the performance of their networks. We will now dive deeper into 802.11 medium contention to understand how it works as a precursor to the final part of this appendix where I'll detail the two main sources of medium contention and how to properly design and optimize wireless networks to prevent medium contention from killing your WLAN performance.

Comparing and Contrasting Wi-Fi and Ethernet

To understand medium contention, it is helpful to understand the wireless medium upon which Wi-Fi operates. Wireless technologies use radio frequencies transmitted across open air, which is inherently an unbounded and shared medium. Wi-Fi in particular uses a medium contention protocol called CSMA/CA (Carrier Sense Multiple Access, Collision Avoidance). In comparison, Ethernet uses CSMA/CD (Carrier Sense Multiple Access, Collision Detection). What they both have in common is the need to perform Carrier Sense (CS) for medium idle/busy detection on a Multiple Access (MA) network segment. One main difference between Ethernet and Wi-Fi is how collisions are identified (Collision Avoidance versus Collision Detection) and how stations are granted access to the medium once it is found to be idle.

 Note: **CSMA/CD is used by legacy half-duplex shared Ethernet. With the advent of full-duplex switched Ethernet, the need for CSMA/CD was eliminated and is no longer used when a full-duplex link is present.**

Ethernet stations can detect collisions over the wire because a portion of energy is reflected back to the transmitter when a collision occurs. Therefore, Ethernet uses a "transmit, then check for collisions" approach to medium contention and collision detection. Technically, this is called 1-persistent CSMA because Ethernet stations transmit with 100% probability when the network is idle. This allows Ethernet stations to minimize overhead by transmitting immediately after the previous frame transmission, once the medium is idle. Additionally, Ethernet stations can very quickly detect collisions on the wire, within the first 50µs of the frame, which is why Ethernet frames must be padded out to a 64-byte minimum length. When stations detect a collision, it immediately ceases transmission of the remaining frame to reduce wasted network overhead and reactively implements a backoff procedure to minimize the probability of a subsequent collision.

However, Wi-Fi stations cannot detect collisions over the air and use a more cautious, "randomized access" medium contention approach. Technically, this is called p-persistent CSMA, where "p" indicates the probability of transmission when the medium is found to be idle after it was previously busy (perhaps due to a previous frame transmission). This is largely due to the inherent differences of electromagnetic signaling over guided versus unguided media (copper or fiber cabling versus the air). Therefore, Wi-Fi stations must implement collision avoidance instead of collision detection, which randomizes network access among multiple stations. Randomized network access is beneficial when multiple stations have queued traffic awaiting transmission, yet the medium is busy. The previous frame transmission and access deferral serve to align subsequent transmission attempts by multiple stations without randomized access; therefore, there is a much higher probability of frame collisions. Coupled with the inability to detect collisions over the air, multiple stations would continue transmitting at the same time for the full length of the frame, wasting large amounts of airtime and causing significant network overhead.

Wi-Fi Collision Avoidance Mechanisms

Wi-Fi collision avoidance mechanisms include inter-frame spacing for different high-level frame types (for instance, control versus data frames) and a contention window to introduce randomness into the distributed medium contention logic of radio transmitters, since there is no central source of coordination between Wi-Fi stations.

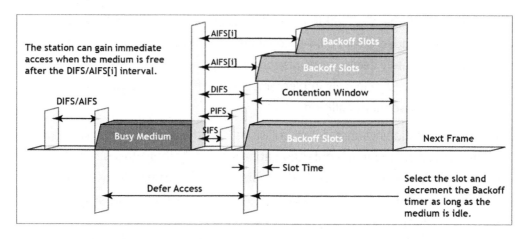

Figure D-3—Wi-Fi Collision Avoidance Mechanisms

Inter-frame spacing provides priority access for a select few types of control frames necessary for proper network operation. The Short InterFrame Spacing (SIFS) value is used for acknowledgements that must directly follow the previous data frame; DCF InterFrame Spacing (DIFS) is used for non-QoS data frames; Arbitrated InterFrame Spacing (AIFS) is used for QoS data frames and is variable based on the WMM Access Category (AC) to which the frame is assigned. Before every frame transmission, Wi-Fi stations select a random timer value within the contention window range and countdown until the timer expires (unless the medium was idle immediately prior, in which case the contention window timer may be skipped). Only then are stations allowed to transmit the frame if the medium is still idle. If a collision occurs (as implied by the absence of an acknowledgement frame), then the transmitting stations double the contention window size to reduce the probability of a subsequent collision, up to a fixed maximum contention window size. This is called Truncated Binary Exponential Backoff. The initial small contention window size is referred to as the Contention Window Minimum (CWMin), and the capped maximum size is referred to as Contention Window Maximum (CWMax). When WMM QoS is in use, both inter-frame spacing and the contention window size vary based on the WMM AC to which the frame belongs, providing a statistical advantage for higher-priority traffic over lower-priority traffic. This method of probability-based medium contention introduces a large amount of network overhead to minimize the possibility of a frame collision.

 Note: **The term "frame collision" is technically inaccurate for wireless networks. The RF energy from two simultaneous transmitters does not actually collide in the air and affect one another; rather the radio receiver is unable to distinguish between the two signals to accurately decode the data from the desired transmission.**

Positive Frame Acknowledgement

Wi-Fi transmitters are incapable of detecting collisions since there is no direct return path for the RF energy that is dispersed out into an expanding wave front over the air. Therefore, both stations fail to realize that a collision has occurred until the entire frame has been transmitted and there is an absence of frame acknowledgement from the intended receiver. Each retransmission attempt results in the contention window doubling in size (binary exponential backoff), from which the random backoff timer is selected. For these reasons, collisions on a Wi-Fi network are more severe and result in more network overhead than on an Ethernet network where frame collisions can be detected very quickly during transmission of the frame preamble.

Positive frame acknowledgements are required since Wi-Fi stations cannot directly detect collisions over the air and because the medium is not reliable, which can result in frame loss or corruption due to various sources of signal attenuation or RF interference. Therefore, for the Wi-Fi network to provide a reliable link-layer transport of frames between stations, the receiver must inform the transmitter that the frame was properly received. This occurs when the receiver sends back a short acknowledgment frame indicating successful reception of the immediately preceding data frame. Positive frame acknowledgement is a large source of network overhead on Wi-Fi networks. 802.11n/ac stations can minimize both medium contention and acknowledgement overhead by using frame aggregation and block acknowledgements, which allow the transmitting station to send multiple data frames at once and receive one acknowledgement from the receiver. By eliminating the need to acknowledge each individual frame, more network capacity is available for data transmission, resulting in better system performance. This is due, in part, to the half-duplex nature of 802.11, which relies on the same channel (frequency) for bi-directional communication. The block acknowledgement indicates which frames were received successfully and which were not, allowing selective retransmission of only the frames that were not properly received (similar to TCP selective acknowledgements at Layer 4 in the OSI model).

Protection Mechanisms

802.11 protection mechanisms provide backwards compatibility to ensure the coexistence of older WLAN clients with newer ones, as well as to ensure all Wi-Fi stations on the channel are made aware of a pending frame transmission and defer access to prevent frame collisions, reducing hidden node problems. Backwards compatibility is necessary because older clients cannot interpret transmission at higher data rates by newer clients due to different modulation and encoding techniques. Therefore, newer clients need to transmit RTS/CTS or CTS-to-Self control frames at the legacy data rate before transmitting their higher-speed data frames. RTS/CTS ensures that all clients receive the frame and appropriately set their network allocation vector (NAV), which is a type of internal back-off timer to defer transmission for the length of time indicated for completion of the subsequent higher-speed data frame transmission. Most modern clients automatically implement CTS-to-Self mechanisms for protection when the AP indicates that older clients are associated or detected within range. RTS/CTS must be manually enabled, but is more thorough in protecting a frame transmission from collision because it prevents hidden node issues and allows all clients within the cell to hear the CTS frame when it is transmitted by the AP. Protection mechanisms occupy network airtime and increase network overhead by as much as 40%, but can improve network performance in situations where there are hidden nodes or a mixture of old and new Wi-Fi clients.

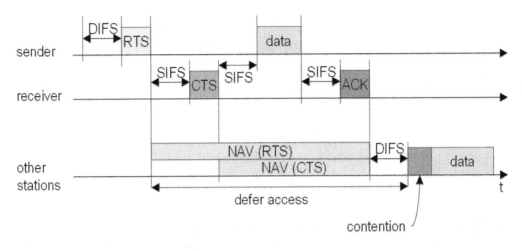

Figure D-4—Protection Mechanisms

Channel Utilization—The Canary in the Coal Mine

Network load (channel utilization) has a large effect on medium contention, frame collisions, the amount of network overhead, and ultimately WLAN performance. As channel utilization increases within an environment, the likelihood grows that multiple stations will select the same random backoff timer from the initially small contention window range. This applies to all Wi-Fi transmitters operating on the same frequency, whether they are APs or clients. When multiple stations select the same timer value they will transmit frames at the same time resulting in a collision.

It is important to understand that there is a breaking point at which channel utilization degrades WLAN performance. As WLAN administrators we need to understand how the network is used, how it changes over time, and continually plan for new use-cases. These days this typically requires the need to perform adequate capacity planning on a recurring basis. The more data that you have to work with from your current NMS the better. Historical data and trends will allow you to understand what applications and devices are on your network, in what quantities, and how your network evolves over time to identify areas of high utilization and plan for growth. Pay particular attention to the channel utilization metrics that your NMS provides for access points in your network. Establish a baseline for each area, trend these metrics over time, and identify appropriate thresholds for alarms to proactively identify areas that need attention to remediate issues or provision greater capacity (re-design).

Now that you know how 802.11 medium contention works, the next step is to learn how to apply this knowledge to improve WLAN planning and design with the goal of optimizing WLAN performance. In the next section, I will detail the two main sources of medium contention, explore Wi-Fi's breaking point(s), and show you how to integrate this into WLAN planning and design.

Push It to the Limit! Understand Wi-Fi's Breaking Point to Design Better WLANs

We all want high-performing WLANs. In order to do that we must push Wi-Fi to its limits!

> *(Cue adapted Scarface Theme, verse 1)...*
>
> *Push it to the limit!*
>
> *Walk along the perimeter edge*
>
> *But don't look up, just keep your head*
>
> *And you'll be finished*
>
> *Survey to the limit!*
>
> *Past the point of no bandwidth*
>
> *You've reached the edge but still you gotta learn*
>
> *How to build it*
>
> *Hit the floor and double your pace*

Laptop wide open like an engineer outta hell

And you crush the speed test

Going for the back of every room

Nothing gonna stop you

There's no wall that strong

So close now, battery near the brink

So, push it!

We walk a fine line when designing wireless networks, attempting to push as many users and bandwidth through our APs as possible, ensuring adequate capacity is available to meet demand, while not overbuilding the network. But what are the limits, and how do we know we've hit them? Or more important, how do we plan and design Wi-Fi networks to make sure we don't hit these limits?

The Right Metrics

Capacity can be defined as the amount of available time for stations to transmit and receive data. Or to put it another way, available capacity is the inverse of network utilization. The question then becomes, how do me measure network utilization?

In order to design, measure, and assess the performance of a WLAN, we need to understand the key metrics that define WLAN health. In wired and wireless networks alike the key metrics are bandwidth (more precisely 'throughput', which I'll use from here on out) and latency. If you'll recall from my earlier post, throughput is really a function of serialization delay, while latency is a function of both geographic delay and contention delay.

 Note: **For the purposes of discussing latency in the remainder of this article, I'll limit my working definition to contention delay at the access layer since most Wi-Fi travels over distances of only a few tens of meters with RF signals travelling near the speed of light, which renders geographic delay negligible.**

However, there is a key difference between wired and wireless networks that must be considered. In wired networks both throughput and latency correspond directly to link utilization; a wired link operates at full-duplex and with a single, fixed speed that allows for predictability and a direct correlation between throughput and latency with link utilization. Therefore, on wired networks we use throughput and latency metrics to directly assess the health of a network.

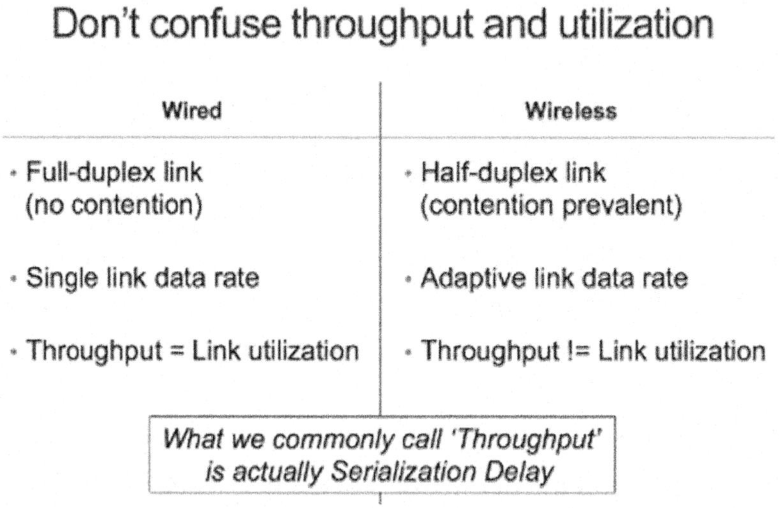

Don't confuse throughput and utilization

Wired	Wireless
· Full-duplex link (no contention)	· Half-duplex link (contention prevalent)
· Single link data rate	· Adaptive link data rate
· Throughput = Link utilization	· Throughput != Link utilization

What we commonly call 'Throughput' is actually Serialization Delay

Figure D-5—Throughput

In wireless networks, the underlying link is half-duplex and operates with a variable-link data rate depending on the combination of AP capabilities, client capabilities, and environmental factors such as RSSI, SNR, and multipath. Therefore, there is no direct correlation between throughput and link utilization. For example, take three different clients that all need to consume the same 10 Mbps throughput: a high-end laptop may result in 4% airtime utilization, a tablet 10% airtime utilization, and a smartphone 25% airtime utilization (these are example figures only and should not be used for planning purposes). Clearly, throughput is not a good measure of WLAN utilization or health. The unique mix of clients and applications on a network determine the airtime utilization on the network and the resulting throughput performance and access latency of the WLAN. WLAN professionals must focus on the underlying airtime utilization in order to assess network utilization, available capacity, and wireless network health.

Airtime utilization is the key metric to measure and assess WLAN health.

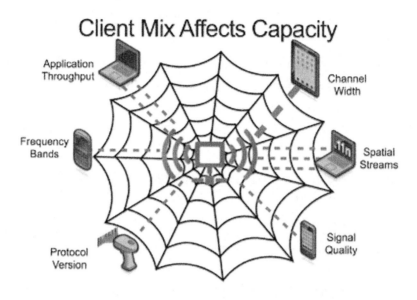

Figure D-6—Client Mix affects Capacity

Airtime utilization (or channel utilization) is influenced by two main factors: external RF interference (non-Wi-Fi energy) and medium contention (Wi-Fi transmissions). External RF interference is fairly straightforward; energy above the CCA ED threshold (Clear Channel Assessment, Energy Detection) causes Wi-Fi stations to sense the medium as busy and defer transmission, thus consuming available airtime from the Wi-Fi station's perspective. Additionally, energy below the CCA ED threshold can raise the noise floor and reduce the SNR for Wi-Fi stations, resulting in the use of lower data rates and possibly higher retransmission rates. Medium contention requires a bit more definition, as the topic is more nuanced and requires greater focus to successfully plan and design a WLAN.

We can classify sources of 802.11 medium contention into two major categories. If there are two limits we need to be aware about in Wi-Fi, it's these two!

1. Airtime Demand—the airtime demanded by stations within an individual AP radio cell.

2. Co-Channel Interference (CCI)—the airtime utilization that results from Wi-Fi contention across all stations (APs and clients) on the same frequency or channel across multiple AP radio cells.

The two result in fundamentally the same effect but are approached differently within the WLAN design process. Airtime demand is addressed through capacity planning while CCI is addressed through coverage planning.

Airtime Demand

The first major source of medium contention is the airtime demand within a single AP radio cell. Simply put, this is the amount of airtime required by all clients of varying capabilities running a variety of applications that are connected to a single AP radio.

Many Wi-Fi professionals and novices alike fall into the trap of guessing the number of clients a single AP should be designed to support, or even worse, deciding how many APs are required based on square feet / meters using a rule-of-thumb. These outdated methods for WLAN design have resulted in capacity forecasts that do not accurately reflect the capacity demand and intended use-case(s) for the WLAN. Often WLANs are deployed with too few access points by following an outdated coverage-oriented design methodology, with too many access points because capacity planning has not been performed, with inaccurate capacity planning methodology, or with the false notion that simply deploying more APs will result in more capacity.

WLAN capacity is heavily dictated by the interaction between the infrastructure and client devices, with the capabilities of each directly shaping the performance of a network reliant on shared airtime. Due to the unique mix of access points and the myriad of different client device types, no two WLANs are alike. Therefore, the measure of WLAN capacity is determining the airtime demand of all stations on the WLAN based on their quantities, capabilities, and intended use (application requirements, user and/or device behavior). From these measurements, coupled with other environmental characteristics, we can derive a capacity forecast, which describes the number of Wi-Fi radios operating on non-overlapping channels (to minimize CCI) in the same physical area that are required to meet the throughput requirements of all client devices.

Capacity is measured by airtime utilization:

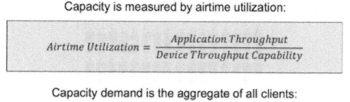

$$Airtime\ Utilization = \frac{Application\ Throughput}{Device\ Throughput\ Capability}$$

Capacity demand is the aggregate of all clients:

Figure D-7—Capacity

The airtime demand placed on the WLAN by each individual client device is determined by taking the application throughput divided by a realistic device throughput capability. Care must be taken to use realistic device throughput capability figures that devices will actually experience throughout the WLAN; avoid using the peak throughput under a best-case scenario. The airtime demand is then summed for all concurrent client devices on the WLAN and distributed between frequency bands to determine the correct quantity of APs and radios to deploy. This provides a forecast of the capacity required on the WLAN.

The key to the capacity forecast is reducing medium contention between client devices by segmenting them into small enough groups operating on non-overlapping channels so that each client can achieve the required application throughput level for an optimal user experience. As depicted in the graphic below, the goal is to find the correct number of AP radios that will segment users into different collision domains rather than overloading AP radios. The breakout or ratio of 5 GHz to 2.4 GHz radios is of critical importance, as well, since the 5 GHz bands offer significantly more channels and capacity.

Capacity planning should result in the optimal number of APs to serve all users without overloading APs.

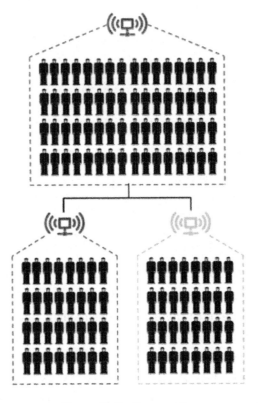

Figure D-8—Segmenting

Co-Channel Interference (CCI)

The second major source of contention is co-channel interference (CCI). Since radio communications are unbounded, receivers must attempt to distinguish the desired incoming signal from all other energy. When multiple transmissions exist at the same time on the same frequency it complicates the ability for receiving stations to accurately determine the correct signal to sync its circuitry to and to receive. Therefore, to prevent frame loss in such situations, most wireless-based systems operate in either a half-duplex (example: Wi-Fi) or simplex (example: FDD) mode. For

Wi-Fi, this means that stations must defer transmission if they detect an existing Wi-Fi transmission in progress on the frequency.

Co-channel Interference (CCI) results from the need to re-use the same radio frequencies (channels) within a multi-AP WLAN deployment due to the limited spectrum resources that we have available. It also results from neighboring WLANs that are within range of one another and using overlapping frequencies due to lack of coordination or limited spectrum resources. When CCI is present, multiple AP radios have overlapping coverage areas and cause Wi-Fi stations to defer transmissions across AP boundaries. In such a case, a transmission in one AP cell causes deferral in an adjacent AP cell. The result is that the two AP cells share available airtime and capacity to a large degree.

It is critical to understand how to design WLANs to minimize CCI. To do this effectively, we must know what the RSSI threshold is where a Wi-Fi station can properly recognize, sync, and decode a frame preamble and PLCP header (physical layer header). Unfortunately, this varies between chipsets and device design. Generically, frame PLCP headers can be decoded at the Receive (Rx) Sensitivity level of the Wi-Fi device at the data rate used to encode the preamble. PLCP headers are hard-coded at low data rates based on the PHY specifications as follows:

- 802.11b with Long Preambles = 1 Mbps
- 802.11b with Short Preambles = 2 Mbps
- 802.11a/g/n/ac (OFDM) = 6 Mbps

The Rx Sensitivity level for many chipsets at these data rates can be very low, in the -90 to -99 dBm range (sometimes even lower for access points). This can result in CCI being detected from very-distant transmissions, causing deferral and loss of airtime and capacity. Some Wi-Fi devices, mainly Aps, also have artificial CCA carrier sense thresholds that can be configured to ignore transmissions below a defined signal level that is higher than the Rx Sensitivity of the device, reducing the negative effects of CCI from distant transmitters.

Savvy readers may be asking, "Why don't they just design the device with a lower Rx Sensitivity in the first place?" The answer is because better Rx Sensitivity improves the reception of frames at all data rates, including higher data rates, improving rate over range across the board. Improved Rx Sensitivity is generally a good thing and improves performance.

The IEEE 802.11-2012 standard also defines a signal threshold for CCA carrier sense and deferral, which is -82 dBm for OFDM PHYs (802.11a/g/n/ac). This level is also a common artificial threshold in APs. Therefore, WLAN professionals commonly design WLANs to minimize CCI using a cell boundary of -82 dBm. It is important to understand just how far an RF signal travels beyond the desired association coverage area (e.g., -66 dBm). The graphic below helps visualize this distance, which is the result of the inverse square law, which states that every doubling of distance in free space results in 1/4th received signal strength, or -6 dB. The practical effect is that CCI can very well cause CCA deferral, shared airtime and shared capacity up to 8x the distance from the AP as the desired client association range!

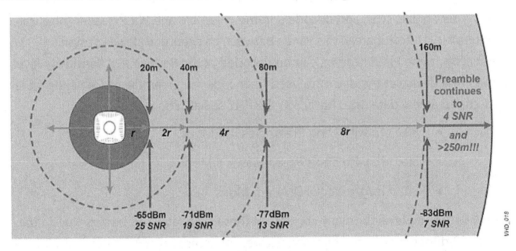

Figure D-9—Graphic Courtesy of the Aruba Networks VHD VRD Theory Guide

The lack of CCI mitigation is one of the major sources of reduced capacity on modern Wi-Fi networks. Oftentimes network architects recognize the need for greater capacity but fail to take into account the negative effects of co-channel interference (CCI) that actually reduces capacity. It is critical to plan for the proper AP quantity, AP placement, antennas, AP channel width and use of DFS channels (affecting the number of channels available for frequency reuse), association coverage threshold, AP overlap for roaming, frequency reuse, and CCI boundaries when designing a WLAN. By installing too many APs or by inadequately implementing a frequency re-use plan, CCI will increase and actual capacity on the WLAN will decrease due to increased overhead from management and control traffic. Additionally, capacity decreases even further because more clients are drawn to connect to APs on the frequency due to higher average RSSI / SNR across a larger coverage area, which brings more stations competing for the shared airtime of the channel. As part of the design process, disabling radios is a tactic that should be considered when appropriate to minimize CCI, especially in the 2.4 GHz band and the de-facto standard of dual-radio APs with fixed frequency bands.

The Breaking Point

Since airtime utilization is the key metric that determines WLAN health, we need to know the breaking point where the amount of airtime utilization results in degraded application performance and user experience. The breaking point varies but is based on application latency requirements and the underlying mechanics of WMM contention handling for different QoS queues. Latency is heavily dependent upon the number of collisions and retransmissions it takes to successfully deliver a frame over the air.

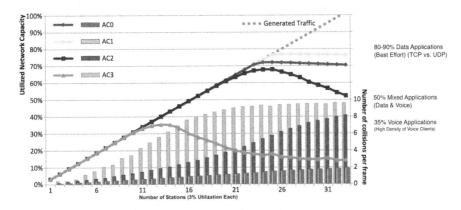

Figure D-10—Network utilization and retransmissions per-frame for each EDCA Access Category (Source: Comsis)

When designing a WLAN, identify which set of applications are in-use on the network and thus which airtime utilization breaking point is applicable:

- Data applications are more tolerant of frame retransmissions since they do not require real-time interaction. The WMM best effort queue is where most data applications are handled, which has a large initial contention window size, accommodating more concurrent users and higher airtime utilization before retransmissions and degraded performance begin to appear.

  - 80% airtime utilization is a good threshold to use for WLANs that only support data applications.

- Real-time applications like voice and non-buffered or interactive video have more stringent latency requirements. The WMM voice and video queues handle these traffic types and have much smaller initial contention window sizes than the best effort queue, resulting in a lower airtime utilization threshold before user transmissions begin colliding resulting in retransmissions, latency spikes, and degraded application performance.

  - 35% airtime utilization is a good threshold to use when the WLAN only supports voice and video applications, which is rare. More commonly, WLANs with voice support a mix of voice and data applications, described next.

- Mixed networks support both voice and data applications. Therefore, the airtime utilization threshold to use is a blend of the best effort, voice, and video queues.

  - 50% airtime utilization is a good threshold to use for mixed-use WLANs.

Integration into WLAN Design

WLAN design should be approached with an emphasis on developing a balanced design, providing appropriate levels of coverage and capacity. A balanced design attempts to provide adequate capacity to meet growing demand while not over-building the WLAN and incurring excessive cost. This approach requires careful analysis of capacity requirements in order to determine the appropriate number of APs to meet current and future demand. Frequency re-use is of critical importance during RF planning in order to ensure that AP density required can be implemented successfully without causing significant co-channel interference (CCI). A balanced design is appropriate for most modern WLANs, which face increasing device density and business reliance on the WLAN, but must be mindful of budgetary constraints and return on investment.

Proper capacity planning must be coupled with RF coverage planning to determine the correct amount of APs for a WLAN, as well as how it should be implemented within a given physical space using correct AP placement, antenna selection, coverage patterns, and frequency re-use. Planning for RF coverage and WLAN capacity require different methods of forecasting and measurement, while at the same time being tied together in a coherent fashion to achieve a successful outcome. Both coverage and capacity requirements should be forecast as part of the WLAN design process and merged together to provide a final WLAN design. Network architects should not rely solely on either coverage planning or capacity planning to design WLANs, but use both processes together.

In some environments, capacity requirements will dictate more access points (on non-overlapping channels) than would be required based purely on RF coverage requirements. In other environments, the opposite may be true. And in high-density environments, the per-user performance may be restricted due to RF spectrum and CCI limitations. It is recommended that network architects perform WLAN capacity and coverage planning in parallel and in an iterative process, balancing the requirements of both before deciding on a final design.

Wi-Fi is a complex technology and the only way to get better is to put in the effort through learning and experience. So get out there and push yourself to the limit!

(Cue adapted Scarface Theme, verse 2)…

Welcome to the limit

(The limit)

Take it maybe one step more

The bandwidth hungry clients still comin' so

You better learn it

Push it to the limit

(The limit)

With no one left but you in your way

You might get careless, but your WLAN's never safe

While you still maintain it

Welcome to the limit

(The limit)

Standing on the perimeter edge

Don't look down just keep your head

And you'll be finished

Cheers,

Andrew von Nagy

CPSIA information can be obtained at www.ICGtesting.com
Printed in the USA
BVOW07s0331110116

432467BV00007B/141/P